The English Parson-Naturalist

Illustration of white and yellow waterlilies (*Nymphaea alba* and *Nuphar lutea*), from William Turner's *Herbal*, 1568.

The English Parson-Naturalist

A Companionship Between Science and Religion

Patrick Armstrong

First published in 2000

Gracewing
2 Southern Avenue
Leominster
Herefordshire HR6 0QF

ISBN 0 85244 516 4

Typesetting by
Action Publishing Technology Ltd, Gloucester, GL1 1SP

Printed in England by Cromwell Press
Trowbridge, Wiltshire, BA14 0XB

Contents

List of illustrations vi
Acknowledgements vii
Preface ix

1 Introducing the English parson-naturalist 1

2 Monks, monsters and the mediaeval mind: the antecedents of the English parson-naturalist 23

3 The flowers of the field 43

4 The birds of the air 71

5 A draught of fishes . . . and beasts and creeping things: vertebrates other than birds 83

6 Go to the ant: insects and other invertebrates 95

7 Clergyman geologists: curates searching for evidence of the Flood? 110

8 Natural history societies, museums and the conservation movement 139

9 To the uttermost parts of the earth 154

10 Retrospect and prospect 171

Glossary 185
Index 193

List of Illustrations

Half title verso: Illustrations of white and yellow waterlilies, (*Nymphaea alba* and *Nuphar lutea*) from William Turner's *Herbal*, 1568.

1. John Ray (1627–1705), 'with who the adventure of modern science begins'.
2. Allegorical frontispiece from John Ray's *Methodus Plantarum Nova*, 1682.
3. Title page of John Ray's *Wisdom of God Manifested in the Works of Creation*, 1692.
4. Illustrations of fossils from John Ray's *Observations, Topographical, Moral and Physiological*, 1673.
5. The Reverend William Kirkby (1759–1850). Rector of Barham, near Ipswich, Suffolk, botanist and entomologist. The portrait shows him in his 90th year. *By courtesy of the National Portrait Gallery, London.*
6. The Reverend Professor John Stevens Henslow (1796–1861). Rector of Hitcham, Suffolk and Cambridge Professor. Teacher and friend of Charles Darwin (note hand-lens).
   By courtesy of The National Portrait Gallery, London.
7. The Reverend Professor Adam Sedgwick (1785–1873), Canon of Norwich Cathedral, who gave Darwin his only formal instruction in geology in a few weeks in North Wales in 1831. Geological map in background.
   By courtesy of The National Portrait Gallery, London.
8. The eccentric William Buckland (1784–1856), originally a diluvialist, he later enthusiastically embraced the glacial hypothesis. Fossils in foreground, geological map in background.
   By courtesy of The National Portrait Gallery, London.
9. Title page of the second edition of William Buckland's *Reliquiae Diluvianae*, 1824.
10. The Reverend William Orpen Morris (1810–1893). Rector of Nunburnholme, Yorkshire. Pioneer in bird protection, and ascerbic critic of Darwinism.
    From an engraving.
11. The Reverend Canon Charles Kingsley (1819–1875). Canon of Chester, Canon of Westminster, Darwinist and controversialist, pioneer in the natural history society movement.
    Cartoon by Adriano Cecioni. *By courtesy of The National Portrait Gallery, London.*
12. Father Julian Tenison Woods (1832–1889). Pioneer Australian palaeontologist, theistic evolutionist, Catholic priest of the Australian outback.
    By courtesy of the Catholic Archives Centre, New South Wales.
13. Canon Henry Baker Tristram (1822–1906). 'The Great Gun of Durham', in shooting attire. Later he was a pioneer in bird conservation.
    By courtesy of Barabara Mears.
14. The Reverend William Warde Fowler (1835–1912). First President of the Yorkshire Naturalists' Union, botanist and entomologist. After a portrait in *The Naturalist. By courtesy of the Yorkshire Naturalists' Union.*
15. The Reverend Adrian Woodruffe-Peacock (1858–1922). Lincolnshire rector, pioneer ecologist and 'ink-slinger'. After a portrait in *The Naturalist. By courtesy of the Yorkshire Naturalists' Union.*
16. The Reverend Edward Armstrong (1900–1978). Vicar of St Mark's, Cambridge, student of bird behaviour. Alighting from an aircraft, Reykjavik, 1947 en route to study the behaviour and ecology of the birds of the Icelandic tundra.
    Armstrong family collection.

p.192 The English Counties: after W. E. Lunt *History of England*, 4th ed. (1956).

Acknowledgements

Part of the reason for the success of the parson-naturalist genre is the geographical nature of the Church of England – a priest (until recently) in every parish, but yet with links to the wider church through deanery and diocese. But this dispersed nature makes for problems for the researcher: the materials (the sites, and archives, the specimens) are scattered around the country – indeed around the world. I have therefore to thank those who assisted me in overcoming some of these difficulties.

I have first to thank, with all my heart, my late father, Edward Armstrong, who remained all his life an Irishman but who was proud to belong to the English parson-naturalist tradition. He taught me the joy to be found in Creation, as well as the importance of understanding 'the way things once were'. Thanks Dad.

Thank you, Moyra, for your love, care and support while I have been in a study of a rural rectory in the 1850s instead of doing odd jobs around the house in Nedlands in the 1990s. Bless you, Darling.

I thank the staff of libraries and archive and record offices in many parts of England for making available published and archival sources. These include the Sydney Jones Library, University of Liverpool; the University Library, Palace Green, Durham; the Cambridge University Library; the Bath Library; the Ipswich and East Suffolk Record Office; the Ipswich Museum; the University Zoological Museum, Downing Site, Cambridge; the Newton Library, Cambridge; the Liverpool City Library; the Southport Library. For assistance in Australia I acknowledge the assistance of the Reid Library of the University of Western Australia.

The work has been completed while I have been in the employ of the University of Western Australia, and I am indebted to the University for opportunities for study-leave and other types of support. Host institutions while I have been on that leave have included: Darwin College, Cambridge; University College, Durham;

St Deiniol's Library, Hawarden, North Wales. The last two of these provided substantial support for the work: all provided superb environments for research. Amongst a number of stimulating colleagues at St Deiniol's I thank particularly Peter Francis and Robyn and Alan Cadwallader (that latter two now of Adelaide, South Australia).

The following have provided bed, breakfast and stimulating discussion when I have dropped out of the sky on one of my occasional lightning zaps round the UK: Ros and Nick Philpott; Robert and Sheelagh Hetherington; Tim Armstrong (senior); Nathalie Armstrong-Boursier and Tim Armstrong (junior); Margaret and Ian Boston; Debbie and Michael Uttley; Penny and Andrew Banks; Jill and Phil Rutherford; Geof Martin; Rachael and Nigel Jones; Liz and Rendel Williams; Anne and Bill Bright; Mary and Duncan Crawshaw; Vanessa and Mark Seaward. There were others. Some of these didn't know how (or how much) they were helping.

Sandy Baker helped by providing copies of his papers and obscure references: it is a special pleasure to acknowledge the help of another historian of natural history with links to Durham. Alan Cadwallader, Jill Rutherford and Mark Seaward read drafts of the (more-or-less) complete text, and helped enormously by commenting from their respective viewpoints.

I won't list all the colleagues and students at the Geography Department of the University of Western Australia who have provided ideas, tolerance and companionship. They have been legion. Some of what I've been researching over the last decade or so stretches the definition of what should be considered geographical research to its limits, so I particularly thank successive heads of department for allowing me to push against those boundaries.

May God Bless you all, whether or not you believe in him or her.

Nedlands, Western Australia
April, 1999

Preface

The village churchyard, wild flowers nodding along the boundary hedge and peeping between the lichen-covered gravestones, perhaps with the parson chatting in the church porch to one of the churchwardens, is one of the most idyllic, and enduring images of the English countryside. Today the country parson, as rector of a united benefice, is likely to have responsibility for two or three, possibly as many as seven such churches. The desk in the study in the rectory (or church office if there be one) is likely to be piled high with buff envelopes full of forms, circulars, policy documents and reports. He or she is likely to be a very busy and hard-pressed person indeed.

It was not always so. There were times in the past when the vicar or rector of a rural parish had the cure (or care) of just a couple of hundred souls, and at a time when administrative duties were less onerous than today, time must sometimes have hung heavily. Some of these country clergy of earlier eras were poets, some musicians. Some of them made a special study of dialect or of languages, or wrote on local history. A few were political activists, campaigning for the rights of the common people (or occasionally in defence of landed interests) in disputes about tithes or enclosures.

Many were naturalists. There were theological reasons for this, many seeing a delight in nature as an expression of Christian piety; some had other theologial postures that could be declaimed from the naturalist's viewpoint on the world. Some expressed their interest in natural history in little more than the compiling a list of wild flowers occurring in their parish; some achieved high scientific honours for their work on fossils or fishes, mites or mosses, sponges or spiders. Oftimes the wives and children of the rectory or vicarage must have helped them, but the records are frequently, and most unfortunately, silent on this. Nevertheless a few parson's wives of the nineteenth century appear as competent naturalists in their own right: one feels there must have been more.

This book is about these parson-naturalists, the plants and animals, rocks and fossils they studied, their views on the world, and particularly the social milieu in which they worked. There were literally hundreds of these people: only a small sample can be discussed here (my apologies if your favourite figure has been omitted). I have included a range of examples that illustrated the diversity of interests and approaches of these men, but that also brought out particular themes. Some of them are well-known figures, some are less conspicuous in the scientific Parthenon, but made a significant local contribution. Even with this strongly selective approach, to keep the work within bounds only botanists, zoologists and geologists are discussed. There were many parsons who made important contributions to astronomy, the physical sciences, archaeology or meteorology (the study of the weather): except where these men also worked in the other fields of natural history mentioned above, they will not be discussed in any detail. Obviously most of my examples are English (the English have been great travellers), but from time to time I have glanced briefly at a few individuals from elsewhere.

The matter of the citation of sources perhaps requires brief comment. Reference is made to several hundred individuals in these pages, and to quote the exact source of every scrap of information given about each of them, would make the text unreadable, or burden it with superscripts and notes to an unacceptable extent. And yet the requirements of scholarship (and the needs of some readers) require that references be given. I have attempted a compromise: I have tried to quote all the main sources, but have not always repeated a citation every time it is used. Biographical details such as dates of birth and death, and particulars of school and university education, I have frequently obtained from established reference works, particulary *Crockford's Clerical Directory*, and the *Dictionary of National Biography* (in their various editions), without giving formal acknowledgements in each case. I acknowledge that this rationalization will not please all.

Chapter One

Introducing the English parson-naturalist

On the 12th July I had a fair opportunity of contemplating the motions of the *Caprimulgus*, or fern-owl, as it was playing round a large oak that swarmed with *Scarabaei solstitiales*, or fern-chafers. The powers of its wing were wonderful, exceeding if possible, the various evolutions and quick turns of the swallow genus. But the circumstance that pleased me most was, that I saw it distinctly, more than once, put out its short leg while on the wing, and, by a bend of the head, deliver somewhat into its mouth. If it takes any part of its prey with its foot, as I have the greatest reason to suppose it does these chafers, I no longer wonder at the use of its middle toe, which is curiously furnished with a serrated claw.[1]

The tradition

So wrote Gilbert White, in the autumn of 1771, to his fellow naturalist, Thomas Pennant, in a letter that was eventually included in *The Natural History of Selborne*, first published in 1789. In the passage above we see much of what has made this book so notable. Gilbert White's style possesses what Richard Jefferies called, in introducing a nineteenth-century edition of *Selborne*, the quality of repose: restful, direct and yet evocative. One can almost feel the air of the warm, still, English summer evening, on the edge of a wood, perhaps, and hear the swish of the nightjar's wings as it twisted and turned, and the occasional bump of the large insects as they collided with some obstruction in the gloaming. Yet here is the observant naturalist; the description of the incident, although concise, misses no significant detail: here is a careful study of the behaviour of a living creature, made at a time when the study of the behaviour of organisms was in its infancy. Here, too, is the comparative approach – the behaviour of one species is compared with another. And here is shrewd deduction – from the behaviour of the living bird, the purpose of the comb-claw feature previously noted in a dead specimen is illuminated.

Gilbert White in many ways provides a typical example of the phenomenon of the parson-naturalist – a significant figure in English science and the English church for several centuries – and to some extent he can serve as a template. He came from a family of clergy: although not wealthy, he was comfortably off. He was born in Selborne, Hampshire on 18 July 1720, and after schooling with a private tutor for a few years, in nearby Basingstoke, he was admitted to Oriel College Oxford on 9 December 1739. He became fellow of his college, and ultimately senior proctor. He eventually returned to Selborne in 1755, holding the curacy of the neighbouring parish of Farringdon until 1784, in which year he was appointed curate of Selborne. Gilbert White continued to reside, at a house called The Wakes, in the village in which he was born, until his death on 26 June 1793. He kept in contact with a network of correspondents, including friends he had made at Oxford, throughout much of his life. Through these letters, many of which still exist, and his diaries of his observation on plants, animals and the countryside, many of which have been published, we know a good deal of his life.[2] In this book we shall meet him frequently.

The beginnings of the parson-naturalist tradition can be seen in some of the monastic scholars and writers of the Middle Ages. Their purpose in writing about plants and animals was very different from those of later naturalists, and there are those who argue that they should not be considered naturalists at all. The extent to which they can be thought to belong to the same tradition to which Gilbert White belonged will be considered later.

But certainly since the time of William Turner (*c.*1508–1568), a great polymath – he wrote on medicine and theology as well as natural history – who was originally from Morpeth, Northumberland, clergy have made a most formidable contribution to natural history in England.[3] Besides Gilbert White himself, one of the best-known figures is perhaps John Ray (1627–1705), with whom, it has been said, 'the adventure of modern science begins'.[4]

However, the brightness of the reputations of these individuals should not blind us to that great host of other luminaries who have, to a very considerable extent, made English natural history what it is today. They include botanists and ornithologists, geologists and entomologists; clerical naturalists have included specialists on spiders, molluscs, sponges, seaweeds and lichens. Some of them, such as geologists Adam Sedgwick (1785–1873), eccentric William Buckland (1784–1856) who was originally something of a fundamentalist and catastrophist, but was later an exponent of the uniformitarian (or gradualist) cause, and Thomas Bonney (1833–1923), mountaineer, acerbic letter-writer and pioneer geomorphologist, had permanent university appointments.[5]

Others originally held academic positions, but were required, as was the tradition in earlier centuries, to renounce them on marriage: such was John Mitchell (1724?–1795) who was Woodwardian Professor of Geology at Cambridge for two years, but who later spent 26 years in the Yorkshire parish of Thornhill.[6] Some, like John Stevens Henslow (1796–1861), Charles Darwin's friend and teacher, combined both an academic position and parochial ministry; he was Professor, successively, of Mineralogy and Botany at Cambridge as well as the much-loved Rector of Hitcham in Suffolk.[7] Of him, on his death it was said:

> He was a first rate man of science, an indefatigable parish priest, an amiable, large-hearted, generous and genial man . . . and a thorough, earnest and practical Christian.[8]

Some parson-naturalists, like Gilbert White, used their long association with a single parish (and incumbencies of over 40 years were not uncommon in the eighteenth and nineteenth centuries) to make a detailed study of a particular locality. Others specialized in a particular biological group. There were men who formed and supported natural history societies and field clubs, those who built up museums, and those who edited county floras, often using their network of clerical colleagues to assist them. There are certainly Scots (including Scots Presbyterian) examples of the genre, and not a few Irish, but the tradition is distinctively an English one; Australian, New Zealand and other 'colonial' representatives in many cases have been English by birth, training or temporary residence. Quite a number, including several parochial clergy, have achieved the high distinction of a Fellowship of the Royal Society.

The nineteenth century was perhaps the hey-day of the English parson-naturalist, although as has been noted above, the genre had its origins much earlier. The tradition also continued into the twentieth century, particularly in the form of a line of distinguished clergyman ornithologists, including for example the Reverend Francis Charles Robert Jourdain, originally a frenetic egg-collector (and author of *Eggs of European Birds*, 1906) but later won over to the cause of conservation. The Reverend Peter Harold Trahair Hartley (1909–1985), on the other hand, was active in conservation (or as it was known earlier in the century 'bird protection') circles throughout much of his life. He was a member of the fine tradition of Suffolk naturalists, combining parochial ministry, ornithology and the position of Archdeacon of Suffolk (1970–1975). My own father, Edward Allworthy Armstrong (1900–1978), an Ulsterman by birth, but who after working in parishes in the north of England and Hong Kong, was Vicar of St Mark's, Cambridge for many years (1943–1967). He was a naturalist of varied interests, but is chiefly known for his work on bird behaviour (*Bird Display and Behaviour*, 1947; *The Wren*, 1955; *A Study of Bird Song*, 1963).[9] The breed lives on, although the parson-naturalist species seems much rarer than before, in the likes of the Reverend G. Gordon Graham, Vicar successively of Wheatley Hill and Hunwick, author, just as many clergy before him have been editors or authors of English county floras, of *The Flora and Vegetation of County Durham*, published in 1988.

Differences in agenda

Many parson-naturalists have seen their work in natural history as an extension of their work as priests. The early monastic writers about the birds and the beasts sought to elicit moral truths, or used tales of their antics as allegories of the Christian life. John Ray (botanist, ornithologist, entomologist, palaeontologist, theologian) set out the notion that 'design implies a designer' in *The Wisdom of God* in 1692 (see Plate 3). Gilbert White referred respectfully to 'the excellent Mr Ray'. These ideas were recycled, without full acknowledgement, by William Paley (1743–1805), Archdeacon of Carlisle, first in 1802, but reprinted and revised many times, as the doctrine of 'natural theology', in his eponymous book, subtitled *[E]vidences of the existence and attributes of the Deity collected from the appearances of nature*. The notion was that the complexity and appearance of design in the natural world provided evidence of the existence and nature of a Divine Creator. Paley argued, for example:

> It is a step to have it proved, that there must be something in the world more than what we see. It is a farther step to know, that, amongst the invisible things of nature, there must be an intelligent mind, concerned in its production, order and support. These points being assured to us by Natural Theology, we may well leave to Revelation the disclosure of many particulars.[10]
>
> Contrivance must have had a contriver; design, a designer;[11]

it would be from this source that many nineteenth-century ordinands came across these notions. Indeed, Charles Darwin (1809–1882), who went up to Christ's College, Cambridge in 1827 intending to enter the Church of England priesthood, in later life recalled that his reading of Paley was virtually the only study from his Cambridge days that was to be of much use to him in his scientific career.[12] The Paleyan point of view perhaps explains the extraordinary diligence with which some of the notable nineteenth-century naturalists set about their work as recorders, collectors and classifiers; we might mention Miles Berkeley, who described 6000 species of fungi, or Alfred Norman who played a similar role in the distinctly Victorian study of sponges, or Octavius Pickard-Cambridge (1828–1917), who wrote some many dozens of papers on spiders throughout his career, the first in 1859, the last in 1914.[13] Diligence was almost an art-form in itself: no tiny fragment of great diversity and glorious complexity of Creation was to be missed.

Sometimes, it seems, collecting was almost an end in itself. The Reverend Leonard Jenyns (later Blomefield), Vicar of Swaffham Bulbeck, but who later moved to later of Bath, was a fanatical collector of flowering plants and ferns. His collection, of about fifteen thousand specimens, bound in 40 impressive leather-bound volumes, survives in Bath Library. Each specimen is almost a work of art in the way in which it was neatly labelled, and the whole was classified and organised, each folio having its very carefully and neatly written list of contents. The date on each specimen allows the career of this fine naturalist to be reconstructed. There is a specimen of *Equisetum arvense*, collected from Anglesey Abbey, close to his Cambridgeshire parish, in April 1822, and one of *Equisetum sylvaticum* collected by him in the New Forest in July 1881, after he had moved to Bath and assumed the name of Blomefield. Past landscapes can be recreated through the collection. A specimen of *Drosera anglica*, often associated with boggy country, was collected at Whittlesey Mere (then the largest lake in lowland England, drained in 1851) on 30 July 1827. He clearly bought, sold and exchanged specimens in substantial numbers, and his network of contacts can be seen in the names of the collectors of some of the specimens: clergymen-naturalists are of course well represented. Many specimens have the name of J. S. Henslow by them: these include some collected in Henslow's Suffolk parish of Hitcham, but also, for example, a *Lycopodium selagum [L. selago, Urostachys selago]* from Cauldron Snout, Teesdale, obviously taken on an expedition to northern England in August 1833. Others collected lepidoptera or birds with equal passion.

There were others with rather different, or at least more specific, agendas. Some sought to marry the geological record with the Mosaic record of Genesis.[14] Such was the prolific William Brown Galloway (1811–1903), Vicar of St Mark's, Regent's Park, London from 1849 to 1888. In a stream of pamphlets and books over some 60 years, he attempted to demonstrate the literal truth of Scripture. He essayed to prove that the biblical record could be linked to the evidence of science at every point. He was, for example a 'diluvialist' and tried to show scientifically that the flood had occurred exactly the way described in Genesis.

There were many clergy, who, after the publication of *On the Origin of Species by Means of Natural Selection* in 1859 attempted to demonstrate the falsity of evolutionary ideas; others found Darwin's notions liberating theologically, and strove hard to find a way of accommodating them, and attempting to demonstrate that there was no conflict between Christian belief and a modern scientific outlook. Such was Octavius Pickard-Cambridge, who utilized Darwin's ideas extensively in his work on the taxonomy of spiders; another was Henry Baker Tristram, Canon of Durham Cathedral (1822–1906). Indeed, he was quite possibly the first zoologist to use Darwin's ideas in a scientific paper, even before *On the Origin of Species* appeared. He noticed the Darwin-Wallace paper in the *Proceedings of the Linnean Society* late in 1858, and quoted it in a paper in the *Ibis* on the birds of north Africa a year later. 'Writing with a series of about 100 Larks of various species before me' he wrote, 'I cannot help feeling convinced of the views set forth by Messrs Darwin and Wallace.'[15] He accepted at once that change from one species to another occurred and was 'possibly occurring still'. Nevertheless, he did not exclude the possibility of some independent creation.

Yet another who was in broad sympathy with Darwin's ideas was the Reverend Canon Charles Kingsley (1818–1875), a keen naturalist since boyhood. He had collected shells since he had been a young lad in Devon, and wrote popular articles on seashore life. It is said that his *The Water Babies* is partly inspired by Darwinian ideas: it is certainly rich in allusions to natural history. (*The Water Babies* appeared in 1863, four years after the *Origin of Species*.) Even more interesting, as it was published in 1850, is *Alton Locke*, which as well as portraying the terrible living conditions of those who lived in the East End of London at that time, contains a remarkable dream-sequence. The hero of the tale dreams that he is a madrepore [a form of coral] 'the lowest form of created life', as he crawls out of the primaeval ocean he turns into a crab, and then into a mylodon [an extinct giant sloth] amongst the tree-ferns of the South American forests, and then an ape. At last, the hero recalls :'I felt stirring in me the germs of a higher consciousness'. This is clearly an evolutionary (perhaps Lamarckian – the transformation seems to take place from within) portrayal of humanity. The sequence is possibly also an allegory for one the messages of Kingsley's multidimensional life's work, which is that workers should attempt to improve their lot by co-operation and education: evolution within society.

An ornithologist on the opposite side of the evolution debate was

Francis Orpen Morris (1810–1891), rector of a Yorkshire parish (see chapter 4). Papers given before the meetings of the British Association for the Advancement of Science in Norwich (1868) and Exeter (1889) announced the commencement of a twenty-year campaign 'to eradicate Darwinism from English intellectual life',[16] as James Moore put it. Orpen Morris produced a whole stream of anti-Darwin pamphlets.[17] In one of these he expresses his 'Ineffable contempt and indignation' at the 'astounding puerilities' of Darwin's ideas. In the same paragraph he referred to 'childish absurdities', 'utter contempt', 'indignation', 'miserable infidelity', 'wretched system', 'imposture'. There were not words enough in the English language to express his contempt for Darwinism, he declaimed. That, at any rate was a brief synopsis of his views. Although Francis Orpen Morris was a strong evangelical, his prime arguments were on the basis of logic rather than Scripture. He did not like the notion of natural selection. It was absurd, he argued, to say that organisms vary, and yet may also descend from one another.

The nineteenth century was also the great period of imperial expansion and exploration. Often the missionary clergyman was not far behind the explorer, the trader and colonial administrator in Africa, Asia, South America and the Pacific. Many English clergy saw it as with their duty to take the gospel 'to the uttermost parts of the Earth', and some of them packed a botanical vasculum or butterfly net in with the Bible, prayer-book, communion stole and quinine. Such men, along with their close colleagues, the army and naval chaplains, sent back specimens to the Herbarium at Kew, or to the Natural History Museum, or submitted their observations to learned journals edited in the home country.

Slightly different explorers, without imperial or military ambition,[18] were those who took part in a 'Crusade' to the Holy Land. A number of naturalists, archaeologists and geologists in the second half of the nineteenth century saw themselves as part of a *peaceful* crusade, to understand the geography, history and natural history of the Holy Land and indeed the entire Middle East, contrasting themselves with the armies of the blood-thirsty Crusaders of the Middle Ages. An organisation that was in the vanguard of this 'peaceful invasion' was the London-based Palestine Exploration Fund. A leading figure in the crusade, and a leading light in the foundation of the Fund, was Dean Arthur Penryn Stanley (1815–1881), who had first visited the Middle East in 1852, publishing his important *Sinai and Palestine* in 1856. The Reverend Dr Henry Baker Tristram, mentioned above, was an outstandingly competent scientist, and an authority on the plants and animals of the Middle East and North Africa, who published some of his researches in the volume on *Flora and Fauna* in *The Survey of Western Palestine* produced by the Fund in 1884.[19] This monumental work of 500 pages, with fine coloured illustrations, covers every vertebrate and mollusc, and most flowerless and flowering plants then recorded in the area. The following extract from Tristram's *Land of Israel*, 1866 indicates the theological and scientific approach to his investigations in Palestine between November 1863 and June 1864:

> The primary object of our journey was the investigation of physical and natural history, not, however, to the exclusion of other objects of interest. We passed through the land with our Bibles in our hands – with, I trust, an unbiased determination to investigate *facts*, and their independent bearing on sacred history. While on matters of science the inspired writers speak in the ordinary language of their times (the only language which could have been understood), I can bear witness to the minute truth of innumerable incidental allusions of Holy Writ to the facts of nature, of climate, of geographical position, – corroborations of Scripture, which, though trifling in themselves . . . prove the writers to have lived when and where they are asserted to have lived; which attest their scrupulous accuracy in recording what they saw around them and which, therefore, must increase our confidence in their veracity where we cannot have means of testing it. I can find no discrepancies between their geographical and physical statements and the evidence of present facts . . . The Holy Land not only elucidates but bears witness to the truth of the HOLY BOOK.[20]

A sound, 'middle of the road' Church of England approach is seen here. He is respectful of the importance of Scripture, and not too extreme a literalist, appreciating that the biblical authors wrote in the language and thought-forms of their time, and were not to be accepted uncritically on scientific matters.

Many Victorian clergy saw it as part of their task to educate, to improve, and to 'elevate' in every possible way those who were in their charge: parson-naturalists who saw their duties lying in this direction thus sometimes had a social and educational agenda as well as a theological or philosophical one. So often the local rector or vicar also had an important role in the management of the local church school. Henslow of Hitcham pioneered, in the 1850s, the teaching of botany to the children of 'the labouring classes' at the village school there, and his ideas were enthusiastically taken up by the newly formed Department of Science and Art for use throughout the country. Prizes were given to children, 'village botanists', for herbarium specimens and collections at the annual village horticultural show. Henslow claimed that as the result of the 'village botany' at Hitcham school 'Observant faculties have been strengthened, reasoning powers expanded, the intellectual and moral status improved', and that the study fostered 'habits of patience, perseverance and caution'. An Inspector of Schools, another clergyman, commented of Henslow's school botany work that it 'usefully directs the attention of his pupils to observe the beauties of nature amongst which they dwell'. Henslow never lost sight of the scientific importance of botanical teaching, but there was also something of a missionary zeal about his approach to it as well.[21]

The dedication with which many clergy enthusiastically fostered natural history societies in the nineteenth century illustrates the same theme: through a diligent study of Creation, humanity may approach the Creator. A study of the records of the hundreds of local societies and field clubs in different parts of the British Isles, shows that parochial clergy took a prominent part in their organisation throughout much of the nineteenth century. Here, too, other concerns can be identified. Activity was preferable to the devil's aid, idleness; outdoor activity was particularly worthy and 'healthy', and well-directed outdoor activity such as collecting plants, observing geology or watching birds was especially to be encouraged – it was almost a moral and patriotic duty. The eccentric William Buckland ended a geological excursion to Dudley Caverns at the British Association meeting in Birmingham in 1839 with a thundering rendition of 'God Save the Queen'.[22] He also dedicated his book on *Diluvial Geology* to Queen Victoria. Saintly, evangelical Thomas Taylor Lewis (1801–1858), assistant and correspondent of such luminaries as Darwin and Murchison, was probably less of a bizarre personality in the field in his beloved Welsh borderland, but was important as founder of the Woolhope Field Club (see chapter 8).[23]

Yet another contemporary preoccupation was with museums (also discussed more fully in chapter 8). Henslow was an enthusiastic champion, playing an important role in the formation of the Ipswich Museum, 14 miles (22km) from where he lived in Suffolk, in 1848, and also in the development of the British Museum (Natural History). He saw a museum not only as a place of exhibits where all might come to learn, but a centre where science, and in particular natural history, could be taught and discussed. He regularly used to lecture at the Ipswich Museum.[24] Many other examples could be instanced: the Reverend Henry Hugh Higgins (1814–1893) occupied a similar place in the development of the Liverpool Museum.[25] It would be too extreme to suggest that some clergy saw museums as part of an apparatus for social control, but the idea that such institutions might assist in imbuing the common people with a respect for nature, for the Creator, and for authority would not be so far from the truth. Frequently in his *Norfolk Diary* the Reverend Benjamin Armstrong comments favourably on the 'respectful' nature of the 'poor' in a particular parish. Above all else the nineteenth-century gentry – the class of society to which many of the clergy belonged – sought respect.[26]

It is a logical step from a fascination with the works of creation, and a desire that all who wish to might know about them, to having a concern for their welfare. The tradition of a love of animals is an ancient one in the Christian tradition, going back to St Francis of Assisi (1182–1226), and indeed much before. The 'conversion' of Charles Jourdain from egg-collector to conservationist has been mentioned already, and is not without parallels.[27] The Reverend Peter Hartley was active in the Royal Society for the Protection of Birds for many years. In the wider field of of conservation we may mention the role of the Reverend Canon H. D. Rawnsley (1851–1920), Vicar of Crosthwaite, near Keswick, active like the well-known author Beatrix Potter, who lived nearby for long periods, and whom he profoundly influenced and encouraged, in the formative years of the National Trust. Such men would have seen the concern for the conservation of the whole of creation – plant and animal, life and landscape – as part of their Christian duty (see pages 147–150). Coming still closer to the time of writing, one might mention the role of a number of clergy in the work of their local naturalists' and conservation trusts; thus Gordon Graham is an active member of the Durham County Conservation Trust.

Continuity in the countryside

Clergy until relatively recent times often had a very long association with a single location. Thus a man might be able to gain a very close understanding of the natural history, landscape and human inhabitants of a limited stretch of countryside. Gilbert White, born and dying in the parish of Selborne in Hampshire, and living there off and on for the whole of his life, displays in his *Natural History of Selborne*, an intimate knowledge of the soils and landforms, vegetation and weather, settlement patterns and folk-lore of an area that was about thirty miles (around 50km) in circumference. The Reverend Professor John Stevens Henslow, botanist, was at Hitcham for 24 years: he used the area as a field laboratory for many studies including investigations of fungal diseases of plants, and on soil fertility. The Reverend Benjamin Armstrong (1817–1890) kept a diary, often describing events, scenes, personalities and weather of the East Anglian countryside during his 38 years as Vicar of East Dereham in Norfolk.[28] Another notable nineteenth-century incumbency was that of Henry Dew (1819–1901) who was Rector of Whitney-on-Wye for 58 years. The record books suggest however, that the longest of any incumbency in the Church of England was that of another Norfolk man, the Reverend Bartholomew Edwards, Rector of St Nicholas, Ashill for 75 years and 357 days (1813–1889). It is claimed that he was absent from his parish for only three Sundays between 1859 and 1889, the year in which he died within nine days of his hundredth birthday. There is some uncertainty whether the Reverend Richard Sherinton was instituted to Folkestone in Kent, in 1524 or 1529; if the earlier date is correct, his incumbency, which lasted until 1601, was very slightly longer than that of Mr Edwards. The parish of Farringdon, Hampshire, where Gilbert White was curate 1761–1784 had only two incumbents over a period of 122 years (1797–1919). Only slightly less remarkable is the fact that the parish of Kilkhampton in Cornwall had only four incumbents between 1804 and 1940 (136 years): one of them only remained in the living for two years, so the other three had an average incumbency of around 45 years. The Church of England clergy have always been notoriously long-lived. (Not all these individuals were naturalists.)

It was frequently the case that a son followed a father or grandfather as rector or vicar of a parish: Gilbert White was curate where his grandfather had been vicar. There have been a number of instances where a joint father-and-son incumbency lasted for around a century. Yet another Norfolk clergyman, Canon Marcon, Rector of Edgefield, for over 60 years (1875–1937), died in the same room of the rectory in which he had been born in 1850, for he succeeded his father as rector. Archbishop Geoffrey Francis Fisher (Lord Fisher of Lambeth, 1887–1972) was the son and grandson of Rectors of Higham-on-the-Hill, Nuneaton, both of whom held the living for forty years; his brother held the same living for twenty years: the right of patronage of the living has been held by the Fisher family for generations. Even more remarkable is the record of the Southcomb family, whose members held the parish of Rose Ash in Devon for nearly three hundred years; eight generations were successive incumbents from 1675 until 1948. In the adjoining county of Dorset, the Reverend Octavius Pickard-Cambridge (1828–1917) acted first as curate to his father (who was both squire and parson of the parish of Bloxworth – 'squarson'), and then followed him as rector of the parish from 1868 until his death nearly fifty years later. During this time, and right from his earlier childhood wanderings into the nearby countryside, Octavius built up an unrivalled knowledge of the natural history of the Dorset heathlands.[29]

An interesting example of the tight interconnection between family and place in the English clerical tradition is shown by the career of the

Reverend E. Ponsonby Knubley (1850–1931), who was born in Knaresborough in Yorkshire, son of the Reverend Miles Ponsonby Knubley, then curate of the nearby village church at Farnham. With the early death of his father, his mother remarried the Vicar of Steeple Ashton in Wiltshire, where he was brought up. After Magdalene College, Cambridge, and a curacy in Battersea, he returned to Yorkshire in 1878 as Vicar of Staveley in the Diocese of Ripon, scarcely a couple of miles from his father's old parish of Farnham. Nineteen years later (in 1897) he moved back to Steeple Ashton, in which parish he spent the last thirty-four years of his life. He thus could be said to have followed both his father and step-father. In his time he contributed much to natural history in both Yorkshire and Wiltshire, being particularly interested in the study of birds and birds' eggs. Towards the end of his life the Bishop of Salisbury described him as 'a fine example of an English country parson, loved and valued by us all.'[30]

Yet another example of striking continuity is shown by three clergy – grandfather, father and son – all named John Hemsted (the name Hempsted appears in some records) whose lives spanned the period 1660 to 1824. All seem to have held parishes in eastern England, particularly in Suffolk; John Hemsted II, for example was Vicar of Haverhill in Suffolk, from 1730 to 1769. John Hempsted III was born close by at Linton (Cambridgeshire), and was for while curate at St Mary's Newmarket, Suffolk, before becoming Vicar of St Paul's, Bedford, a parish he held from 1782 to 1824, although he seems to have remained resident in Suffolk for some time after his institution to the Bedford living. It is not certain the extent to which all were naturalists, but certainly John III was a competent botanist, supplying many records and specimens for James Sowerby's *English Botany*.[31]

Some of these examples of long family associations with parishes usually arose partly because the *advowson*, or right to appoint the incumbent, was a form of property that might be held by one family, and exercised on its own behalf, or on behalf of another related family, for generations. To take a single example, the right of patronage of the parish of St James, Kilkhampton, Cornwall, already mentioned, was held by the Granville family, and their descendants, eventually the Thynne family, from 1238 until the late 1980s – around 750 years. During that time the rector was a man with the surname Granville four times, these incumbencies totalling 114 years. John Granville (Rector from 1524 to 1580), in his 56 years served under seven bishops, and in the turbulent reigns of Henry VIII, Edward VI, Mary and Elizabeth I. Arthur Christopher Thynne, appointed when Lord John Thynne was patron, was Rector for 49 years, from 1859 to 1908.[32] The Fisher family example was mentioned above. In passing we may note that with the death of Prebendary John Lance in September 1991, at the age of 64, there came to an end a family line that had held prebends (canonries) of the Cathedral of Bath and Wells in Somerset for over 100 years.

Another reason for this extraordinary continuity was the legal doctrine of parson's freehold. An English parson has the freehold of the 'rights, members and appurtenances' as legal documents so splendidly put it, of his position as rector or vicar of the parish. His curates might come and go, but the incumbent of a parish could stay as long as he pleased: this was often until death. It was only in the case of gross misconduct, and following exhaustive legal enquiry that he could be deprived of his living. The system had, of course, serious disadvantages, in that a man might become lazy, drunken, or neglectful of his duties, and it would not be easy to displace him. It protected, however, the parson from the perhaps transient predilections of the Diocesan Bishop or difficult local residents, and it provided a base from which he could preach the Word, as he saw it, without fear or favour. Owen Chadwick, in *The Victorian Church* summarised the situation:

> The freehold gave a man such security that he could say what he liked to his parishioners whether they would hear or whether they would forebear. It enabled him to be prophet or saint, lover of incense or hammer of bishops. It enabled him to neglect his work and yet survive, or denounce his squire for sin, and yet survive. But it made it difficult to change his work to what he needed when he needed . . . The freehold, still a precious right to the incumbent, became a discomfort to those who cared for the welfare of the incumbent.[33]

Geoffrey Grigson (1905–1985) in *The Freedom of the Parish* put it as follows:

> Within his curtain of trees below church and village, my father had difficulty enough in the beginning. He was an East Anglian, not a Cornishman. He was a stranger who had to be teased and tested. His orchard was robbed, coal was taken from the vast cellar . . . But he stayed; and staying makes all the difference. The church in its old wisdom made the parson's living his freehold. The parson entered upon his living, and then shifting him, if he did no heinous villainy, was . . . like trying to shift Helvellyn. If this meant security for the bad priest, it meant security as well for the good, it gave the good man authority and the will, and ability, to resist. Stay, and you are likely to be accepted. My father was accepted, liked, and loved, I think, before the end; for . . . he came from a long line of parsons used . . . to the peculiarities of the country parish. . . . He

> had seven children born in the vicarage, christened in the church and brought up among the farms and cottages.[34]

Such continuity could lead to an intimate bond developing amongst parson, people and countryside. In the case of parson-naturalists it allowed a man to develop an extraordinarily detailed knowledge of the plants and animals of a single location. Such a man was the Reverend Leonard Jenyns (1800–1893), who was incumbent at Swaffham Bulbeck in Cambridgeshire for thirty years. He strongly believed in

> the moral influence a clergyman may acquire over his parishioners, if he reside among them for a sufficient term of years. It is seldom that any lasting good can be effected in a parish by those who, from some cause of dissatisfaction or other, seek to change their living or curacy, as the case may be – perhaps not once only, but twice or oftener.[35]

This is very different view from the modern one, where an incumbent is often considered as outstaying his welcome if he remains above five or ten years in a parish. Jenyns by all accounts was well loved, being given a handsome set of forty-nine divinity books when he left. He also used his time profitably as a naturalist, producing nearly thirty publications in this time, many in the leading journals of the day, and many concerned with the natural history of the woods, fens and fields of Cambridgeshire.

Another example was John William Chaloner (1811–1894), a fine field naturalist of the old school. One obituary writer recalled how 'rare birds came within his ken during his parish walks'; notes of them were sent to *The Naturalist*. He was also described as having 'an irrepressible capacity for storing facts and making observations [on] plants, fishes, birds, beasts, and insects' being compared in that regard to Gilbert White. He was born in St Andrew's Rectory, Newton Kyme, Yorkshire, son of the Rector, also something of a naturalist, who held the living for several decades, until his death in 1830. John Chaloner died in the same house as he was born. Thus father and son between them held the living, with a short break, for nigh on a century.[36]

Another Yorkshire father-and-son team of naturalists and local historians held the parish of St James, Nunburnholme (East Riding) continuously from 1854 until 1910. The Reverend Francis Orpen Morris (1810–1893) (see Plate 10), once described as a 'zoophilist', a prolific writer of semi-popular books on natural history, particularly on birds and butterflies. He was also editor of the journal, the *Naturalist,*[37] for a few years and a pioneer of bird conservation. One of his earlier achievements was the publication of *Bible Natural History*, in 20 monthly parts, 1849–1850. His successor in the living was his son, the Reverend Marmaduke Charles Orpen Morris, who was incumbent from 1893 until 1910. Marmaduke was something of a naturalist, leaving an interesting list of 139 'flowers' found in the parish, but better known as an antiquarian and an authority on the Yorkshire dialect. Like his father he was buried in the churchyard at Nunburnholme. He was responsible for building the tower at St James church, so that it is locally said 'that the church as it now stands is a monument to the Morris family'.[38]

The network

It is difficult for the citizen of the twenty-first century to appreciate that until well into the nineteenth century the two most important ways of diffusing scientific information were through face-to-face personal contact and correspondence. It is not without significance that the best-known natural history book in the English language (White's *Selborne*) should consist of a series of letters written by a parson.

Books there certainly were, but they were expensive, and few in number, so that the publication of a new natural history work was a major event. Public libraries did not exist, reading rooms beginning to appear around 1880. Indeed the personal libraries of some quite eminent scholars did not comprise more than a few dozen volumes. Booksellers were rare outside London and the university towns. There were only a limited number of scientific journals.

In the seventeenth and eighteenth centuries, and indeed to some extent until the time of Charles Darwin, the exchange of specimens and letters by post to a considerable extent fulfilled the same purpose as the publication of the modern scientific paper. Personal meetings in the drawing-rooms and studies of scholars occupied the place of today's scientific conference. The letter that follows, although rather lengthy is perhaps worth quoting in full, as it is typical of the thousands of letters that crossed the country, containing natural history observations, as well as fragments of family gossip. It is from the Reverend Gerald Smith (1804–1881), to a John Barton. Here we see the exchange of publications and specimens proceeding, members of the family assisting with botanical enquiries, an interest in botany passing from father to son, important links with other botanists (including John Henslow) and organizations. Interestingly, towards the conclusion of the letter a theological justification for a delight in nature that would have represented the philosophical position of many a nineteenth-century parson-naturalist. Smith's plants are now held at Oxford, and his letters are mainly at Kew.[39]

Gerald Smith to John Barton Copse Hill [Ashbourne]
9 May [18]56

My dear John
Your letter was cordially welcome, and would have been more promptly answered, had I been able to give a clear account of my views on bog-violets, which, I confess, removal from the south to the north and from east to west has tended to mystify considerably. When at dear East Marden, I believed in V. canina, flavicornis & latea: but the plants of Yorkshire, Merioneth, Derbyshire and Worcestershire have united in supplying materials for good bridges over the gulphs and appeared to separate those species one from another. Here we have one violet only: a plant with the old and dead shoots below those of this spring – with a small flower of variable hue, & with stipules ciliated or entire. We have not, so far as I have seen, the plant with large flat faced flowers so frequent in the south of England upon calcareous soil. I enclose an Osmaston violet, V. Canina, & with it two plants, which are very normal states of V. punila (including V. flavicornis & lactea), & of V. canina: but the remarks made about the branches of the past being above the branches of the present year I have no means of verifying: my herbarium which is not poor in this genus affords us proof of this being the case with V. pumila at least. As to V. flavicornis, distinct as the compact plants of that upon waste places of the North Downs appeared to be – the limb so azure, the spur so yellow, the leaves so narrow & the stipules jagged & large, in Cheshire, near Chester I observed the hedge violet – V. canina with yellow spurs and brilliant blue limbs while the foliage was broadly cordate & the habit that of the common V. canina. Again as to the azure colour of V. lactea – I have specimens from Brombourne Leas (?) & from North Malvern with white flowers & herbage of variable breadth and length: but I confess that I am not sure that V. lactea is not a species, & that the plants I speak of are white varieties of V. canina. The Tunbridge Wells & Cockbush (?) common V. lactea are exactly alike, & occupy similar stations among heather upon peaty soil. I left in the garden at East Marden a variety of V. canina from the downs above Elstead truly pink, & tufted – I have seen it dilute blue also, & thus so far as the colour is concerned, no rule can be made: but the straggling habit & attenuated points of the leaves of V. lactea seem to be more trustworthy characters. The best test would be the cultivation of the seeds of the supposed species: & I would recommend you also get dear Elizabeth and Annie to work, to send you living plants of the violets now in blossom from the banks and woods, & the high downs around Chichester, to compare with your

> local forms. Comparisons in this case are happy & useful. You would presently see whether you could group together forms under different types, or whether they undulate the one into the other like waves upon the water & prove they are successive modifications of the one form. I have omitted to mention that in V. lactea the direction of the leaves is, so far as I have seen, upwards & not spreading. Sowerby's figure shows that character, if I remember right. It is very pleasant to think of you taking up the garland which fell from your Father's hand, & I do hope you will never forsake his (botanical) friend, but that we may enjoy much refreshing & improving intercourse amidst nature's lovely scenes, or at least in the study of flowers. I thank you for the account of Professor Henslow's lecture: I have read of his Parochial class in Botany, & shall send him, if I am permitted, an order soon for dried plants. He & I once exchanged frequently. Both Edinburgh & London Botanical Societies have made that a business which used to be a private pleasure – I mean the exchange of plants & people are apt to become selfish where exchange is made. I do not apply this remark to the Professor. He was always very liberal. Can you send me a few fresh specimens of Anenome pulsatilla? I have received this and roots of Anenome ranunculoides from Waltham Abbey woods. But I must finish. Our mutual pastimes have, I trust, a true bearing upon the great end in life. 'Great are the works of the Lord, sought out of all of them that have pleasure in Him'. To His care and love I commend you. Mrs Smith unites with me in affectionate remembrances. We both blame Joseph for passing us & not coming to us: but he is in love. Believe me, ever,
>
> dear John, your affectionate friend

The natural history student of the generations of John Ray or Gilbert White was therefore much more dependent upon his network of personal contacts than his modern analogue. The English parson-naturalist of the eighteenth or early nineteenth century was perhaps uniquely well-positioned in this web of connections. He belonged to a relatively small middle or upper-middle class: he had in all probability been to one of two universities, Oxford or Cambridge – four following the foundation of Durham in 1832, and King's College London in 1829. (University College, London, founded in 1827 was initially known as 'That Godless institution in Gower Street'.) Then as now, the friends and contacts made at university proved lifelong. He was, above all, linked to his clerical and scientific colleagues (so often one and the same) by bonds of family and marriage.

The constancy of the tightly-knit nature of English clerical families, more-or-less up until the First World War, is remarkable. For generation after generation almost all the sons of a family would be clergy, and almost all the daughters married into rectories and vicarages. This interconnection by marriage over several generations inevitably meant that such families were related, and also that cousins frequently married. One estimate has it that in total about a third of all the children of clergy married the children of clergymen. The family of Parson White of Selborne provides an example of the network of kinship connections that developed.

The grandfather of the famous Selborne naturalist, also called Gilbert White (1650–1729), was Vicar of Selborne from 1681 until 1729. His first son John (1688–1758) qualified as a barrister, but never seems to have practised. He married Anne Holt, a rector's daughter from Streatham. John's sister Dorothea married the successor to Gilbert White senior in the living at Selborne, the Reverend Basil Cane; his other sister, Elizabeth, married a cousin, the Reverend Charles White. John White, the father of Gilbert White junior had, besides the son who achieved his temporal immortality through his authorship of *The Natural History of Selborne*, four other sons who survived into their majority. Two took orders: John (1727–1779) who became Chaplain to the Forces in Gibraltar, and Henry ('Harry', 1733–1788) who followed Gilbert and John to Oxford and into the church, and who in due course became Rector of Fyfield, some twenty-five miles to the north-west of Selborne. Thomas (1724–1797) became a London merchant, and Benjamin (1725–1794) a bookseller: not in holy orders themselves, they both married the daughters of parsonages. Benjamin in 1753 married Anne Yalden, daughter of the Vicar of Newton Valance, the Reverend Richard Yalden; when she died, he married her father's widow, Mary. Thomas White married the widow of William Yalden (Anne's brother). The family circle was indeed a tight one.[40]

Gilbert White's closest, lifelong friend (their acquaintanceship dated from their time at Oriel College, Oxford) was John Mulso (*c.*1720–1791) was similarly connected. Both his brothers, Thomas and Edward became parsons, and visited Gilbert at Selborne from time to time. There were times when some five or six Mulso, White and other clergy were staying at The Wakes or nearby at one time. A number of them corresponded with Gilbert on natural history and the countryside.

Half a century later, John Stevens Henslow (Plate 6) was the centre of another extensive network of clerical and scientific connections. Henslow himself married the sister of the Reverend Leonard Jenyns, an all-round naturalist (mentioned above), but particularly well-known as the describer of the fish specimens from the *Beagle* voyage. Leonard

Jenyns, as well as being the son of a parson himself, was kin to another clerical naturalist of note, the Reverend Leonard Chapplelow, and married (in 1844) the daughter of the Reverend Andrew Daubeny (1784–1877). One of Henslow's daughters was the god-child of the Reverend Adam Sedgwick, distinguished Professor of Geology in the University of Cambridge for 60 years, as well as Canon of Norwich Cathedral. Indeed the bond between Adam Sedgwick and the whole family seems to have been a close one, for in a letter written to his god-daughter much later in life, he recalled how on summer afternoons in Cambridge he used to visit the family for tea and 'laugh and play' with the Henslow children. Another Henslow daughter married Joseph Dalton Hooker, also a close friend of Darwin. On her death, Hooker made an equally auspicious second marriage, to the widow of zoologist Sir William Jardine, herself a daughter of the Reverend W. S. Symonds, a pioneer geologist, author of *Old Stones*, and founder of Malvern Field Club. Another clerical geologist, the Reverend John Gunn, one time president of the Geological Society of Norwich, was a more distant connection of the Hooker family. John Henslow had two sons who became parsons. The elder was Leonard Ramsay (presumably named after his uncle), who followed his father to St John's and then to Hitcham as curate (1854–1856), before, like his uncle, moving to Bath, where he became Rector of Zeals. His younger brother George (about four years younger) went to Christ's College, Cambridge (there's the Darwin link again), and was a competent botanist. And so on.[41]

It was through this network, held together through the links of kinship and marriage, that information was passed in letter form, and through personal contacts. These latter were important: a close acquaintance-ship with one member of the the fraternity meant that one had entrée into the circles of others. If a clergyman-naturalist were to take a living in some distant part of the country, he would already have a ready-made suite of clerical and scientific associates. There would be someone in the neighbourhood with a link, through school, university or kinship, who could introduce him. Specimens, as well as clerical gossip, were exchanged at rural deanery meetings and other clergy gatherings. When a man sought information on the natural history of another part of the country, or from the colonies, or on a biological group or other topic of which he had little personal knowledge it was often to a clerical colleague that he turned. Thus when the Reverend William Purchas, Vicar of Alstonfield, Ashbourne, Staffordshire in the Diocese of Lichfield from 1870 until his death in 1903, then living outside the county, needed a collaborator for his *Flora of Herefordshire* (1889), the Reverend Augustus Ley, Vicar of Sellack with Kings Capel was able to assist him. The Reverend W. E. Symonds, FGS (Fellow of the

Geological Society), Rector of Pendock provided a note on the geology of the district. (In fact the theological positions of the Purchas and Symonds were rather different, and this led to difficulties later, see chapter 7.[42])

Conclusion

The tradition of the English parson-naturalist has thus proved an extremely persistent one. The beginnings can be seen in the writings of some of the clerics of the later Middle Ages, and clergy naturalists had a near-dominating influence in the natural science of late eighteenth and nineteenth centuries, the tradition remaining strong through to the Edwardian period. Although much less numerous than previously, there are still some who uphold the fine amateur tradition in English natural history while exercising a parochial ministry. The reasons for the persistence and importance of the clergyman-naturalist role in the English countryside and in English science, are complex. There are strong theological imperatives as to why the roles of naturalist and parson should be combined, but this does not explain why the tradition should be so much stronger in the established church than in the free churches and in the Roman Catholic Church. The tradition's strength may be partly explained by the strength of the parochial system: in each country parish, no matter how small, was a parson. Sometimes the community was so small, perhaps just one or two hundred souls, that the total amount of work cannot have been very onerous. In the 1870s one country doctor said that the 'great disease that afflicted country clergy was want of work'.[43] The legal doctrine of parson's freehold meant that some incumbencies were long, and indeed, because of the system of patronage, on some occasions lasted for more than one generation. An intimate association with a particular locality could thereby develop. There existed a very tight social network through which information passed, and which may have contributed to the stability of the system in general.

In the chapters that follow an attempt will be made to describe the extent to which the preoccupations of the clergy, in regard to their natural history, have remained constant throughout the last few centuries, and the extent to which it has subtly changed. While a broadly 'taxonomic' treatment is adopted, with naturalists being discussed under the headings of the main biological groups they studied, biographical information about a range of individuals from different periods is included, and several other themes will be discussed. These will include the identification of some naturalists with a particular theological position where this is relevant to their work, the contribution of the genre to the development of science as a whole, together with the importance of the notion of the fellowship of parson-naturalists as a social network.

Notes

1 Letter 37, Gilbert White, *The Natural History of Selborne*. 1st edition, 1789.
2 Mabey, R., *Gilbert White* (London, Century, 1986); Foster, P. G. M., *Gilbert White and his Records* (London, Christopher Helm, 1988).
3 Raven, C. E., *English Naturalists from Neckam to Ray* (Cambridge University Press, 1947); Jones, R. D., *William Turner: Tudor Naturalist, Physician and Divine* (London, Routledge, 1988).
4 Raven, C. E., *John Ray: Naturalist* (Cambridge University Press, 1942).
5 Amstrong, P. H., 'Thomas Bonney (1833–1923)', *Geographers: Biobibliographic Studies*, 17, 1997, pp. 9–16.
6 Geikie, A., *Memoir of John Mitchell* (Cambridge University Press, 1918).
7 Russell-Gebbett, J., *Henslow of Hitcham* (Lavenham, Terence Dalton, 1977).
8 *Illustrated London News*, 22 June 1861.
9 Armstrong, E. A., *Bird Display and Behaviour* (Cambridge University Press, 1947), *The Wren* (London, Collins New Naturalist, 1955), *A Study of Bird Song* (Oxford University Press, 1963).
10 Paley, W., *Natural Theology: Evidences of the Existence and Attributes of the Deity Collected from the Appearances of Nature* (London, C & J Rivington, 1825 ed.), p. 377.
11 *ibid.*,p. 9.
12 Barlow, N., ed., *The Autobiography of Charles Darwin* (London, Collins, 1958).
13 Pickard-Cambridge, A. W., *Memoir of the Reverend Octavius Pickard-Cambridge, MA, FRS, by his son* (Oxford, privately printed, 1918).
14 Gillispie, C. C., *Genesis and Geology* (Cambridge, Mass., Harvard University Press, 1951); Livingstone, D. N., *Darwin's Forgotten Defenders* (Edinburgh, Scottish Academic Press, 1987).
15 Tristram, H. B., 'On the ornithology of Northern Africa . . . Part III, the Sahara, continued', *The Ibis*, 1, October 1858, pp. 415–435.
16 Moore, J., *The Post-Darwinian Controversies* (Cambridge University Press, 1979), p. 196.
17 Morris, F. Orpen, *Difficulties of Darwinism* (London, William Pool, 1869); *All the Articles of the Darwin Faith* (London, William Poole, 1875); *A Guard Against the Guardian: Letters on Evolution addressed to the Guardian Newspaper* (London, William Poole, 1877); and *The Demands of Darwinism on Credulity* (London, Partridge, 1890).
18 Although Haim Goren, Galilee, Israel (personal communication) has suggested to me that the measure of competition that existed between the Palestine Exploration Fund, and its German analogue Der Deutsche Verein zur Erforschung Palästina's (German Society for the Study of Palestine) was to some extent a manifestation of national rivalry.
19 Tristram, H. B., *Flora and Fauna* in *The Survey of Western Palestine: Flora and*

Fauna (London, Palestine Exploration Fund, 1884).

20 Tristram, H. B., *The Land of Israel: a Journal of Travels in Palestine undertaken with Special Reference to its Physical Characters*, 2nd ed. (London, SPCK, 1866).

21 Russell-Gebbett, 1977, op. cit.

22 Gillispie, 1951, op. cit., pp. 200–201.

23 Collom, B., *Victorian Country Parsons (*London, Constable, 1977), pp. 34, 112–123.

24 Russell-Gebbett, 1977, op. cit.

25 Ford, W. K., 'The Rev. Henry Hugh Higgins, MA, a Liverpool biologist' *Liverpool Libraries, Museums and Arts Committee Bulletin* 1[2] 1952, pp. 67–79.

26 Armstrong, H. B. W., ed., *Armstrong's Norfolk Diary: Passages from the Diary of Benjamin John Armstrong* (London, Hodder and Stoughton, 1963).

27 Allen, D. E., *The Naturalist in Britain: a Social History* (Harmondsworth, Penguin Books, 1978).

28 Armstrong, H. B. W., op. cit.

29 Armstrong, P. H., 'Three parson-naturalists from Durham', *The Naturalist*, 120, 1995. pp. 65–75; Pickard-Cambridge, 1918, op. cit.

30 'F.A.M.', 'Canon E. Ponsonby Knubley, MA (1850–1931)', *The Naturalist*, [57], 1932, pp. 17–19.

31 Oswald, P., 1991, 'The Revd John Hemsted (1747?–1824) *Nature in Cambridgeshire*, 33, 1991, pp. 26–34.

32 Greener, W., *Kilkhampton Church* (Privately printed, 1993).

33 Chadwick, O., *The Victorian Church*, Part 2, (London, Adam and Charles Black, 1970), pp. 169–170.

34 Grigson, G., *The Freedom of the Parish* (London, Phoenix, 1954).

35 Blomefield, L., (late Jenyns), *Chapters in my Life* (Bath, privately printed, 1889).

36 Emett, J., 'In memoriam: John William Chaloner', *The Naturalist*, [19], 1894, pp. 113–115.

37 This journal is sometimes cited as *Naturalist (F. O. Morris)*, London: it ran from 1851 to 1858. It was nothing to do with the Yorkshire Naturalists' Union, publisher of *The Naturalist*, which commenced in 1854.

38 Lambert, M., 'F. O. Morris' list of Yorkshire birds', *The Naturalist*, 117, 1992, pp. 113–125.

39 Shaw, G. A., 'Some botanical correspondence of the mid 19th century', *The Naturalist*, 103, 1978, pp. 31–33.

40 Mabey, 1986, op. cit.

41 Russell-Gebbett, 1977, op. cit. and Allen D. E., 1978, op. cit.

42 Purchas, W. H. and Ley, A., *Flora of Herefordshire* (Hereford, Jakeman & Carver, 1889). See also Armstrong, P. H., 1995, op. cit.

43 Chadwick, O., 1970, op. cit., p. 166, quoting Church Congress Reports, 1893.

Chapter Two

Monks, monsters and the mediaeval mind: the antecedents of the English parson-naturalist

The mediaeval countryside

The inquirer transplanted from the English countryside of the twenty-first century to that of the Middle Ages would find much that was familiar.

The topography would have changed but little in under a millennium. The meanders of a lowland river might have shifted their position: here and there along the coasts, as at Dunwich in Suffolk, and a few places along the south coast, appreciable areas have been eroded. But in general the form of the land, the disposition of highland and lowland, has undergone little change over the few hundred years.

The proportion of woodland in the landscape would not be markedly different, although the distribution was more uneven than at present during the mediaeval period (say from the Norman Conquest to the sixteenth century). There were substantial parts of the kingdom that at the time of the Domesday survey in 1086 were largely devoid of tree cover: the Yorkshire Wolds, the Suffolk Sandlings, a good deal of Lincolnshire, and some of the Fens, for example. However, these were balanced by regions where timbered land was more continuous: the Weald was largely wooded, and the county of Worcester was probably about 40 per cent forest covered. Over much of the country a good proportion of the primeval wildwood had already been cleared by the time of King William I's arrival, and the landscape was one of pockets of wood, seldom more than a few acres in extent, surrounded by open country – a mosaic of meadow and farmland. Moreover, many of the woods that formed features of the mediaeval landscape still exist; for example, in the year 1251, Hugo de Northwold, the Lord Bishop of Ely, had a survey of his estates compiled: the result was the Old Coucher

Book of Ely (the original of which is in the British Museum: there are copies in Gonville and Caius College, Cambridge, and the Ely Diocesan Registry). Within this document is the entry:

> The Wood. There is one wood which is called Heyle which contains fourscore acres. Item there is another wood which is called Litlehund, which contains thirty two acres . . .[1]

Hayley Wood in Cambridgeshire had probably been in existence within more or less the same boundaries for several centuries when the Bishop's surveyors made these observations, to which they added some comments on management. Another survey of the Bishop's estates made in 1351 shows woods with the same names of approximately the same size, and incidentally, being managed in much the same way with the regular cutting of underwood. After the dissolution of the monasteries, Queen Elizabeth I leased Hayley Wood to one John Spurling for 21 years in 1584, and its continued existence, notwithstanding its occasional expansion and contraction, can be checked in leases, valuations and reports down to its present ownership by the Wildlife Trust of Bedfordshire and Cambridgeshire.[2]

Certainly major parts of the open country surrounding the woods were in open fields during the mediaeval period. A single example will illustrate the general character of the landscape in the mid-fourteenth century. The West Fields of Cambridge comprised some 1480 acres of arable land, divided into some 3350 selions or strips, each about half an acre in area, typically measuring one furlong by two perches (220 yards by 11 yards).[3] These were grouped into 68 furlongs, and these into four large fields. Each year approximately one third of the land, one of the larger fields or the two smaller ones, was left fallow, the remainder being cultivated. The vast fields adjoined similar expanses in the nearby villages. Such an open landscape is of course different from the planned, enclosed landscape that followed the enclosures of the eighteenth and nineteenth centuries with its varied network of boundary hedgerows in lowland England, and drystone walls in the uplands. Yet in its openness, and ecological poverty it was probably not so very different from the 'arable prairies' that have resulted from the removal of those hedgerows in the decades since the Second World War over much of the country.

Most of the plants and animals of England's mediaeval countryside would be familiar to the modern field naturalist. The oak, ash, maple, elm, aspen, hazel, blackthorn, and the two species of hawthorn (*Crataegus monogyna* and *C. oxyacanthoides*) and of birch (*Betula pubescens* and *B. verrucosa*) now growing at Hayley would all have been familiar to the mediaeval woodsman, who would understand the characteristics and uses of each. The beaver had already disappeared from English rivers by the Conquest, and the wolf had almost gone: one was killed in Surrey in 1212, and there are a few scattered mentions from the remainder of the century: a few may have continued on the North York Moors until the end of the fourteenth century. The rabbit was first introduced into England at the beginning of the twelfth century, and by the 1160s was probably familiar over much of the country. The raucous cough of that bird beloved of poachers, the pheasant, seems to have part of the English woodlands' sound-scene from about the same time: the species was certainly present by 1170.

If Bishop Hugo were able to view his woodland and farmland properties today he would find much that was familiar in the mosaic of open arable areas, occasional grasslands, scattered villages, and compact copses of mixed deciduous woodland. The landscape of his mind, however, and the thought processes with which he and his contemporaries evaluated the world about them, would have been very different indeed.

Mediaeval mental maps

It was not just that the whole structure of society was different, and that what was regarded as important and what of minor significance differed, but the basic assumptions behind everyday life, including such basic concepts of cause and effect, and the role and position of humanity in relation to the universe, were fundamentally dissimilar. The nature of natural history, and the way in which its study was undertaken in the mediaeval period has to be considered against very different yardsticks from those applied to the science of later centuries.

At one level, people were in close contact with their environment – the plants, the animals and the soils that supported them. Activities in field and coppice were tightly constrained by the weather. Towns were small, and the majority of England's (indeed Europe's) population was rural. Communities, of necessity, acquired, through experience and trial and error, a compendium of practical knowledge about plants used as sources of food or for decoration or medication, fish taken from the rivers, lakes and the sea that were eaten, animals and birds that were hunted, as well as on such matters as soils, weather patterns and the management of woodland. Familiarity in some cases led to appreciation: the masons who designed and carved the capitals of the chapter house at Southwell Minster around 1295, decorated them with the brilliantly natural leaves (and occasional flowers) of oak, buttercup, hawthorn, white bryony, crab apple, wild rose, potentilla, ivy, maple and hop. They clearly had an affection for the plants of the woods and fields nearby. The carvings are bursting with life and the workmen must have brought in bunches of foliage to serve as models.[4] Likewise the woodcarvers who sculpted the intricate and lively detail of a family of fox-cubs and a couple of displaying herons on the oak misericords in Chester Cathedral around 1380 must have had a perceptive eye for the mammals and birds of the local countryside.[5] Another splendid set of misericords decorated with animals and plants is to be found in the choir of St Mary's church, Richmond, Yorkshire. There, in carved stalls brought from Easby when that monastery was dissolved (1535) is to be seen a bat, hanging upside-down, with its large ears carefully carved: no detail has been missed; even the bone structure of the film-like wings is portrayed. Again the carver must have closely inspected a specimen before he put his tools to the timber.

Similarly the monks who decorated manuscripts with cameo depictions of flowers in amongst the illuminated capital letters and festoons of leaves around the borders of the text must surely often have had fresh specimens before them as they worked. It is also to monastic sources that we must turn for the very rare written accounts of animals that seem to be firmly based upon first-hand knowledge; such details are interpolated more-or-less incidentally into accounts with quite a different emphasis. The twelfth-century Thomas of Ely, inserted into the account of Hereward the Wake in *Liber Eliensis* (a manuscript preserved in the library of Trinity College, Cambridge) the following lively and enthusiastic piece about the Isle of Ely:

> The isle is within itself plentifully endowed, it is supplied with various kinds of herbage, and for its richer soil surpasses the rest of England. Most delightful for its charming fields and pastures, it is also remarkable for its beasts of the chase. Its woods and vine-yards are not worthy of equal praise, but it is beset by great meres and fens as though by a strong wall. In this isle there is an abundance of domestic cattle: stags, roes, goats and hares are found in its groves and by these fens. Moreover there is a fair plenty of otters, weasels and pole-cats, which in a hard winter are caught by traps, snares, or by other devices. But what am I to say of the kind of fishes, and of fowls, both those that fly and those that swim? In the eddy at the sluices of these meres are netted innumerable eels, large pike ['water wolves'] – even pickerel, perch, roach, burbot and lampreys which we call water snakes . . . As to fowls there are numberless geese, . . . coots, grebes, cormorants ['water crows'], herons and ducks, of which the number is very great. At midwinter, or when the birds moult their quills I

have seen them caught by the hundred, and even by three hundreds more or less, sometimes they are taken in nets as well as by bird-lime.[6]

In the details of land-use, soil, the barrier-like nature of the swamps and meres surrounding Ely and organisms present, the account chimes well with descriptions written several centuries later. Indeed some of the fish species mentioned are still to be caught in Fenland drainage lodes, and the birds are amongst those found in the patches of fen that remain, or along the slow rivers of the region. There is, however, little detail in the descriptions of species, nothing on behaviour or what we would now call ecology. The birds, mammals and fish are apparently valued as food, or in the case of the otter and stoat, presumably, for their fur, or perhaps because they prey upon animals felt to be useful. The account is an economic document, not a scientific one.

But even so, such practical details were rare: it was as though there were a barrier between those who had such personal and practical knowledge, and the scholars who attempted to store, classify and evaluate knowledge concerning the world about them. Between the mason or woodcarver with an eye for nature's detail, the woodsman who knew that cutting a copse would permit the woodland to regenerate in such-and-such a manner, the countryman who knew the ways of trout and hare – between these men on the one hand, and the writer surrounded by his books in his library, on the other, 'was a great gulf fixed'.

Let us examine why this should be so, and why therefore, the mediaeval view of the world was so very different from our own.

The church in mediaeval England was an influential force in the land. The abbots of the monasteries were wealthy magnates, and the higher clergy were persons of great consequence. The church was responsible for much education, and it was within the walls of the abbeys and monasteries that most scholarship was practised. Writers on natural history, usually clergy themselves, of course, were less concerned to expound the details of the reality around them, but to use nature 'as a storehouse of symbols of a different and more perfect world'. Much of nature – plants, animals, rocks, stars – was seen to contain allegorical lessons on the nature of God, and preferred human moral conduct. The Kingdom of Heaven, and the Life of the World to Come were seen as infinitely more important than the details of immediate reality: the nature of that Kingdom and the human relationship with it were of far greater consequence than the relationships between the kingdoms of this vain world or indeed, the relationships within the local stretch of countryside.[7] For this notion the the mediaeval church was especially indebted to St Augustine (354–430), who, in *City of God,* argued that the secular world was corrupt, and of little value. What a plant or bird might be able to teach humanity about the story of Christ's redemption of the world was therefore much more important than details of its appearance, or distribution. Moral truth was infinitely superior to the 'scientific' truth that was to be gained from observation. An acquaintance with the doings, and supposed doings, of nocturnal creatures might help good Christian folk, when they heard a barn owl give its eerie screech on flying from its home-barn of an evening, to be on guard against the Evil One. Watching sparrows copulate and bicker on the cottage roof was a warning to humans about the evils of licentiousness. The female pelican was believed to pierce her breast with its beak in order to sustain her young with her own lifeblood; this story would remind mediaeval women and men of the charity and self-sacrificing blood of Christ. The ibis was said to 'clean out its bowels with its own beak' and to enjoy eating corpses, snakes' eggs and dead fish. A bestiary put it as follows:

> This bird is typical of carnal man, who goes in for deadly dealings as if they were good spiritual food – by which his miserable soul gets nourished for punishment.
>
> You, on the other hand, good Christian fellow – who are born again by water and the Holy Spirit to enter the spiritual oceans of God's mysteries – on you he bestows the very finest food which he mentioned to the apostles, saying: 'The fruit of the Spirit is affection, peace, praise, forbearance, long suffering, etc.'[8]

Sometimes there was a root for these stories and anecdotes, which occur time and again, in the writings of mediaeval 'naturalists'. The idea of the pious pelican no doubt originated from the fact that pelicans have a large bag-like structure attached to their lower bill in which masticated fish and other food are held. The bag is pressed against the bird's breast as the food is expelled when the young are fed. Ibis can often be seen picking up scraps of carrion or fish from along the strandline, and twisting their necks so as to preen their hind quarters with their long bills. However, often the moral lessons to be drawn from vignettes of the countryside such as a white barn owl screeching in the churchyard, or sparrows scuttering around the farm were the product of pious minds that had little or no real knowledge of, or interest in natural history.

As late as 1635 in *Emblemes* Francis Quarles wrote:

> Before the knowledge of letters God was known by his Hieroglyphics. And what indeed are the heavens, the earth, nay every creature, but Hieroglyphics and emblems of his glory?[9]

Sometimes it may be almost impossible to disentangle the fragments of accurate observation, the moralizing imagery, biblical teaching, and the depictions of mythical monsters inserted for their entertainment value. Yet another set of misericords, in Ripon Cathedral, dated between 1489 and 1494, show this intermingling. An owl in flight swoops towards the observer, every feather detailed, talons outstretched, hooked beak protruding and large eyes staring ahead. But to what extent was the carver showing a creature with which he was familiar, and to what extent was he portraying a bird that was seen as a symbol of evil, because of its alleged inability to see in daylight, itself equated with the Jews failing to recognize Christ? Oak leaves, vine leaves and grapes are carved accurately, but such emblems alternate with a griffin (a winged quadruped with a lion's body and an eagle's face) and dragons. A representation of Jonah cast overboard into the jaws of a whale is next to a comic portrayal of two piglets dancing to the music of a bagpipe played by a sow: the pig is a symbol of gluttony and lust, the bagpipes a 'low' instrument, rousing animal passions. A pelican in her act of piety is near to another comic caricature: a man is wheeling a woman clutching a bottle and a stick in a barrow: depictions ridiculing women, revealing them as shrew-like or as gossips were common motifs. There are also wyverns (two-legged dragons), demi-angels, and a mermaid holding brush and mirror, symbolizing pride and vanity, and luring men to sin and damnation. A pair of realistic bears face one another, as do two birds eating fruit in a tree: the latter may provide an allegory for Christian souls eating the fruits of salvation. A series of three carvings provides an early strip cartoon. In the first misericord a fox stands in a pulpit, preaching to a cock and a goose: wandering friars had become notorious for their greed, and the image is thus a biting satire on certain travelling preachers. The second shows the fox running off with a goose, the outcome of being hoodwinked by the sweet words of the preaching fox. In the third the fox himself is being set upon by dogs. The foxes, geese and dogs are all portrayed quite realistically, but the moralistic component dominates. To add to the complexity of interpretation of the whole array, some of the designs are based on prints – including engravings of ornamental flowers, and a popular woodblock book, the *Bibilia Pauperum*; the woman in a wheelbarrow is taken from a German engraving of the 1470s. Here we see respect for published authority, a theme to which we return below. It might be observed that the creators of these carvings were not clergy, but travelling craftsmen of whom we seldom know even the names. However, as with the fragmentary illuminations of animals and plants in manuscripts, mentioned earlier, the inspiration was usually clerical.[10]

The pastime of falconry or hawking, and the lore associated with it, illustrates a number of aspects of the mediaeval view of the world and society. Feudal society was strictly hierarchical – in theory a man owed duties to, and might be owed rights from, those above and below him in the hierarchy. Certainly the privileges of some feudal lords were jealously guarded, and a number of statutes were passed protecting game resources, setting out who might take part in hunting game, and establishing stern punishments for those who poached. Falconry was the preserve of the elite, and indeed the *Boke of St Albans* (1486) sets out the type of bird appropriate to certain ranks, descending from an eagle for an emperor, a gyr falcon for a king, a 'falcon of the rock' for a duke, down to a hobby for a young man. A peregrine was regarded as the appropriate bird for an earl, and a merlin for a lady. A sparrowhawk was listed for a priest.[11] Each position in the complex hierarchy had a token allocated to it.

It seems that it was not unusual for the higher clergy to indulge in the sport of falconry. Richard de Swinfield, Bishop of Hereford, in 1289–1290, seems to have owned several falcons, and appointed one Adam Hairpin as falconer to look after his birds. In March 1290, the Bishop had one of his favourite birds sent to the Cathedral in Hereford for cure. In the following century, the Bishop of Ely attended a church service in Bermondsey, Southwark, leaving his hawk in the cloister. While the Lord Bishop was attending to ecclesiastical duties within, the hawk was taken. When the Bishop discovered his loss he promptly pronounced excommunication upon those who had stolen it.[12]

Hawks were regarded as status symbols, and persons of high rank would often travel with their birds. Indeed it was regarded as dishonourable for a man of rank to give up his hawk. The ownership of a good hawk was thus a piece of personal vanity to which the senior clergy were not immune. Because of their importance as a valuable form of property, a good deal of lore was accumulated concerning birds of prey: where they nested in the wild, their growth and development, the diseases from which they suffered. One of the earliest of the clerical naturalists who took note of some of this knowledge was Gerald de Barri (*c*.1146–1223) (his name is usually latinized to Giraldus Cambrensis), who although Welsh, travelled in England. Giraldus was born at Manorbier in Pembrokeshire, son of William de Barri and Princess Nesta; he was partly educated in Paris, and ordained in 1172. He visited Ireland in 1184–1185, writing extensively about that country in *Topographica Hibernica* in 1188. For a long period he was Archdeacon of Brecon. He was deeply involved in ecclesiastical controversy, twice being elected to the Bishopric of St David's but failing to obtain consecration.[13]

In *Topographica* Giraldus includes a number of details of hawks and hawking that appear to be based on careful personal observation. He describes the hawk soaring in wide circles, the swift stoop and the attempts of the quarry to escape as it 'Flits from side to side, now high, now low, while all the spectators are filled with delight.' He also made another interesting observation, eight hundred years before Darwin expounded the notion of 'the struggle for existence':

> It is, however, a remarkable fact in the history of this tribe of birds, that their nests are not more numerous than they were many centuries ago; and although they have broods every year, their numbers do not increase.[14]

Giraldus also noted the absence of snakes from Ireland, and the presence of the beaver in parts of Wales. He describes the distributions of fish such as the salmon, trout and grayling in rivers such as the Usk and the Wye. He has descriptions of both a woodpecker (probably the green woodpecker, *Picus viridis*) and of the golden oriole (*Oriolus oriolus*), mentioning its clear musical note. He stated that the nightingale has never entered Wales, and distinguished carefully between the whooper and the mute swan.[15] Not all of Giraldus' observations were, however, of the same high quality. Here is an account of barnacle geese, apparently read to the scholars and dignitaries of Oxford in 1186, after his return from a journey in Ireland:

> There are in this place many birds called Bernacae: Nature produces them against nature in a most extraordinary way. They are like marsh geese but somewhat smaller. They are produced from fir timber and are at first like gum. Afterwards they hang down by their beaks as if they were seaweed attached to the timber, and are surrounded by shells in order to grow more freely. Having thus in process of time been clothed with a strong coat of feathers, they either fall into the water or fly freely away into the air. They derive their food and growth from the sap of the wood or from the sea, by a secret and most wonderful process of alimentation. . . . They do not breed and lay eggs like other birds, nor do they ever hatch any eggs, nor do they seem to build nests in any corner of the earth.[16]

He claimed to have seen 'more than a thousand' of these creatures hanging in their shells from a piece of driftwood. He added that certain 'Bishops and religious men' dined on these birds at times of fasting on the basis that they were more fish than flesh or fowl.

There is evidence that the origins of the story may lie in the Near

East: there are similarities with Jewish and Arab tales. But it was typical of Giraldus to combine snatches of accurate observation with weird traditional tales. Canon C. E. Raven wrote of Giraldus that he was: 'Pompous and monstrously conceited, in consequence quarrelsome and vituperative; credulous and inaccurate and unable therefore to present an objective picture of nature or history.'[17] There was at that time no strong tradition of careful separation of direct observation from hearsay.

Another important tradition in mediaeval writing was that of extreme respect for earlier writings. As well at the Bible, the Greek and Latin classics were revered, studied, copied and expounded. Interestingly classical writers sometimes were used in a similar way to stories of animals and plants mentioned above. Writers such as Homer, Virgil and Ovid were, as Raven put it, 'translated into subtle revelations of the Christian truth'.[18] The *Aeneid* was seen as an allegory for the journey through life, and the ultimate triumph of wisdom and virtue over folly. Classical authors with rather more to say about natural history that were studied included Aristotle and Pliny the Elder: these two were well known to mediaeval writers on plants and animals.

The two traditions, that of recycling, sometimes with interpretive expansion, the ancient authorities, and that of providing a Christian or moralistic exegesis of sources, go some way towards explaining the character of the bestiary in mediaeval Europe. Its origin is to be sought in the Physiologus, a strange collection of stories on animals and their habits written in Greek, in Egypt, in about the fourth century AD. One author has declared that it had 'no scientific or literary merits whatever'.[19] It was translated first into Latin, and then, with additions and alterations, into almost every European language. In it (and the bestiaries based upon it) were to be found not only many animals familiar in the eastern Mediterranean at the time of the Physiologus' original compilation (and thus in many cases quite unfamiliar in mediaeval Britain and western Europe many centuries later), but also beings that were completely fabulous – the unicorn, wyvern, griffin, and phoenix (the mythical bird of Arabia, supposed to live five thousand years and then to build a funeral pyre of spices and aromatic wood, settle on it and die: from the ashes a new phoenix arose). Canon Raven wrote of the mediaeval bestiaries: 'That there is not a single statement in the bestiaries which can be accepted as fact may be an exaggeration, but it is plain that it was not with fact but with doctrinal significance and moral implications that the authors were concerned. [These books are] .... violently unscientific'.[20] The criticism that most of what was to be found in these mediaeval books on 'natural history' was not the result of observation would not have entered the minds of those, clerical and lay, who read them.

One such reader would have been Alexander Neckam (1157–1217), whose name was sometimes Latinized to Nequam (thus becoming the source of a good deal of donnish punning; the Latin word translates to 'Worthless'). Born in St Albans and educated there, he was sent to be master of a school in Dunstable, about 12 miles (20km) away, but left to study in Paris, then probably the greatest centre of learning in western Europe, where he studied medicine and law, as well as theology. In about 1186 he returned to his mastership in Dunstable, although for a while he seems to have taught at Oxford. He then applied for admission to monastic orders at St Albans, apparently unsuccessfully: *Si bonus es, venias: si nequam, nequaquam* ('If you're any good, you're already here: if you're worthless, you aren't'). He went to the Augustinians in Chichester some time before 1203, becoming their abbot in 1213. Towards the end of his life he seems to have moved to Gloucestershire, and he was buried in Worcester Cathedral. Neckam wrote *De Naturis Rerum* (Concerning the Kingdom of Nature); this was a sort of mediaeval encyclopaedia, embracing the entire universe as it was perceived at the time: it thus gives an insight to mediaeval cosmology, and the view-of-the-world of the era's writers on natural history. The account starts with a discussion of God, his angels, and the heavens – those parts of creation that were unaffected by the Fall of Man and Nature. The earth is considered at the centre of the universe, and the sun, moon, stars and planets are discussed in that order. Neckam then moves on to the four elements of fire, air, water and earth, an arrangement that influences the order in which the living creatures that are described in chapters 21–80 of Book I, and chapters 22–117 of Book II. The chameleon, the only animal that was supposed to live entirely on air was considered first, even before the birds and flying insects. Fish belong to the watery element, and so come before minerals, plants and many quadrupeds. Fish included the mermaid and the hippopotamus; amongst the birds were the phoenix and the 'grips', a bird that digs for gold; other animals mentioned included the basilisk, the dragon and the *amphisbaena* or two-headed snake. Of the basilisk, he wrote that it emerged from an egg laid by a cockerel in old age, and hatched by a toad. Concerning plants, Neckam does not have a great deal more to say than to offer lists of herbs, fruits and a few flowers.[21]

Neckam was typical amongst mediaeval writers in the deference he paid to the early authorities. Much of his material is copied from *Polyhistor*, a third century AD compilation by Caius Julius Solinus, itself incorporating material from Pliny the Elder. Other sources include the *Variarum libri*, of the sixth-century Christian writer Magnus Aurelius Cassidorus, and the works of the poets Virgil, Martial and Ovid. Long sections are taken *verbatim* from some of these authorities, as was the custom of the day. There are express or implied references to the Bible. For example there is a mention of parrots at Mount Gilboa. In 2 Samuel 1. 21 a curse was placed: 'Ye mountains of Gilboa, let there be no dew, neither let there be rain upon you', and so the region was assumed to be rainless; parrots were alleged to nest there as rain was supposed to be fatal to them. Neckam mentions the fable of the origin of barnacle geese ('bernekke') from the wood of conifers steeped in the sea, apparently deriving his material from Giraldus (above), but he displays his scepticism: 'Rumour has it that by a process of Nature firwood steeped in the sea gives off young birds. This is done by viscous humour: what public opinion asserts, philosophy indignantly denies.' He also states another point perhaps gained from Giraldus (there is little evidence that before the 1180s when *De Naturis Rerum*, was written, Neckam was in the right part of the country to have made the observation personally), that there is a river in Wales, where the nightingale only sings on the bank nearer to England.

Neckam rehearses the oft-told tale of the wren that hid itself under the wing of the eagle in the competition to see who could fly highest, and thus claim the dignity of the king of all birds: the tiny wren flew out as the eagle was at its apogee, so claiming the prize. Dominion is not always given to the rich and powerful.

The moral lesson from another tale about the eagle is rather different:

> There was once a king in Great Britain who was very fond of hawking and particularly admired the skill and speed of one of his goshawks. One day this goshawk was chased by an eagle, and to save himself flew or crept into a wattled enclosure made for sheep. The eagle went pecking round this enclosure, trying to find a way in, and while so doing put his head through one of the wattles and got his head stuck there; the goshawk took advantage of his predicament and killed him. By this time the courtiers had come up and began to extol the goshawk for his victory over the much stronger enemy; but the king would have none of it, deeming that the goshawk was guilty of treason and lese-majeste for killing the king of his own tribe, and ordered the unfortunate victor to be hanged.

As Canon Raven puts it, the tale has 'a moral admirably suited to feudal ideas' although it could not be based on 'any sort of eyewitness'.[22] There are, in the entire corpus of Neckam's work, few facts that it can be asserted unequivocally as the result of his own observations. Some, therefore, would argue that Neckam was no naturalist at all – Nequam. But before we accept this verdict we should note that his purpose was to edify, to warn, to turn the incidents of life into parables, rather than to convey accurate factual information. He liked a fine tale, and is more interested in the bizarre and the quaint than the commonplace, certainly, but here and there one can sense a critical approach, some of the excesses of the bestiary he rejects, and he at least makes an attempt at a scholarly approach, quoting, now and again, what he regarded as reliable sources.

Roger Bacon (*c.*1214–1292) was born in Ilchester, Somerset, a couple of years before Neckam's death in nearby Gloucestershire. He studied in Oxford, and then in Paris, until about 1250. In the Franciscan convent in Paris he came to know the priest who was later to become Pope Clement IV, and expounded to him his ideas on the inadequacies of contemporary theological education. A return to Oxford was cut short in 1257 by a summons to return to Paris by his Franciscan superiors, and he was confined there for several years. In 1266 his friend became pope, and bade him send a statement of his teachings mistakenly believing that they were already in writing. Roger set to work and in 1267 sent him the *Opus majus*, amongst other things on the importance of philosophy in understanding theology, and on the importance of the study of languages for an understanding of Biblical texts. There were also sections on mathematics, optics and the experimental sciences. The *Opus minus* and *Opus tertium* were to some extent summaries, but also partly elaborations of ideas set out in the *Opus majus*. Alas, Clement IV died in 1268, and any chance for the general acceptance of his propositions was lost. Bacon returned to England, and in 1271 produced the *Compendium philosophiae*, which contained an outspoken attack on the ignorance of the clergy. In 1277 he was condemned by the authorities of the Franciscan Order for 'suspect novelties' and 'dangerous doctrines', and again imprisoned. Pope Nicholas IV seems to have been particularly opposed to his views. He died, apparently at liberty, in Oxford.

As one might expect from one who was learned in languages, and who set great store by such expertise, he attached great importance to the names of organisms, particularly those mentioned in the scriptures. He discusses in great detail what was meant by *chirogrillus* in the Latin versions of his day of Leviticus 11. 5 and Deuteronomy 14.7: 'coney' in most modern English versions (Hyrax, an animal completely unfamiliar to him). Bacon thought the rabbit was meant.

He also has an interesting elaboration of the pelican story. 'It kills its young, mourns for them for three days, and then brings them to life again by sprinkling them with its own blood.' Bacon is ambivalent about the veracity of the tale: it is as though the scholar in him does not fully believe it, but Bacon the churchman saw the possible insight into the significance of Christ's death and resurrection to be gained from it. 'This is not contradicted, nor need be rejected, though it is not an opinion that must be held.' He admitted that at least one early authority spoke of it as no more than a popular tale.

Much of his work can be seen as a plea for rigour in scholarship: the need for a knowledge of the original languages of the classics and the Bible. He regrets the unavailability of original manuscripts, and deplores defects in education. But he also pleads the need for observation, and the importance of the exact knowledge of things in themselves, and careful experiment and observation. He has been credited with forecasting that the application of science would lead to powered ships, vehicles and aircraft. In *De Nullitate Magiae* he declaimed that magic was unworthy of study by the serious philosopher. To that extent, to our way of thinking he represents a step forward.

A close contemporary of Bacon was the Franciscan monk, Bartholomaeus Anglicus, Bartholomew the Englishman. Bartholomew's origins are uncertain; a sixteenth century source claims him as one of the earliest of Suffolk naturalists, but there is no real evidence of an East Anglian origin. He seems to have been sent by his order to Saxony in 1231, and to have taught theology in Paris a decade or so later. His *De Proprietatibus Rerum* (Concerning the Nature of Things) seems to have been produced around 1250, or a little later. The oldest known copy is one in the Bodleian Library in Oxford, dated 1296. It was widely copied and translated into many European languages, and in the sixteenth century, printed. It has been claimed that a version of it was the most important source of natural history information in the time of Shakespeare. It was encyclopaedic in scope, and had a similar general structure to Neckham's work. Commencing with a discussion of God, the angels and the rational soul, but, considering humans a little below the angels, considers the body and its members, before going on to heaven and earth, times and seasons. Like Neckam, Bartholomew considers the four elements and the life-forms associated with them: fire; air and birds: water and fish; earth, with headings for countries, stones, trees and herbs, animals and so on. Bartholomew's sources include the Bible, Aristotle, Pliny, Isidore (the seventh-century Archbishop of Seville), and Bede; often material, originally from these sources is taken via intermediaries. Raven comments that the only fragment in the whole section of the work dealing with birds that could be based on observation is the note on swans twisting their necks during courtship. Most of the material is simply legend. The sea eagle (osprey) is described as having one foot 'close and hoole' like that of a gander 'therewith she ruleth herself in the water', the other having sharp claws 'with the which she taketh her pray'. He tells of whales on which earth accumulates and bushes grow, so that sailors mistake them for islands and of mountain goats which break their fall from high rocks with 'their owne hornes'. He has a whole tribe of semi-human monsters such as the mermaid, the cyclops with its one eye, and dog-headed creatures. On the other hand the metamorphosis of the tadpole into the frog, and of the caterpillar into a butterfly are accurately described. In the latter case, the spinning of a web, and the insect's wrapping that web around itself are carefully noted. The plants are described for their food or curative values; the vine is considered in particular detail, but he describes the characteristic three-cornered cross-section of the sedge (*Carex*) and the way in which it can cut a person's hand when sharply drawn across it.

The occasional vivid glimpse of nature that may have been gleaned from life should be noted for its rarity, and should not blind us to the real purpose of what the mediaeval monastic author was trying to do. C. E. Raven summarized Bartholomew's work, and indeed that of many mediaeval clerical scholars who wrote about plants and animals, in these terms:

> From internal evidence Bartholomew is a *nudum nomen*, a mere cipher. His book draws its charm from the quaintness and variety of its subject-matter, not from the quality of its author. He is content to amuse, instruct and edify by the recital of tradition . . . but of concern for truth in the scientific sense, indeed of any love of nature apart from books and legends, he shows not a trace. And this is characteristic of his age and general outlook. 'Guard that which has been entrusted to you' – guard it and improve upon it – was a text faithfully followed.[23]

Saintly messengers

Of earlier origin but overlapping in time and in the nature of their content and approach are the often fragmentary accounts of animals, and occasionally of plants, weather effects and other aspects of nature, that occur in the accounts of the lives of the saints, particularly the Celtic saints. Reginald, a Durham monk of the twelfth century, described in *Miracles of Cuthbert* (1167), the way in which the eider ducks (*Somateria mollissima*) nested 'in the houses and even under the beds' of Saint Cuthbert, on the Farne Islands, off the coast of Northumberland. The ducks allowed themselves to be handled; eider ducks still do nest in the sheds and old stone buildings of the islands. The purpose, however, of such accounts was to demonstrate truths about the saints, their special powers, and therefore their sanctity, and some of the stories stretch the credulity of the modern naturalist rather more than that of eiders roosting amongst the saintly Cuthbert's blankets. The same Reginald of Durham, in a biography of St Godric of Finchale (a monastery just outside that cathedral city) describes how Godric drove a hare from the garden. He had been growing vegetables for the poor, but before banishing the creature, tied a bundle of greens to it so that it might not starve. The good Godric is said to have sheltered hares fleeing from huntsmen in his dwelling, freed animals caught in traps, warmed those that were frozen, and 'in his wise solicitude watched over the very reptiles and creatures of the earth'. Cuthbert is also said to have been warmed by otters after a lengthy devotional exercise involving a vigil in the sea (the cold waters off Lindisfarne [Holy Island], Northumberland). This anecdote, because of occasional accounts of tameness in otters, is perhaps not totally fanciful.[24] The story of St Ciaran who was helped in the task of digging a cemetery at Saighir by a wild boar, using its tusks, or that of the blackbird that nested in St Kevin's outstretched hands are more obviously contrived (although blackbirds do nest very close to habitations – even in outhouses amongst garden tools). And the tale of the twelve (a significant number – the number of the apostles) wolves that stood quietly with Columbanus while he was singing psalms is even more extraordinary, from the point of view of the modern student of natural history, but quite understandable given the function of the tale to demonstrate the saint's sanctity and power.

Many of these accounts may be traced back to the influence of Irish monks, who were active as missionaries in north-east England. In an extreme example, St Hild (sometimes Latinized to Hilda) of Whitby is said to have turned the snakes to stone: hence the occurrence of ammonites, fossils which to the uneducated eye resemble coiled snakes in stone, in the shaley cliffs along that part of the Yorkshire coast. One local form of ammonite has been given the scientific name *Hildoceras*. In Ireland the legend is that the absence of snakes from that country is due to the worthy St Patrick driving them out. Or we may note the story of St Columba (the first Abbot of Iona, 563–597, originally from County Donegal, in Ireland), that was recounted by the ninth Abbot, St Adamnan (679–704). Saint Columba, standing on an elevated spot on the plain of Iona, declaimed:

> From this hour's space, the poisons of no vipers shall in any wise be able to hurt either men or cattle in the lands of this island, so long as the inhabitants of this same place of our sojourning observe the commands of Christ.[25]

When one notes that the account of St Columba is replete with cameos of the saint curing the sick, stilling great storms by prayer, foretelling the future, even raising the dead – in short comporting himself in a way similar to the way Jesus is described as acting in the gospels, and in a manner similar to some of the prophets in the Old Testament – it becomes clear that whatever scraps of natural history are embedded in such stories are purely incidental, and that their real import lay elsewhere. Nevertheless some pleasant glimpses persist, as in the account of the whale spotted in the sound between Iona and Tiree, whose arrival was said to have been foretold by the Saint to one of the brethren:

> In passing over the wider reaches of the ... sea, he [i.e. St Columba] and the sailors that were with him look[ed], and behold a whale of wondrous and immense size, lifting itself up like a mountain, while floating on the surface, it opened wide its yawning mouth ...[26]

The Saint made a similar prophesy to another of the brethren about to make the voyage, but assured him that his faith would hold him safe. When the whale duly appeared, the brother who had been primed by Columba:

> with both his hands upraised he blessed the sea, and the whale. And in that very moment the huge monster dived under the waves, and no where appeared to them again.

The whale itself, of course, is incidental. The point of the anecdote was to illustrate the special authority of the Saint, but anyone who has, from close at hand, watched a member of one of the larger species of whale lift itself from the sea as it rises to breath, and arch itself over as it dives, disappearing from view, will have a transitory affinity with this author.

Elsewhere, in a moralizing little lay about a poacher, one Erc by name, St Adamnan describes the seals (sea-calves) breeding on a little islet; the malefactor

> came alone and secretly from the island of Colonsay, and through the day tries to hide himself under his coracle covered in hay, among the sand-hills, that by night he may sail over to the little island where the sea-calves that are ours by right, are bred and breed, that the greedy and most thievish fellow may fill his coracle with them when savagely slain ...[27]

The sea around Iona is sprinkled with rocky islets on which seals breed today, so there is every reason to suppose that particles of observation were embedded in the matrix of moralizing. (The thief came to a sad end.)

Such was the nature of the accounts of animals that permeated much monastic writing. Many of the tales were of Irish or Scots origin, like Adamnan's accounts of Columba, but were recycled, sometimes with elaboration and change, by English monks, for the edification of other audiences. There may possibly have been a factual basis to some of these anecdotes, but they were not intended to be actual accounts of animal behaviour. They were to demonstrate the piety and spiritual power of the saints.

There is still another way of interpreting some of these incidents. Columba is reported to have foretold the arrival at Iona of a crane from Ireland: the monks were enjoined to care for it and feed it as they would a pilgrim.[28] Yet a pig on the Isle of Skye, being pursued by fierce hunting dogs is not rescued but the Saint holds up his hand and commands it to die: it does so. The crane represented Ireland, the land of his fathers; the pig was Pictish, and in Pictland Columba was constantly being opposed by the king and his associates. Gilbert Markus interpreted the situation thus: 'Animals do not represent nature here. They represent political relationships.'[29] Rather in the way perhaps, that George Orwell used animals in *Animal Farm*.

Mediaeval, and pre-mediaeval, accounts of plants and animals, and indeed most descriptions of the environment, are to be seen in a very different light from those of later naturalists. Occasionally a fragment of lively description that has the ring of truth shines from an historian's chronicle, an early biographical account, or a legal document, but such inclusions are usually almost accidental. For the most part, accounts of plants and animals are described for what they can tell the reader about Christian truths, about the life of the World to Come, and about morality. The animals in accounts of saints appear strangely docile; they were included to edify the reader rather than educate him. Other creatures behave in the strangest ways. Weird monsters mingle freely with recognizable beasts of the field both in the mediaeval encyclopaedic compilations and in the carvings of wood and stone in the churches; they were there to entertain and to elevate. The idea that the suggestions in some of the more bizarre accounts should be experimentally investigated would not have occurred to these writers: in some cases they were borrowing material from biblical writers, and those of the ancient classics, and thus the creatures and plants they described – those of the south of Europe, North Africa or the Near East – were quite unfamiliar to them. Inevitably mistakes were sometimes made as to the identity of some of the species mentioned. This mattered little, for the task of the scholar was to respect the ancient authorities, not to test ideas in what we would regard as a scientific way.

The society was a feudal one, and hierarchical distinctions were important. Land was the principal source of wealth. Hunting and falconry, which depend upon access to large areas of land, were ways in which these distinctions were displayed and thus the animals and birds associated with these activities attracted particular attention. The mediaeval church was a centre of temporal as well as spiritual authority, and monasteries owned massive estates, which were managed on as sound an economic basis as possible: the documents associated with this sometimes provide an insight to the plants and animals present. The fact that the dignitaries of the church mingled with feudal lords means that in their accounts (and those of their scribes) they were wont to display similar predilections. The natural history of the Middle Ages, if such it can be called, comes from a very different world, and served a very different purpose from that of later centuries.

Notes

1 Rackham, O., *Hayley Wood: its History and Ecology,* Cambridge, Cambridgeshire Naturalists' Trust, 1975, p. 9.
2 ibid. p. 26 ff.
3 Hall, C. P. and Ravensdale, J. R., *The West Fields of Cambridge* (Cambridge Antiquarian Society, 1976).
4 Anon, *Southwell Minster* (London, Pitkin, 1972)
5 Bennett, B. T. N., *The Choir Stalls of Chester Cathedral* (London, Pitkin, 1968).
6 Marr, J. E. and Shipley, A. E., *Handbook to the Natural History of Cambridgeshire* (Cambridge University Press, 1904), pp. 6–7.
7 Raven, C. E., *English Naturalists from Neckam to Ray* (Cambridge University Press, 1947), chapters 1 and 2, pp. 1–35.
8 White, T. H., *The Book of Beasts* (London, Jonathan Cape, 1954), pp. 119–120.
9 Raven, C. E., 1947, op. cit., p. 2.
10 Grossinger, G., *Guide to Ripon Cathedral* (Ripon, 1989)
11 Berners, Dame Juliana, *The Boke of St Albans* (1486: Facsimile ed., William Blades, 1881).
12 Gurney, J. H., *Early Annals of Ornithology* London, Witherby, 1923), pp. 52, 64.
13 Raven, C. E., 1942, op. cit., p. 23.
14 Gurney, J. H., 1923, op. cit. p. 44, quoting a nineteenth-century translation of Giraldus.
15 Raven, C. E., 1947, op. cit., p.25, quoting from Giraldus' Itinerary.
16 Armstrong, E. A., *The Folklore of Birds* (London, Collins, 1958), p. 226. quoting Giraldus.
17 Raven, C. E., 1947, op. cit., p. 23.
18 Raven, C. E., 1947, op. cit., p. 3.
19 James, M. R., 'The Bestiary in Europe' *History*, April 1931, pp. 1–11.
20 Raven, C. E., 1947, op. cit., p. 4.

21 Raven, C. E., 1947, op. cit., pp. 4–6.
22 Raven, C. E., 1947, op. cit., p. 6–7.
23 Raven, C. E., 1947, op. cit., p. 18.
24 Armstrong, E. A., *St Francis: Nature Mystic* (Los Angeles, University of California Press, 1973); but see also Bradley, I., 'How Green was Celtic Christianity?', *Ecotheology*, 4, January 1998, pp. 58–69.
25 Fowler, J. F., ed., Adamni vita S. Columbae: *Prophesies, Miracles and Visions of St Columba, First Abbot of Iona . . . by St Adamnan, Ninth Abbot* (London, Henry Frowde, 1895), p. 80.
26 Fowler, J. F., 1895, op. cit., p. 25,
27 Fowler, J. F., 1895, op. cit., p. 42.
28 Fowler, J. F., 1895, op. cit., pp. 48, 78.
29 Markus, G., 'Columba: Monk, Missionary and Hijack Victim', *Spirituality,* 12, May–June 1997, pp. 131–135.

Chapter Three

The flowers of the field

Consider the lilies of the field (Matthew 6.28)

Plants are directly or indirectly the source of all human food, they have for centuries been utilized for their healing properties, they have long had symbolic significance and many are of great beauty. For these reasons plants have been the subject of human curiosity for millennia.

William Turner: father of English botany

Although, as we have seen, a certain amount of plant lore is to be found in the writings of Giraldus, Neckham and their mediaeval contemporaries, it is probably fair to say that systematic botany begins in England with William Turner (1508–1568). He was born and brought up in Morpeth, Northumberland, and as a young lad, explored the coasts and fields of that county. In his writings on botany he describes seeing sea holly (*Eryngium maritimum*) on the coast near Holy Island. He entered Pembroke Hall, Cambridge, in 1526, and was associated with theological controversy, and indeed political intrigue, through much of his life, being associated with the Cambridge Reformers. In 1551 he became Dean of Wells.

In his *New Herbal*, Part 1 of which was published in 1551, he broke entirely new ground (a revised edition, including corrections, appeared in 1568). It was the first book of real consequence describing the plants of the English countryside in the English language. Approximately 300 plants are accurately described, often with perceptive comments on their habitat and ecology, and their medical properties: Turner was medically qualified, as well as being ordained. It is not too much of an exaggeration to say that William Turner is the father of English botany: he brought system and order where there was previously only an array of scraps of information. He identified, as far as he was able, the modern English (and sometimes continental) names with those of ancient authors. His work was magnificently illustrated.[1] (See Frontispiece.)

Here is his account of the dodder (*Cuscuta europaea*):

> Doder groweth out of herbs and small bushes, as miscelto groweth out of trees. And neither of both groweth out of the ground. Doder is like a great red harp string, and it windeth about herbs, folding much about them, and hath flowers and knops, one from another a good space, wherein is seed. The herb has neither leaves nor stalk, neither root in the ground. The herbs I have marked doder to grow most in, are flax and tares . . . I have seen it in Germany and in England in plenty.[2]
> (Knop = knob-shaped swelling or protuberance)

The concise, accurate description could hardly be improved upon: the comparison with mistletoe is extremely perceptive, and comes close to identifying the parasitic nature of both.

A slightly ecological approach can be seen in his account of the alder tree (*Alnus glutinosa*):

> The nature of this tree is to grow by water sides in marshy ground. The tree when the bark is off is red, and the bark is much used to dye withal. Pliny sayeth the alder is profitable to set at river sides against the rage of the flood, to help strengthen the bank withal; . . . some say the juice of an alder tree's bark is good for a burning . . .[3]

Here is another quite complex ecological picture: once again, humans are part of the system:

> The Wild Teasel groweth about ditches and watery places; in the beginning of winter the Goldfinches use much to haunt this herb for the seed's sake, wherof there are very desirous . . . in the Wild Teasel is found a worm when the head is full ripe which fishers use as bait . . .[4]

Note well the respectful quotation of authority, the distinction between his own observations and those of others, the careful description, and the emphasis on medical properties and practical uses – these are what set Turner apart from botanists before, and for a century after him. Turner slipped easily from his role as priest, to medical doctor, and to herbalist and botanist. As was not uncommon with the scholars of his day, his work conveys a sense of the unity of knowledge. There was a

> sense that earth and all that is therein is still the Lord's. Specifically, in Turner's case, not only do we find his religious and social analysis decked out with ornithological analogies, but more fundamentally important is the fact that all his works derive from one central ethos. For Turner was concerned with the body material, the body politic and the body spiritual as but three aspects of a unitary whole.[5]

This polymath character remained something of a tradition amongst English parson-naturalists.

William Turner's life spanned the period of the Reformation in England; an early and enthusiastic member of the Protestant party, and not always a man to hide his light, or his opinions, under a bushel, he became, at various times in his life, something of a marked man, and twice he had to flee abroad (into Italy and Germany). Disruptive though this must have been for his family, it allowed him to improve his medical qualifications, and to see a great deal of continental botany. However, it also meant that at one stage he had to take lengthy legal action to recover his position (and income) as Dean of Wells, for during his absence it had been taken by another.

John Ray: pioneer plant taxonomist

There are similarities between the lives of William Turner and John Ray who lived a century later (1627–1705) (see Plate 1). Both had relatively humble origins. Turner was the son of a tanner from Morpeth, Northumberland; Ray that of a blacksmith from Black Notley in Essex. Both were enthusiastic botanists as schoolboys (John Ray's mentor was the local herb-woman). Both went to Cambridge – Turner to Pembroke, Ray to Catherine Hall, later moving to Trinity. Both spent time on the continent. (It may be noted, however, that John Ray was not ordained until 23 December 1660, when he was thirty-three.) Both were brilliant polymaths, publishing in a whole series of disciplines. Both wrote on birds and fishes as well as on botany. Both, too, were the victims of contemporary religious tensions, for following the passage of the Act of Uniformity of 1662, fellows of colleges were required to declare that those who had taken oath under the Solemn League and Covenant were not obliged to keep that oath. Ray had not taken this oath, but, as a man of principle, he could not bring himself to declare such an oath was not binding, and he resigned his fellowship. Both William Turner and John Ray had something of a history of ill-health, but it could also be said that in both cases it was illness that opened the door to the natural world.[6]

Thus it was that illness struck John Ray in 1650; he seems to have had a chest complaint, but possibly he had been overworking, for some of his symptoms seem to be those we would associate with a nervous breakdown. Recovering from his illness, whatever it was, he started exploring the surrounding countryside, redeveloping his interest in plants:

> When I was forced, following an illness that affected me both physically and mentally, to rest from more serious studies, and to spend my time riding and walking, I had leisure in the course of my journeys to contemplate the varied beauty of plants and the cunning craftsmanship of Nature that was constantly before my eyes, and had so often been thoughtlessly trodden underfoot.
>
> First I was fascinated and absorbed by the rich spectacle of the meadows in spring-time; then I was filled with wonder and delight at the marvellous shape, colour and structure of the individual plants.[7]

Wanting to find out more of the subject of botany, he searched throughout the University of Cambridge for someone to instruct him. But to his astonishment he 'among so many masters of learning and luminaries of letters' found no-one to help him. But he did not despair: he resolved to teach himself.

> Why should not I, endowed with ample leisure, if not with great ability, try to remedy this deficiency so far as my power permitted, and advance the study of phytology, which had been passed over and neglected by other men?[8]

He describes how he gradually became familiar with the subject, comparing the plants that he found in the Cambridgeshire countryside with pictures in books, gradually becoming familiar with the relationships between plants, considering to what 'tribe and family' each new species he encountered belonged. He started collecting 'simples', herbs used medicinally, and growing them in the garden outside his room in Trinity College. His objective was 'to illustrate the glory of God in the knowledge of the works of nature or creation.' The idea that the beauties of nature provided an insight into the mind of the Creator he was to develop later in *The Wisdom of God*.

In his *Catalogus Plantarum circa Cantabrigiam nascentium* (Catalogue of the plants of the Cambridge area), the first English local flora, published in 1660, he gives a thorough, annotated bibliography, and detailed descriptions of the plants, that one commentator has described as setting 'high standards for descriptive botany' and marked a transition from the old to the new scientific botany, emphasising system, order and classification.[9] The hundreds of local floras that followed, for different parts of England, thus had a lofty target at which to aim. Ray listed 558 plants in the *Catalogus* that he had seen personally. Some he merely names, perhaps adding a note on the locality in which the species was to be found. Thus:

> Geranium haematodes [*Geranium sanguineum*] Bloody Cranes-bill. Found on Newmarket heath in the Devil's Ditch, also in a wood adjoyning to the highway betwixt Stitchwort and Chidley.[10]

Ray would be pleased to know that the species still grows in the same locality, its only site in lowland England.

Sometimes he gives a more detailed description:

> Cruciata [modern name *Cruciata chersonensis*, *C. laevipes*] Crosswort or Mugweed. In hedgerows and woods. On the square stem there are always two leaves placed alternately on opposite sides (thus called winged); it is possible to see at a short distance two others at right angles to the first; thus four arise from the four sides . . . You will never find three or five or more.[11]

And sometimes he delivers quite a lengthy essay. Under the ash tree, for example, he goes into perceptive detail on the use of tree-rings for the determination of the age of a tree.

Canon Raven wrote of the *Catalogus*:

> The knowledge that he gained of the flora of Cambridgeshire would have been remarkable if he had possessed the books and collections of a modern student: considering his handicaps, the lack of any reliable authorities, the pressure of his other work, the difficulty of travel, it is evidence not only of rare energy and powers of observation, but of a genius for natural history; a flair for locality combined with a fine sense of the characteristics of plant life.
>
> The greatness of the book lies not only in what it accomplished, but what it foreshadowed. . . . Without Ray's preliminary work there would have been no Linnaeus.[12]

Over the next ten years John Ray made many journeys throughout England (and also parts of Scotland and Wales), often with his great friend and patron, Francis Willughby, and in a Herculean effort, had extended the Cambridge *Catalogus* to the whole kingdom. The *Catalogus Plantarum Angliae et Insularum Adjacentum* (Catalogue of the Plants of England and the Adjacent Islands) appeared in 1670, with a second improved edition in 1677.

A catalogue of European plants, based on his travels in the Low Countries, Germany, Italy and France (1663–1666) followed in 1673. It was issued as an annex to a book describing his travels: *Observations Topographical, Moral and Physiological made on a Journey*. This traverse across northern Europe has been compared in its importance to that of the *Beagle's* voyage of Charles Darwin 170 years later. By its end he had seen more plants growing in their natural state than any contemporary or previous botanist; he had added new species to the European flora, collating a variety of authorities in their identification, besides establishing links with many leaders in European natural history. A second edition appeared in 1738, after his death. The journey was adventurous: Ray and Willughby travelled by sailing-boat, cart and coach; once in a carriage drawn by ten oxen. In 1666 the King of France ordered all Englishmen out of the country, and Ray made his way to Calais in a fishcart.[13] It has been suggested that a later work on the natural history of fishes may have its origin in this incident, but in view of the fact that there is definite evidence that Ray was recording the fish he saw in northern England and Wales some years earlier, this is probably erroneous.[14]

In a great hurry shortly after his return from the continent, John Ray was asked by another clerical member of the Royal Society, Bishop Wilkins (Ray himself had been elected in 1667), to compile a simple classification of plants. Only three weeks were available for the task, and severe constraints were imposed. The classification, *The Table of Plants*, was not a success, but represented a theme important in much of the rest of his life's work. Two papers were read to the Royal Society on 17 December 1674. In 'On the seeds of plants' Ray showed that some plants have two seed leaves or cotyledons in their seeds, some only one. The separation of moncotyledons from dicotyledons is one of the fundamental divisions in the Plant Kingdom, and although Ray did not appreciate its full significance at the time, the paper represented a major step forward in plant taxonomy. The second paper was 'On the specific differences of plants'; this was extremely important as it attempted to establish precise criteria for the determination of what was a species. A large number of characteristics were 'accidental'; colour, size, taste, smell were not suitable for use in establishing specific distinctions. Overall structure or morphology should be the main criterion.[15]

The years of work on the theory of classification continued, and in 1682 the *Methodus Plantarum Nova (New method of [classification of] plants)*, a slim volume of 166 pages appeared. It has an interesting allegorical bookplate showing two children sorting plants under the benign gaze of a muse-like figure, while in the background may be glimpsed an extremely formal garden where plants are being put into a number of evenly spaced and equal sized rectangular beds (see Plate 2). His introductory remarks, as translated by Canon Raven (1942), explain Ray's motives fully:

> The number and variety of plants inevitably produce a sense of confusion in the mind of the student: but nothing is more helpful to clear understanding, prompt recognition and sound memory than a well-ordered arrangement into classes, primary and subordinate. . . . But I would not have my readers expect something perfect or complete; something which would divide all plants so exactly as to include every species without leaving any in positions anomalous or peculiar; something which would so define each genus by its own characteristics that no species be left . . . homeless or common to many genera. Nature does not permit anything of the sort. Nature . . . makes no jumps and passes from extreme to extreme only through a mean. She always produces species intermediate between higher and lower types, species of doubtful classification linking one type with another and having something in common with both . . .
>
> In any case I dare not promise even so perfect a Method as nature permits – that is not the task of one man or one age . . .[16]

There are touches here that anticipate Darwinian thought. He goes on to reject totally the use as food, medicine or ornament as a reliable basis of classification, concentrating on 'the likeness and agreement of the principal parts, root, flower and its cap seed and its vessel'. He attaches particular attention to the petal. Bearing in mind that Ray had no access to a microscope, that the study of marine plants was in its infancy (he did single out the Algae as a distinct group), this was an important piece of work. Some of the families that Ray distinguished still hold today.

All these botanical works, however, can be seen as preparatory to his *Historia Plantarum* (The history of plants), published in three volumes in 1686, 1688 and 1704. These three massive folios (each weighing about 8kg), contained 2,600 pages of close print. The work contained, as far as possible, detailed descriptions of all known plants, arranged in accordance with an improved version of Ray's method of classification. It is impossible to view it without, as Raven says, 'a sense of awe'.[17]

Still the work went on. John Ray had hoped that a new edition of his *Catalogus Plantarum Angliae* would appear when earlier editions sold out. Then, as happens today, difficulties between authors and publishers and printers developed, and this was not to be. The new material was published as a *Fasciculus Stirpum Britannicum* (Fascicule of British Plants) in 1688. The *Synopsis Britanium* (Flora of Britain) followed in 1690, and has been described as 'the culmination of all his previous work from the Cambridge Catalogue'.[18] 'It gave any student of the country's plants a working guide to identification, locality and habit . . . apart for Linnean nomenclature, we have a modern hand-book'.[19] The identifications are secure, and remarkably accurate; the classification, even if it was not scientifically perfect (what classification is?), was logical. The work was very successful going into several editions, the last, with a splendid series of plates, appeared 20 years after the author's death. It continued to be used by students until the end of eighteenth century.

After the publication of the *Synopsis*, John Ray turned, for the most part, away from the field of botany: his work was on zoology, geology, and philosophical and theological subjects. Yet his work on plants was not quite finished. He produced an update of his *Catalogue of Foreign Plants* in 1694, and a list of plants from each county for Camden's *Britannica* in the same year. The latter was not very complete, but is important as it stimulated the interests of others in compiling county floras. In 1695 he produced a rejoinder to an attack upon his approach to classification by the French botanist, de Tournefort, entitled *Dissertatio Brevis* (Brief Dissertation). Finally, in 1703, there was the culmination of his life's work on classification, the *Methodus Plantarum Emendata et Aucta*, a final revision of his classificatory system. He died on 17 January 1705 after a long illness, having devoted fifty years of his life to the scientific study of the natural world.

A plant physiologist

In the spring of 1669, during a stay at Wollaston, John Ray and his friend Willughby did some simple experiments on the movement of sap in plants. They bored holes into the trunks of trees of several species – willow, sycamore and birch – and studied the movement of sap under different conditions. Their work was published in *The Philosophical Transactions of the Royal Society* in June 1669 as a paper entitled 'Experiment covering the motion of sap in trees made this spring'. The experiments were not particularly notable but are interesting as they represent one of the first studies of plant physiology.

But the parson-naturalist who was to develop the study of plant physiology was Steven Hales (1677–1761), who entered Corpus Christi College Cambridge in June 1696. In February 1703 he was elected a fellow, and shortly after that started work in what was known as the 'elaboratory' in Trinity College. Whilst working there he must have met with Sir Isaac Newton, going to and from his rooms in the north-east corner of the Great Court of Trinity College. He left his fellowship after a few years, and in 1709 he became perpetual curate of Teddington, where he remained for the remaining 52 years of his life. He is said to have done a great deal for the fabric of his church building. He provided the parish with a water supply, and was well respected locally: the poet Pope (who was a near neighbour) called him a 'worthy and good man'. His most important work was *Vegetable Statics*, which, partly, perhaps because it was published in the fiftieth year of its author's life, has been compared to *On the Origin of Species*. It appeared in 1727.[20]

Hales conducted the first experiments on plant transpiration (water loss). He covered the soil of a plant pot in which a sunflower was growing, leaving a stoppered opening for the plant to be watered, and cemented the plant in. He measured the rate of water-loss, making due allowance for loss from the pot, and then estimating the total area of leaf on the plant, calculated loss per unit area. He compared the rate of 'perspiration' of a sunflower with that of a cabbage and of a vine, and the rate of loss by day with that by night. He commented on the way in which the sunflower followed the sun, and conducted several experiments on the flow of sap. He also measured the power of root-pressure in a vine by attaching tubes containing mercury to the stumps of vine branches, to determine the pressure, in terms of the height of the column of mercury that could be supported. Most important of all, Hales understood: first, that plants drew part of their food from the air, and second, that light had an important role in the story. He took as his starting point some of the ideas of Sir Isaac Newton, who, as we have seen, he probably knew quite well while he was in Cambridge. Air, Hales stated, made up 'a very considerable part of the substance of vegetables', and 'particles of air' are in due course wrought into the substance of plants.[21] Finally he did experiments on the growth of plants, marking both the stems and leaves of growing vines, and demonstrating that the most rapid growth was closest to the tip.

Taxonomy as an art form

There are a number of clerical naturalists who dedicated a large part of their working lives to the investigation of less popular biological groups. These groups are often extremely difficult taxonomically, but yet in some environments are extremely important ecologically. Among botanists who devoted their lives to the working-out of the taxonomy and the ecology of unfashionable groups was the Reverend Miles Joseph

Berkeley (1803–1889), who, as well as following a career as the parson of a Northamptonshire parish, effectively revolutionised mycology (the study of fungi) and also the study of algae.

Like so many parson-naturalists, he had a deep interest in natural history during his schooldays: he made an extensive collection of shells, first at Oundle Grammar School, and then at Rugby. He entered Christ's College, Cambridge in 1821, graduating in 1825. While at Cambridge, like Charles Darwin, just a few years his junior and who went to the same college, he came under the influence of John Henslow, who was connected by marriage and consanguity to a wide network of naturalists. He was ordained in 1826, and was initially a curate at St John's, Margate, Kent. In 1833 he became perpetual curate of Apethorpe and Wood Newton, Northamptonshire, and in 1868 he was instituted as Vicar of Sibbertoft, near Market Harborough.

Living in a seaside town for the first few years after his ordination, he took an interest in marine algae or seaweeds. In 1833 he published *Gleanings of British Algae*, a series of detailed studies of both freshwater and marine British species. Subsequently, he turned to fungi, and as one biographer put it, 'it was in the field of mycology that his laurels were won'. Simply viewed as statistics, the facts are impressive. His first major volume, the second part of the Cryptogamia supplement by Sir W. J. Hooker to Smith's *The English Flora*, contains all the British fungi known at the time, some 1360 species, belonging to 155 genera, most of which were studied in the living form. Shortly after he moved back to his native Northamptonshire he began a long series of articles, partly written in collaboration with his friend C. E. Broome, in the *Annals and Magazine of Natural History*. Between 1837 and 1883 he enumerated 2027 species of fungi, many of them not recorded previously in Britain. He studied specimens, including those sent from all over the world to the Natural History Museum in London, and described around 6000 species new to science. In addition to several massive volumes, some of them profusely illustrated, he was the sole author of over 400 scientific papers, and joint author with others of several hundred more. In 1879 he presented his collection to Kew. It contained 10,000 species, hundreds of which were new species he had described himself. It is probably true to say that he was one of the greatest authorities on the world's fungi who has ever lived. He was somewhat belatedly elected a Fellow of the Royal Society at the age of 76.[22]

North of the Scots border, a Presbyterian minister at Saltcoats was hard at work on the seaweeds of the Ayrshire coast. He was the Reverend David Landsborough, author of *A Popular History of British Seaweeds*, which eventually ran to three editions. With the assistance of his children, Landsborough prepared many hundreds of collections of pressed seaweeds, which were sold in aid of kirk and school.[23]

Often the parson's wife was the helpmate in both her husband's work in natural history as well as his pastoral work, but a Yorkshire clergyman's wife who was a quite distinguished naturalist in her own right was Mrs Margaret Gatty (commemorated in the name of the genus *Gattya*). In 1848, ill and weak after the birth of her seventh child, she was sent to Hastings, on the Sussex coast for several months to recuperate. A local physician suggested that she take up the study of seaweeds, no doubt hoping that it would both relieve her boredom and get her out into the sea air. She published *British Seaweeds* in 1863. She seems to have been a determined and perhaps slightly eccentric woman. In her book she included instructions in the matter of dress for ladies embarking on the systematic study of seaweeds: 'Anyone really intending to work in the matter', she declaimed, 'must lay aside for a time all thought of conventional appearances.' She suggested 'a pair of boy's shooting boots' waterproofed with neat's-foot oil.[24] Petticoats should not reach below the ankle, a hat was preferable to a bonnet, stockings of merino wool to those of cotton, and gloves were indispensable. Despite her individuality, she was sufficiently conventional, in the terms of her class and day, to advise that a low-water-mark shore-hunt should be undertaken under a gentleman's protection.[25]

It would be possible to detail a clergyman-botanist whose name is associated with almost every botanical group, no matter how obscure: mosses, liverworts, lichens, slime-moulds (Myxomycetes or Mycetozoa), as well as ferns and flowering plants. A couple of further examples will have to suffice. The Reverend W. A. Leighton, was another of those who owed their career in natural history to John Henslow (Leighton was also a friend of Darwin, and his senior by four years). Leighton was a pioneer in the field of British lichenology, and in 1871 published *The Lichen-flora of Great Britain, Ireland and the Channel Islands*.[26] Lichens also attracted the Reverend William Johnson (1844–1919) who was the leading authority in northern England on the group for many years. He compiled a collection of some 2000 specimens, including more than a quarter of the entire British lichen flora, listed currently at 1720 species. A large part of his collection survives at the University of Leeds. He worked primarily in Durham, Northumberland, Cumberland and Yorkshire, although also in Scotland, Wales and Norway. Between 1894 and 1918 he published the thirteen fascicles of the *North of England Lichen-Herbarium* (printed in Newcastle, Darlington and Manchester).[27]

The phenomenon of the county flora

The nineteenth century was the great age of botanical inventories. More familiar than the specialised catalogues of algae, fungi, lichens, etc., is the county flora, the compendium of all the plants (usually just the vascular plants) of a single county, often with information on where they are to be found. John Ray had shown the way with his Cambridge *Catalogus* in 1660. A trickle of floras appeared in the eighteenth century (for example the Reverend Charles Abbot's *Flora Bedfordiensis*), but the first floras for most English (and a number of Welsh and Scottish) counties followed in the nineteenth, many of them compiled, authored or edited by clergymen. The *Flora of Oxfordshire* (and adjoining counties) was edited by the Reverend Richard Walker (1791–1870), appearing in 1838. It was the Reverend W. A. Leighton who compiled the *Flora of Shropshire* in 1841, paying tribute to his former teacher in the dedication to John Henslow: 'These simple fruits of his labours are dedicated by his grateful pupil.' The Reverend W. H. Coleman, in preparing the *Flora of Hertfordshire* between 1840 and 1847, used a method that has been compared (by Allen) to that used to compile the *Atlas of the British Flora* well over a century later. Each of the assistants was given sole responsibility for a limited district, so that 'having a local interest in the reputation of their respective districts, [they were] stimulated to increase their diligence'. The Reverend Professor Charles Cardale Babington provided an updated *Flora of Cambridgeshire* in 1860. In 1869 the *Flora of Middlesex* appeared; this was ostensibly by Henry Trimen and W. T. Dyer (later Sir William Twistelton-Dyer, director of Kew Gardens, but apparently owed much to the Reverend W. W. Newbould, described (by Allen) as 'a fine scholar but morbidly self-effacing': he contributed a long historical section anonymously. A *Flora of Herefordshire* appeared in 1889, edited by the Reverend William H. Purchas and the Reverend Augustin Ley (*c*.1815–1911), Vicar of Sellack with King's Capel, Herefordshire. Both were interesting individuals: the Reverend A. Ley was a plant collector on a gargantuan scale, the rarer the better: he is said to have contributed 15,000 specimens to the Botanical Exchange Club, an organisation that staggered on following the financial collapse of its progenitor, the Edinburgh Botanical Society in the 1840s. Purchas was described as 'an evangelical type of clergyman' of a somewhat fundamentalist outlook (he disapproved thoroughly of the views of Lyell and Darwin, adhering to the belief that the book of Genesis should be interpreted literally). The flora had a detailed regional subdivision, with an account of each of the 'botanical districts' of the county 'with notes on their geology'. The task of preparing these notes fell to the Reverend W. S. Symonds,

FGS (Fellow of the Geological Society), Rector of Pendock, who was of more modern views, describing the manner in which the rocks were laid down over long periods of geological time and subsequently eroded. Purchas was not amused. The *Flora of Sussex*, by the Reverend F. H. Arnold, Rector of Raston, appeared in 1889, second edition 1907, beautifully illustrated by his daughter – another family involvement.

Suffolk had several 'clerical' floras; this is unsurprising since Suffolk probably has had more clerical botanists than any other county. The Reverend Professor John Henslow (1798–1861), Rector of Hitcham, co-operated with a Bury St Edmunds dispenser, Edmund Shepper (1825–1867) to produce one in 1860; they were assisted by the Reverend Edwin Nearson Bloomfield (1827–1914), of Great Glemham. This was followed in 1889 by *Hind's Flora*; the Reverend William Marsden Hind (1815–1894), Rector of Honington, was assisted by the Reverend Dr Churchill Babington, Rector of Cockfield (a relative of Professor Charles Cardale Babington, author of the 1860 *Flora of Cambridgeshire*). Hind's Suffolk Flora was the authoritative work for several decades, although some supplementary notes, in part based on Hind's original herbarium specimens in the Ipswich Museum, were produced by a C. E. Salmon, assisted by the Reverend William Moyle Rogers in 1907. In 1911 an account of the 'Botany of Suffolk' was included in the *Victoria County History*, vol. 2; the account was prepared by several authors including the Reverends E. N. Bloomfield, J. D. Grey, W. M. Rogers and F. R. Bullock-Webster.

Coming further into the twentieth century, and into the adjoining East Anglian county, the Reverend Kirby Trimmer published the *Flora of Norfolk* in 1914. The two world wars provided a lull in activities and then the Reverend H. J. Riddesdell (along with two others) prepared the *Flora of Gloucestershire*, published by the Cotteswold Naturalists Field Club in 1948.

Somewhat surprisingly, but delightfully, the tradition continues. In 1988 the Reverend G. Gordon Graham, edited the superb and exhaustive *Flora and Vegetation of County Durham*. In the preface to this work, the television naturalist and conservationist (and strong churchman) David Bellamy describes Gordon Graham as a 'voucher specimen' amateur naturalist.

Of course, the editing and writing of a county flora is just a part of the story. Many parochial clergy, with their long-acquired and detailed knowledge of their particular patches, sent in records. Here was one of the areas where the tight-knit clergy network showed its strength. Among the list of assistants noted as sending information or otherwise assisting with Purchas and Ley's *Herefordshire Flora*, mentioned above, are no fewer than nine clergy, including the Reverend Sir G. H. Cornewell, Bart.,

Rector of Moccas and the self-effacing W. W. Newbould. Of the 23 informants acknowledged in Henry Baines' *Flora of Yorkshire*, one of the first generation of floras, four were clergymen. Similarly, of the forty or so persons who assisted George Claridge Druce with records, or in other ways, for the 1886 *Flora of Oxfordshire* at least nine were in Holy Orders.[28] When, in 1901, Herbert D. Geldart edited the 'Botany of Norfolk' account for the *Victoria County History* of that county, a number of clergy assisted him in various ways: these included the Reverend G. R. Bullock-Webster, who wrote on Characeae, the Reverend J. M. Crombie on Lichens, the Reverend E. F. Linton on the genus *Rubus* (bramble) and *Rosa* (wild rose) and one or two others.[29]

An earlier example of the same sort of link is provided by the the Reverend John Hemsted (1747?–1824), who was curate of St Mary's Newmarket, 1781–1782, and then Vicar of St Paul's Bedford from 1782 until his death. He was the third in a line of clergy, all of whom bore the same name. There is some evidence that at least one of these forebears was also a naturalist. John Hemsted III, although he does not seem to have published much, was described in 1792 as 'a very intelligent industrious botanist', and was a node in a network of botanical correspondents, clerical and lay. He may have been an important source of specimens for illustration in James Sowerby's (1757–1822) great work, *English Botany* (published in 36 volumes between 1790 and 1814, second edition 1828), the text of which was mostly written by Sir J. E. Smith (1759–1828).[30]

The Reverend Dr Charles Sutton provides a comparable instance of a dominant figure in such a network. He too seems to have been an important source of information for Hind's *Flora of Suffolk*. A charming manuscript exists, entitled '*Iter litorale*, or a week's botanical excursion to the Sea-Coast at Orford', which describes a botanizing expedition to the then quite wild heathland and coast of the Suffolk Sandlings in August 1787, by the young Sutton in company with two friends. One was William Kirby (1759–1850) (see Plate 5), later in Holy Orders himself, who came from a long line of Suffolk naturalists, local historians and topographers. Kirby was a competent botanist, although his own emphasis was on entomology (he was eventually a Fellow of the Linnean Society, and an FRS); his sister was to marry Sutton. The other was the Reverend Peter Lathbury (1760–1820), whose posthumous son, the Reverend Nathaniel Peter Edward Lathbury (1820–1855), also made botanical records acknowledged by Hind. Dr Sutton's account, which was not published until relatively recently, gives a lively impression of three young men out on a bit of a spree (food and wine figure quite prominently in the description) but the essay appears to have the first Suffolk record for a number of species. These include *Epilobium angustifolium* (rosebay willowherb, now *Chamaenerion angustifolium*), *Serapias palustris* (now *Epipactis palustris*), *Statice limonium* (now *Limonium vulgare*) and *Aster triopolium apetalon*. The last two Sutton notes growing in the marshes near Orford, where they continue to flourish.[31]

Local floras and the beginnings of plant ecology

Sometimes a clergyman's detailed knowledge of his parish manifested itself in a local or parochial flora, a much less ambitious project than a county catalogue. Such was the character of the work of the Reverend (later Canon) William Fowler (1835–1912) (see Plate 14), who although he spent much of his ministry in the neighbouring county of Yorkshire (Vicar of Liversedge, 1864–1910), was born and died in the village of Winterton, Lincolnshire. He was a lifelong student of the flora of that county, one of his early papers entitled 'The rarer plants of the neighbourhood of Winterton, Lincolnshire', appearing in *The Phytologist* in 1858. William Fowler, one obituary put it with some justification, 'was the first oecological student of environment . . . amongst British botanists'. Certainly he published a long series of articles on Lincolnshire plants in relation to soils in *The Naturalist* between 1878 and 1890.[32]

Another pioneer of plant ecology was the Reverend Edward Adrian Woodruffe-Peacock (1858–1922), Vicar of Cadney, just south of Brigg in North Lincolnshire from 1890 to 1920. This is not altogether surprising, for he knew Canon Fowler quite well, getting acquainted with him at the University of Durham, which he attended from 1879 to 1881, after spending a couple of years at St John's College, Cambridge. He had studied science, history and mathematics, switching to divinity at Durham. However, his academic path was not altogether smooth, for, on his own admission, he was 'doing considerable botanizing, boating, lawn tennis and fighting a strenuous [sporting] battle for his Hall.' His college Principal pointed out to him 'he had not kept half a dozen days that half term, and that he was 'using the university as a club'. The Principal added, in a dignified way: 'I shall have to send you down if you do not reform. The University is not a club, Sir', so Adrian 'scratched' from the BA examination, leaving Durham with a Licentiate in Theology rather than a Bachelor's degree.[33]

'Woofler' as he liked to be called, was a very competent all-round naturalist, and wrote many hundreds of scientific papers and shorter contributions, especially to *The Naturalist*, *The Transactions of the Lincolnshire Naturalists' Union* and *The Journal of Botany*. Amongst these was a check-list of Lincolnshire plants (1909) and a 'Critical catalogue of Lincolnshire Flowering Plants' (1894–1900). He was a pioneer of the detailed, small-scale ecological survey. One such was 'The ecology of Thorne Waste' (1920–1921), a peat-bog area on the border between Lincolnshire and Yorkshire.[34] As this included Woodruffe-Peacock's observations going back to 1874 when it had the characteristics of a 'quaking bog' with a layer of *Sphagnum* peat over a layer of water, it represented an early study that emphasized the response of a plant community to land use change. Another paper from the same vintage was 'A fox-covert study' (1918), which appeared in the *Journal of Ecology*.[35] He was a very early member of the British Ecological Society, and met the founder, Dr A. G. (later Professor Sir Arthur) Tansley on a Society field-trip to Mildenhall, Suffolk, in June 1918. They became correspondents and friends. For many years Woodruffe-Peacock worked on a detailed *Rock-Soil Flora of Lincolnshire*, discussing the plants of the county in relation to soil and environment. In its day, this was an innovative approach, and A. G. Tansley was so impressed by the manuscript that he offered to have it published at his own expense. Had it been published at the time, it would have been ecologically far ahead of, and quite different from, other county floras. Post-World War I inflation, and the author's continual tinkering with the text meant that it was never published, although it is held in the archives of Cambridge University Botany School, where it has been used by scholars seeking early plant records.[36]

As with many parson-naturalists, much of his knowledge came from travelling round his parish. One obituarist described him as 'Full of enthusiasm . . . an indefatigable observer and note-taker.' Originally he used a bicycle, but a medical specialist at one stage advised against this, and he became a prodigious walker, often averaging six or eight miles a day. Tansley wrote of the *Flora*:

> It carries out the central thought of ecology. You go for twenty to thirty years to work the same bit of ground annually to discover its changes. As you are willing to sacrifice any time to get the facts, you have discovered the obscure laws behind them.[37]

Interestingly, to supplement his small stipend as a country vicar, he did some consultancy work for horse-stud and game conservation interests. He must have been one of the first ecological consultants in England.

Adrian Woodruffe-Peacock was an innovator in many other ways. He was a pioneer in plotting the distributions of plants in his native Lincolnshire. As early as 1894 he had 20,000 'place notes' on the distribution of plant species tabulated in his 'Locality Register'. He appealed to all botanists to send him 'full notes of rare Lincolnshire plants in their private collections, with parish, name of collector, and date appended'. He was also one who appreciated the vital importance of mechanisms of dispersal, a neglected aspect of British ecology. He approached this through the careful study of microhabitats. As the result of 'half a dozen visits' to a sandbank in a Lincolnshire beck during a dry summer when the water was low, he noted over 58 species growing, in his view as the result of the dispersal of seeds by the stream. In May 1892 he 'examined two Pollard Willows in Cadney, not far from the village, and in their large open heads, about seven feet from the ground', found no fewer than twelve species of plants (mainly species of trees and shrubs). The implication, although it is not actually stated, is that the seeds and fruits must have been distributed by birds.[38]

Rather different was the ecological approach of the Reverend Philip Mauleverer Garnett (1906–1967), another 'one off' individual. Educated at St John's College, Cambridge (BA, 1927; MA, 1931), he was a schoolmaster for a number of years. Several years of distinguished Navy service in the Second World War followed (DSO, MBE). Then after an abortive period of agricultural training, he went to theological college, and was ordained in 1952, doing curacies in Hampshire, and then Kirkbymoorside with Bransdale and Farndale, in North Yorkshire. Later he was appointed Vicar of Ledsham with Fairburn, and rural dean of Selby. His botany involved the detailed study of the ecology of a single plant species. While at Kirkbymoorside in the North York Moors, he made a study of *Chamaepericlymenum (Cornus) suedicum* (dwarf cornel). He found this species in five North Yorkshire localities. He confirmed one old record, taking careful note of the species' ecological requirements, developed theories about where, in similar settings, the species might be found, and then went to look. Sometimes he was remarkably successful. He applied a similar technique to a number of rare North of England species, confirming old records, and finding new locations.[39]

East Anglia is replete with examples of 'local botanists'. One was the Reverend Francis Gilpin (1855–1945), who was curate at Redenhall, Norfolk, in the Waveney Valley, from 1883 to 1887, and in 1888 published an account of *The Flowering Plants, Ferns and Allies of Harleston*; he incorporated many of the earlier records of the Reverend E. A. Holmes, of St Margaret's. Nearly a century earlier, in the same part of the country, the Reverend George Crabbe, the poet whose verse embodies so much of the spirit of the East Anglian coast and countryside, had held curacies at Aldeburgh, Great Yarmouth and Framlingham. He compiled a list of 226 flowering plants, published in Loder's *History of Framlingham* in 1798. A modern variant here, still in Suffolk, is the Reverend R. Addington, Vicar of Charsfield, near Woodbridge who, as a contributor to a modern scientific mapping scheme, carefully recorded all the wild flowers in a 2km by 2km tetrad in the 1990s. Careful study of the ecology of some of the churchyards in his care produced some interesting records, including woad (*Isatis tinctora*) which proved to have been sown by some church flower ladies who had used the plant in arrangements.[40]

Alas, the work of some significant local clerical botanists never saw the light of day in their lifetimes. Such are the annotations of William Gawthorp, Rector of Ripley, near Harrogate from 1736 until his death (and burial in the churchyard) in 1759. William Gawthorp owned a copy of *A Synopsis of British Plants in Mr Ray's Method*, published in Newcastle-upon-Tyne in 1744. In this book he made hundreds of annotations concerning the flora of the area around Ripley. These notes form both an account of his botanizing exploits and a record of his findings. He seems to have been particularly fond of botanizing around Fountains Abbey, and his notes provide information about a number of species found there. The reference to the 'low end of Fountains wood near Studeley Park pales plentif' probably refers to *Paris quadrifolia* (no longer a locality for the species); 'out of the rocks above Fountains Abbey' grew *Helleborus foetidus* (stinking helleborine), *Asplenium viride* (green spleenwort, a fern) grew in the ruins of 'the Dormitory of Fountains Abbey, south end', and *Lactuca virosa* (green prickly lettuce) was also found. 'In the pasture above Fountains' grew *Botrychium lunaria* (moonwort, another fern). In the 'Lane going from Fountains Hall to Aldfield' he stumbled upon yet another fern no longer found at the locality *Asplenium adintum-nigrum* (black spleenwort); 'below Tanfield down the River Bank' he found *Filipendula vulgaris* (dropwort) happily still found nearby. The annotations were not published until 1986, but they, and others like them, document the changing nature of the flora of a local area, and also give an indication of the way in which amateur botanists of earlier centuries went about their activities.[41]

Memorabilia such as these, and letters and diaries, and indeed writings of a quite ephemeral nature can frequently give an insight to the way in which the work of botanical field-work was actually done. Often natural history was quite a lonely activity, but not always. A social phenomenon of the nineteenth and early twentieth century was the 'reading party'. A group of young men from Oxford and Cambridge would settle for two or three weeks, often at an inn but sometimes a country house in, perhaps, the Lake District or Wales, for reading, discussion, walking and the odd burst of high spirits. Sometimes they included natural history amongst their activities. A group staying at

Beddgelert, North Wales, in the summer vacation of 1848, the height of the Victorian fern craze, included botanizing, some not-always-successful angling (and a little backgammon) in their round of activities. Almost all the members of the team became leading clergy of their generation. One was Brooke Foss Westcott (1825–1901), later a master at Harrow School, Regius Professor of Divinity at Cambridge (1870–1890) and Bishop of Durham (1890–1901), a lifelong enthusiast for botany and geology. Here he, and one or two others of the group, are descending from Snowdon on a fine day in early August.

> [W]e scrambled and wriggled ourselves down the fearful precipice of Clogwyn and Garedd. A rare fern grows there, which is not to be found in England tho' it is on some of the Alps and the higher mountains of Scotland. But every one said the search for it was so great that we had no chance of meeting with it. However in our descent we came to a place which even Moorsom said was impracticable and Westcott, unwilling to give it up, went a little way to see, and there in a cleft in a rock was this fern. Didn't we gather it at great risk to our necks. They talk of going there again soon – there are so many curious plants to be found . . . I got separated but saw them crossing the lake in a ferry.[42]

Although B. F. Westcott published little scientific material, his interest in science influenced his theology, in for example his *Gospel of Creation*. His continued interest in botany and geology is demonstrated by his correspondence. His children in later life complained that a cart was needed to bring home the ferns and rock specimens he collected on holiday.[43]

The popularizers

The nineteenth-century county or parochial flora was not generally illustrated, and the style was scientific and full of compressed detail. There has long been a demand for a different kind of volume, for natural history books that are a lighter read, and with illustrations that are easy on the eye. Clerical naturalists were often quite successful at filling this particular niche. The Reverend Charles Alexander Johns (*c.* 1818–1875), graduate of Trinity College, Dublin (1841), a Cornish curate and schoolmaster, first published *Flowers of the Field* in 1851: it then cost two shillings and sixpence. It had many pictures and was extremely popular, running through many editions over several decades.[44] Although he was often considered something of a 'lightweight', Johns seemed to have the knack of producing the type of natural history books the public wanted. He wrote a number of other works of similar genre; titles included: *Botanical Rambles, Forest Trees of Britain,* and . . . *Gardening for Children.*

This is again a tradition that has continued closer to the present time. The Reverend William Keble Martin (1877–1969), like so many, was an enthusiastic insect collector and amateur botanist in youth. Early in his career he worked in parishes in Lancashire and Yorkshire, and had little time to pursue his natural history interests. From 1920 onwards, he settled in Devon, where he was successively incumbent of livings at Coffinswell, Torrington and Milber. There he took up his old interest. In the course of a sixty-year career, he produced a quite delightful, and yet detailed and accurate series of paintings of British flowering plants, sometimes travelling on night trains to reach distant parts of Britain, to work on his paintings for a day, returning overnight, working on the drawings as he travelled back to his parish in Devon. In all he completed illustrations of 1486 species of flowering plants. Keble Martin had written only a modest amount previously – an account of the history of one of his parishes in 1920 and a *Flora of Devon* in 1939 – and although his plates were exhibited, no publisher wished to incur the high cost (at that time) of colour reproduction. It was only with the intervention of the Duke of Edinburgh that a publisher was found (George Rainbird) and *The Concise British Flora* appeared in 1965. The delightful illustrations were accompanied by descriptions of the plants to assist in identification. It was an immediate success: in 1967 some of the illustrations were used to illustrate United Kingdom postage stamps.

There is a further anecdote connected with Keble Martin's flower book worthy of note. Around the time of the publication of the book, at the age of eighty-seven, he proposed to his housekeeper, a Mrs Lewis. She refused, saying she liked the name Lewis, and would suffer financially if she remarried. Six weeks later, his publisher telephoned him to say that Prince Philip had agreed to write a foreword to the flower book. Keble Martin reported: 'In the joy and excitement of the moment, Mrs Lewis forgot her reserve and threw her arms around me.' They were married a few weeks later.[45]

The Lincolnshire botanist the Reverend E. Adrian Woodruffe-Peacock mentioned above was also a popular writer. Although he seldom wrote out sermons in full, he declared fairly late in life that even as a student in Durham he had 'a certain reputation for being an ink slinger'. He had written for *Science Gossip* from the age of fifteen, and had been 'on the scribble' ever since. He earned a modest income from his hundreds of pieces for a whole range of local and national newspapers and magazines, ranging from the *Boston Guardian*, *Grimsby Daily*

Telegraph and *Lincolnshire Times*, through the *Huddersfield Advertiser* and *Manchester News*, to *Country Life*, *Farmer & Stock Breeder*, *The Field* and *Shooting Times*. He used a wide variety of pseudonyms, so some of his writings are almost impossible to trace. Those pseudonyms that are known include 'AQ', 'GOB', Gregory O. Benoni, 'NL', 'Q', 'QED' and Walter Adam Wallace. Under this last name in 1889 he wrote a rather strange novel with the title *Only a Sister? A Tale of Today*. Although one reviewer thought the author 'clever' and 'daring' another thought the work 'silly'. In one review the publishers were congratulated on the 'good clear type and remarkably handsome cover', presumably because the critic was not terribly impressed by what lay within.[46]

A family Darwinian link

The importance of the Reverend John Henslow, Rector of Hitcham and Professor of Botany at Cambridge, as a node in the mid-nineteenth-century network has been stressed. Through his family links, and network of clerical acquaintances, he played an important role in the flow of information (and specimens) in nineteenth-century natural history, particularly botany. He assisted in placing his disciples in important positions: the most significant example of this was his role in placing Charles Darwin aboard the *Beagle*. John Henslow entered St John's College, Cambridge in 1814. In 1819 he (along with Darwin's other teacher, Adam Sedgwick, amongst others) founded the Cambridge Philosophical Society 'as a point of concourse [and], for scientific communications'. Henslow, then at Little St Mary's, Cambridge, was elected to the Professorship of Mineralogy in 1823 (at the age of twenty-six), moving to the Chair of Botany in 1827, following the death of the previous occupant, the Reverend Professor Thomas Martyn, who had held it for sixty years. Henslow reorganized the teaching of science in general, and botany in particular, in the University, and played an important part in establishing the Botanic Gardens. He encouraged field and practical work. Interestingly some of his research papers were not unrelated to his most famous student's later interest – the species question, variation, hybridization. One paper was 'On the examination of a hybrid *Digitalis*'. He also wrote on the classification of the Pimulas, and on 'monstrosities'. Perhaps more important was his constant support of Darwin before, during and after the Voyage,[47] even after the publication of the *Origin of Species*. He published an account of the plants that Darwin found in the Cocos (Keeling) Islands, in the Indian Ocean, that the *Beagle* had visited in April 1836.[48]

Henslow's own theological views were entirely orthodox: he once said that he did not wish to change one word of the Thirty-nine Articles of religion. Correspondence shows that he was at variance with some of Darwin's evolutionary outlook: after the publication of the *Origin* he wrote to Leonard Jenyns that he thought Darwin had attempted 'more than is granted to man, just as people used to try to account for the origin of Evil – a question past our ever finding out. However his book is a wonderful book & will do good.'[49] Yet his son-in-law wrote on his death that Henslow was 'a man with strong enough religious convictions of his own, [who] had the biggest charity for every heresy so long as it was conscientiously entertained.' Darwin replied: 'I fully believe a better man than Henslow never walked this earth.'[50]

John's son, the Reverend George Henslow (1835–1925) held the positions of Lecturer in Botany at St Bartholomew's Hospital, and Professor of Botany at Queen's College, London. He was a prolific writer and published a large number of books, some popular in character. He was particularly interested in the botany of the Holy Land,[51] seeing this as one avenue for the harmonisation of religion and science. Although he accepted the notion of evolution, writing *Genesis and Geology: A Plea for Evolution* in 1871,[52] the idea of natural selection did not appeal to him at all; the directionality of evolution was too clear for it to be attributable to random variations. He was a very competent botanist, writing: *The Origin of Floral Structures* (1888), and *The Origin of Plant Structures* (1895).[53] The mechanism he relied on would be closer to that of Lamarck than that of his father's close friend and colleague. In his *The Heredity of Acquired Characteristics in Plants*, published in 1908, George Henslow argued that protoplasm possessed 'directivity', a force that enabled living things to respond to their environment.[54] He preferred to speak of adaptation rather than design, as there was no evidence that the Deity had actually 'designed' life-forms before they came into existence. In *The Argument of Adaptation or Natural Theology Reconsidered*, in 1897,[55] he asked:

> [I]s there a Divine Being, who has impressed the forces of life upon inorganic matter? In other words, has He not created living protoplasm with all its wonderful powers of heredity, variability, responsiveness, and adaptability, powers practically illimitable for as the variations in the combinations of the surroundings are infinite, so are the numbers of responsive adaptations of the beings in the midst of them.[56]

The directivity of organisms, and their ability to respond in an immediate way to their surroundings, meant that they evolved. There was pattern, order amidst the complexity; Paley's 'natural theology' remained an appropriate model. There was no tension between science and religion. He developed these views in: *Christian Beliefs Reconsidered in the Light of Modern Thought,* 1884, and *The Theory of Evolution . . . and the Application of the Principles of Evolution to Religion, Considered as illustrative of the Wisdom and Beneficence of the Almighty*; 1873.[57] The title of the latter work (which won the prestigious Actonian Endowment Prize) has a distinctly Paleyan ring. George Henslow despite the personal link with Darwin, and the strongly evolutionary thrust of some of what he wrote, represents something of a restatement of Larmackian views rather than Darwinian orthodoxy (see glossary).

Applied botany

We should also remember that Gilbert White was one of the most successful popularizers of English natural history of all time. (Like many other botanists, he learnt part of his plant lore from a local healing-woman.) Important as matters of identification and taxonomy were to him, he was a strong advocate of the employment of plant science in the service of humanity. Here is Letter 40 to the Honourable Daines Barrington, bearing the date 3 July, 1778. It is so far in advance of its day that it is worth quoting almost in full:

> The standing objection to botany has always been, that it is a pursuit that amuses the fancy and exercises the memory, without improving the mind or advancing any real knowledge: and where the science is carried no further than a mere systematic classification, the charge is but true. But the botanist who is desirous of wiping off this aspersion should by no means be content with a list of names; he should study plants philosophically, should investigate the laws of vegetation, should examine the powers and virtues of efficacious herbs, and graft the gardener, the planter, and the husbandman, on the phytologist. Not that system is by any means to be thrown aside: without system the field of Nature would be a pathless wilderness: but system should be subservient to, not the main object of, pursuit.
>
> Vegetation is highly worthy of our attention; and in itself is of the utmost consequence to mankind, and productive of many of the greatest comforts and elegancies of life. To plants we owe timber, bread, beer, honey, wine, oil, linen, cotton, etc . . .
>
> The productions of vegetation have had a vast influence on the

commerce of nations, and have been great promoters of navigation, as may be seen in the articles of sugar, tea, tobacco, opium, ginseng, betel, paper etc. As every climate has its peculiar produce, our natural wants bring on a mutual intercourse; so that by means of trade each distant part is supplied with the growth of every latitude. But without the knowledge of plants and their culture, we must have been content with our hips and haws, without enjoying the delicate fruits of India and the sulutiferous drugs of Peru.

Instead of examining the minute distinctions of every various species of each obscure genus, the botanist should endeavour to make himself acquainted with those that are useful. You shall see a man readily ascertain every herb of the field, yet hardly know wheat from barley, or at least one sort of wheat or barley from another.

But of all sorts of vegetation the grasses seem to be most neglected; neither the farmer nor the grazier seem to distinguish the annual from the perennial, the hardy from the tender, nor the succulent and nutritive from the dry and juiceless.

The study of grasses would be of great consequence to a northerly, and grazing kingdom. The botanist that could improve the sward of the district where he lived would be an useful member of society; and he would be the best commonwealth's man that could occasion the growth of 'two blades of grass where one alone was seen before'.

This letter may be seen in the context of late eighteenth-century mercantilism, but there are perhaps, other influences. Can one perhaps see the notion of the brotherhood of all mankind in the paragraph about the vegetable productions of the various climatic zones? And still further beneath the surface, maybe, the Christian image of the many parts making up a whole:

We are members one of another. (Ephesians 4.25)

It should not be forgotten that the final words of the letter are a quotation, not quite verbatim, from that campaigning Anglican clergyman, the Dean of St Patrick's, Dublin, Jonathan Swift (1667–1745), who went on to stress that the man who could make two blades of grass when one grew before was more use 'than the whole race of politicians put together'. Gilbert White was not a social reformer or a profound theologian (though he seems to have preached a good sermon), but it is interesting to see how in the writings of the parson-naturalist, scientific, religious and social ideas are sometimes intermingled.

We met Miles Berkeley as a pioneer in the taxonomy of the fungi and algae. It is tempting to assume that he and others like him who devoted so much to the elucidation of a lowly group of plants or animals were rejoicing in God's diversity and complexity and diversity: no tiny fragment of creation was to be neglected. Miles Berkeley was not just a taxonomist, however; he made a number of careful ecological studies, investigations of the life histories of several parasitic fungi, to the extent that he has been called the 'originator and founder of the science of plant pathology.' His investigations of potato blight, published in 1846, during the Irish potato famine, disposed of whole rafts of wild theories about the disease, and showed that it was caused by a fungus now known as *Phytophthora infestans*. He then turned his attention to vine-mildew, and a number of other plant diseases of immense economic and social importance.[58]

The emphasis on plant pathology can be seen alongside John Henslow's interest in the study of soils and natural fertilisers in his Suffolk parish of Hitcham, part of a concern for agricultural improvement, and thus for the amelioration of the conditions of the common people of the countryside. From December 1842 onwards, Henslow frequently attended meetings of the Hadleigh Farmers' Club (Hadleigh was the small town about 6 miles (10km), from Hitcham) and he used to give occasional lectures and contribute to the discussion, in an effort 'to convert them from 'the art of husbandry' to the 'science of agriculture'. 'We must' he said, 'have more out of the land than our fathers had'.[59] Christianity has been described as being one of the most materialistic of religions, and its clergy have always seen the relief of poverty as an important part of their duties.

Finally we should look back to one of the important groups of originators of botany in England – the herbalists and apothecaries. John Ray is said to have learned his plants from a herb-woman; William Turner was a medical doctor as well as priest, naturalist and theologian. And Gilbert White had a passing knowledge of the medicinal uses of herbs:

> *Helleborus foetidus*, stinking hellebore, bear's foot or setterwort, [is found] all over the High-wood and Coney-croft-hanger: this continues a great branching plant the winter-through, blossoming about January, and is very ornamental in shady walks and shrubberies. The good women give the leaves powdered to children troubled with worms; but it is a violent remedy, and ought to be administered with caution.[60]

The idea of concern for the body going hand in hand with that of the soul can be traced back to St Luke and indeed the Supreme Physician himself. This link, together with the fact that plants show such beauty and diversity (it is frequently asserted reflecting the glory of God), together, perhaps with the transience of flowers, like that of human life, pointing therefore to the Life of the World to Come, perhaps explains why botany has been a particular concern of the clergy for many centuries.

Notes

1 Raven, C. E., *English Naturalists from Neckham to Ray* (Cambridge University Press, 1947), op. cit., chapters 4–7, pp. 48–137; Jones, D., *William Turner: Naturalist, Physician and Divine* (London, Routledge, 1988).
2 Jones, D., *ibid.*, quoting *New Herbal.*
3 Jones, D., *ibid.*, quoting *New Herbal.*
4 Jones, D., *ibid.*, quoting *New Herbal.*
5 Jones, D., *ibid.*, p. 49.
6 Raven, C. E., *John Ray: Naturalist* (Cambridge University Press, 1942). See particularly pp. 21–71.
7 Preface to the Reader in *Catalogus Plantarum circa Cantabrigiam nascentium.* Ewen, A. H. and Prime, T., (eds), *Ray's Flora of Cambridgeshire* (Hitchin, Wheldon and Wesley, 1975), p. 22.
8 *Ibid.*, pp. 22–23.
9 Ewen, A. H. and Prime, T., 1975, op. cit., pp. 7–19.
10 *Ibid.*, p,67.
11 *Ibid.*, p. 58.
12 Raven, C. E., 1942, op. cit., Chapter 4, pp. 87, 98.
13 *Ibid.*, p. 138.
14 *Ibid.*, p. 340–341.
15 *Ibid.*, Chapter 8, pp. 181–201.
16 *Ibid.*, p. 193.
17 *Ibid.*, op.cit., Chapter 9, pp. 202–242.
18 Baldwin, S. A., *John Ray (1627–1705) Essex Naturalist* (Witham, Baldwin's Books, 1986), p. 41.
19 Raven, C. E., 1942, op. cit., p. 258.
20 Hales, S., *Vegetable Statics* (1727)
21 *Ibid.*, p. 211.
22 Allen, D. E., *The Naturalist in Britain: a Social History* (Harmondsworth, Penguin Books, 1978), pp. 78, 128.
23 Allen, D. E., 1978, op. cit., p. 131.
24 *Neat cattle* were cattle that were clean and undiseased. *Neat's foot oil* was an oil extracted from the feet of such cattle, especially oxen, after slaughter, used for treating leather and boots to render them waterproof.
25 Allen, D. E., 1978, op. cit., p.131.
26 Further editions appeared in 1872 and 1873; biographical and bibliographical details are provided in Hawkesworth, D. L. and Seaward, M. R. D., *Lichenology in the British Isles 1568–1975* (Richmond, Richmond Publishing, 1977).
27 Seaward, M. R., 'William Johnson's lichen collection', *Naturalist*, [97], 1972, pp. 13–14; Mark Seaward, University of Bradford, personal communication.
28 Druce, G. C., *Flora of Oxfordshire* (London, Parker and Co., 1886).

29 Geldart, H. R., 'Botany of Norfolk', in *Victoria County History: Norfolk* (1901), p. 44
30 Oswald, P., 'The Revd John Hemsted (1747?–1824)', *Nature in Cambridgeshire*, 33, 1991, pp. 26–34.
31 Garthorn Hardy, R., '*Iter litorale*', *Transactions of the Suffolk Natural History Society*, 11(2) 1959, pp. 1–15.
32 Woodruffe-Peacock, E. A., 'William Fowler: In memoriam', *Naturalist*, [37], 1912, pp. 121–123.
33 Woodruffe-Peacock, E. A., *Reminiscences of University Life in Durham*, unpublished manuscript, n.d.. Copy in the possession of Mark Seaward, University of Bradford.
34 Woodruffe-Peacock, E. A., 'The ecology of Thorne Waste', *Naturalist*, [45], 1920, pp. 301–304, 352–356, 381–384; *Naturalist*, [46], 1921, pp. 21–25.
35 Woodruffe-Peacock, E. A., 'A fox-covert study', *Journal of Ecology*, 6, 1918, pp. 110–125.
36 Seaward, M. R. D., 'Biographical Notes on the Reverend E. A. Woodruffe-Peacock, 1858–1922', *Lincolnshire History and Archaeology*, 6, 1971, pp. 113–124.
37 Quoted in obituary: Anon, 'In memoriam, E. A. Woodruffe-Peacock', *Naturalist* [47], 1922, pp. 137–139.
38 Woodruffe-Peacock, E. A., 'A study of Seed-dispersion in Lincolnshire' *Naturalist* [19], 1894, pp. 19–24.
39 Crackles, E., 'Philip Mauleverer Garnett (1906–1967)', *Naturalist* [92], 1967, p. 104
40 Addington, R., 'Not so Wild', *White Admiral*, Newsletter of the Suffolk Naturalists Society, 23, 1992, p. 21.
41 Cundall, R. D., 'Botanical notes made by William Gawthorp of Ripley, near Harrogate in the eighteenth century', *Naturalist*, 111, 1986, pp. 147–150.
42 Letter: J. Frederic Wickenden to J. B. Lightfoot; 3 August 1848, Dean and Chapter Library, Durham.
43 I thank Alan Cadwallader, of St Barnabas' College, Adelaide, South Australia, for his insights into the Westcott's theology, and family life, and for bringing the letter in the preceding note to my notice.
44 Johns, C. A., *Flowers of the Field* (27th edition, London, SPCK, 1892).
45 Keble Martin, W., *Concise British Flora* (London, George Rainbird, 1965); Keble Martin, W., *Over the Hills* (London, Michael Joseph, 1968); Hinde, T., *A Field Guide to the English Country Parson* (London, Phoebe Phillips/Heinemann, 1983), pp. 74–75.
46 Seaward, M. R. D., 'E. Adrian Woodruffe-Peacock (1858–1922): a pioneer ecologist'; unpublished manuscript, 1998.
47 Barlow, N., *Darwin and Henslow* (London, John Murray, 1967).
48 Henslow, J. S., '*Florula Keelinensis*: an Account of the Native Plants of the Keeling Islands', *Annals of Natural History*, 1, 1838 pp. 337–347.
49 Letter: J. S. Henslow to L. Jenyns, 26 January 1860, Bath Library. In the same letter Henslow wrote:

> . . .My views correspond with yours. The Book is a marvellous assemblage of facts & observations – & no doubt contains much legitimate inference but it pushes hypothesis (for it is not a real theory) too far.

50 Barlow, N., 1967, op. cit., p. 19.
51 Henslow, G., The *Plants of the Bible* (London, Bible Tract Society, no date, *c.* 1892); *Spiritual Teaching of Bible Plants* (George Stoneman, London, 1897).

52 Henslow, G., *Genesis and Geology: A Plea for Evolution* (London, Robert Hardwicke, 1871).
53 Henslow, G., *The Origin of Floral Structures through Insect and other Agencies*, International Scientific Series, vol. 64 (London, Kegan Paul, 1888); *The Origin of Plant Structures by Self-adaptation to the Environment*, International Scientific Series, vol. 77 (London, Kegan Paul, 1895).
54 Henslow, G., *The Heredity of Acquired Characteristics in Plants* (London, John Murray, 1908).
55 Henslow, G., *The Argument of Adaptation or Natural Theology Reconsidered* (London, George Stoneman, 1897).
56 Henslow, G., 1897, *ibid.*, p. 64.
57 Henslow, G., *Christian Beliefs Reconsidered in the light of Modern Thought* (London, Frederic Norgate, 1884); *The theory of evolution . . . and the application of the principles of evolution to religion, considered as illustrative of the wisdom and Beneficence of the Almighty* (London, Macmillan, 1873).
58 Allen, D. E., 1978, op. cit.; Russell-Gebbett, J., *Henslow of Hitcham* (Lavenham, Terence Dalton, 1977), p. 94; Miles Berkeley – Leonard Jenyns Correspondence, Bath Library.
59 Russell-Gebbett, 1977, op. cit, pp. 91–96.
60 *Natural History of Selborne,* Letter 41, to the Honourable Daines Barrington, 3 July 1778.

Chapter Four

The birds of the air

He shall arise at the voice of a bird (Ecclesiastes 12.4)

Numerous commentators have attempted to explain the extraordinary popularity of bird-watching. David Allen, in his *Naturalist in Britain: a Social History* pointed out that 'ornithology had scarcely any hope of support on the pretext of economics. It was a totally useless subject: another amateur field, *par excellence*, largely ignored by even nonutilitarian academics'[1] What is therefore the reason for the extraordinary numbers of devotees that it has attracted, and their single-minded enthusiasm? David Allen went on:

> Its secret lay in numbers. Birds had a breadth of appeal that no other branch of natural history could rival. The quantity of species likely to be met in this country [Britain] was small enough to be manageable, yet large enough to provide an appetizing ration of rarities. For most purposes Latin names could be dispensed with.[2]

He goes on to say that as birds move about, sometimes in very large numbers, bird-watching became a co-operative activity, lending itself to the harnessing of large numbers of separate observers.

It should perhaps also be noted that bird-watching requires very little equipment. Although there are a few devotees who still use a telescope for watching the waders on a lake or estuary when it can be secured at a single point, such as in a hide, the expansion in its popularity coincided closely with the availability of cheap binoculars, the emblem of the bird-watcher. Of course it is possible for the action of walking around the countryside with field-glasses to be misinterpreted. It is asserted that holder of the living of Stonegate, Sussex, the Reverend Andrew John Young (1885–1971), poet and more-or-less full-time eccentric, who was originally a Presbyterian minister, switched from bird-watching to botany because his parishioners would believe he was off to the races.[3]

What's hit is history; what's missed is mystery

There are other factors that explain the popularity of bird-watching: birds are the right size – they are easily seen, and are not too difficult to identify (consider fish, spiders, sponges, micro-organisms, lichens, mosses and liverworts in comparison). Birds are obviously very lively and active: this provided another dimension of interest, particularly once ethology became an established field of enquiry. Many birds are brightly coloured and attractive: this also gives them an intrinsic appeal. Here is a quotation from a book on taxidermy by William Swainson:

> In nothing has the growing taste for natural history so much manifested itself, as in the prevalent fashion of placing glass cases of beautiful birds and splendid insects on the mantle piece or side table. The attention of the most indolent is attracted, the curiosity of the inquisitive awakened.[4]

Perhaps this reveals an important part of the story: bird-watching is a development of the hunting instinct. Some birds had been shot for food and sport for centuries. Collecting, skinning, stuffing and displaying them followed. The hunting and shooting parson existed in the countryside until very recent times, and the story goes that the Reverend Alexander Forsyth, a minister in Aberdeenshire with an enthusiasm for wildfowling, became so exasperated by the way in which the ducks dived or flew on seeing the 'flash in the pan', the detonation of the gunpowder before the shot hit them, that, after a series of experiments in 1807 he patented the detonating or percussion cap.[5]

Many naturalists, clerical and lay, were introduced to natural history by collecting – eggs as well as adult birds. The egg-collector was essentially a Victorian phenomenon: the blow-drill was only invented in 1830, and by the third decade of the twentieth century, egging was already becoming unfashionable, as the conservation movement gathered momentum. Nevertheless for several decades, a specimen was regarded as a requirement of any legitimate record of a rare species, hence the adage: 'What's hit is history, what's missed is mystery'.

Some of the stories of collecting from the nineteenth century are little less than horrific to the modern ear. The Reverend Canon Henry Baker Tristram (1822–1906), Canon of Durham Cathedral, was a fine pastor and a distinguished scientist (see Plate 13). He was, in 1868, elected a Fellow of the Royal Society. He wrote a most detailed series of books on the natural history, geology and human communities of North Africa and the Near East. He had a remarkably up-to-date and integrative geographical approach (in, for example, *The Great Sahara*, *The Land of Israel*, *The Natural History of the Bible*, *The Topography of the Holy Land*).[6] Later in life he went on expeditions to China and Japan. But he was a COLLECTOR. He once boasted, as evidence of his 'love of nature': 'Before I was 14 years old, I had taken with my own hands the eggs of the peregrine, the red kite, common buzzard, marsh harrier, hen harrier and the raven.'[7] He began as he meant to go on: here are some quotations, taken at random from *The Land of Israel*:

> I sallied forth with my gun. I succeeded in shooting three small owls and the great grey shrike.
>
> Immense numbers of warblers and red-backed shrikes were breeding on the southern slopes, and in those three or four hours we obtained about twenty nests, chiefly of the Orphean warbler and lesser whitethroats.
>
> We had a most successful natural history exploration in these caverns [in Hyrcanus' Castle] having taken away amongst us, the nests of two vultures, the large Egyptian owl, lesser kestrel and our first nest of the russet swallow, besides the bulbul in the castle. We also captured specimens of a new species of bat, a new lizard and gathered some curious plants, and three very fine species of beetle.

This 'sweep through the Holy Land' as he called it, lasted for many months; it was a journey, an account of which is sufficient to induce minor trauma in the modern conservation-minded ornithologist.

Another ardent collector seems to have been the Reverend H. H. Slater, of Irchester, Wellingborough, who in an enthusiastically written article in the *Naturalist* entitled 'A winter visit to the Farne Islands' in 1884 describes the cavalier way in which several eider ducks, a cormorant, two golden-eyes, a gannet, 'a few good specimens of purple sandpipers in winter plumage and a turnstone' were shot 'with a liberal expenditure of ammunition'. So too were a couple of red-necked grebes, one of which was described as 'still retaining a good deal of the chestnut colour of the summer plumage on the neck'. All this before breakfast.[8]

The Reverend John Chaloner (1811–1894) was yet another north country rector who had 'an unerring eye and often some shot' for a rare bird. Ruff, bittern, gooseander, mergansers, skua, phaleropes, scoters 'and scarce birds generally' were taken by him and many of them adorned his 'beautiful collection'.[9]

Lessons from bird life

By no means all nineteenth-century parson-naturalists were so keen on this slaughter: many were happy simply to record in detail what they saw. The Reverend Leonard Jenyns, Vicar of Swaffham Bulbeck in Cambridgeshire, once claimed he had 'never fired a gun in his life', although he often had a brother or a servant to hand to do the job for him. Once, puzzled by the identification of warblers he wrote 'I must endeavour to have one shot, whilst in the act of singing'. This extract from his 1825 natural history diary concerning the discovery of a meadow pipit's nest on the Devil's Ditch in Cambridgeshire illustrates his sensitivity, as well as his attention to detail. It is typical of the many diaries of the era:

> May 14
> Amongst the long grass . . . on the sloping bank of the ditch we found the nest of the tit-pipit (Anthus pratensis). It was composed of dry grass bents & stalks of plants: patched on the outside with a small quantity of green moss, & lined within with fine dry grass, & long horse-hair. – The eggs were five in number; in colour, some were a thick muddy purplish brown, somewhat darkest at the larger end; others were of a dirty brownish white, closely set all over with spots of reddish brown.[10]

Although he would not have described himself as a scientific ornithologist, a clergyman with whose name bird study will ever be linked, is the Reverend Francis Orpen Morris (1810–1893), born in County Cork, educated at Worcester College, Oxford, ordained in 1834. He worked in parishes in Nottinghamshire and Doncaster, but held the living of Nunburnholme in the East Riding of Yorkshire from 1854 until his death. Collecting formed an important role in his formation as a naturalist: he collected both birds and insects while at Bromsgrove School in the 1820s. His first publication was *A Guide to the Arrangement of British Birds* (1834), a catalogue primarily designed for those labelling collecting cabinets. Around the same time he compiled 'A catalogue of British birds which have occurred at different times in Yorkshire', but it was only published in 1840 (in the *Doncaster Chronicle and Farmers' Journal*). This early interest in nomenclature, scientific and vernacular, caused him to develop an extremely wide network of correspondents and acquaintances, which provided the basis for his later writing. Alas, much material was reproduced quite uncritically, and his *Natural History of British Birds* (1850–1857), originally issued as a part-work (four species a month) contains a feast of anecdotes and elevating tales, many of them totally unreliable. A parson of traditional theological and political views, he lost no opportunity of making a moral point. In his preface to *British Birds* he remarks:

> I have endeavoured . . . throughout to import a religious character to this treatise on some of the most interesting works of the CREATOR, as indicated on the very first page by the motto 'Gloria in excelcis Deo' prefixed to the account of the 'birds of the air', and . . . 'De profundis ad Dominum' attached in like manner to that of the waterbirds, whose home is more or less in the 'great deep'.[11]

Many accounts are packed with allegory. He draws attention to the way in which a cormorant takes a lower rock, when higher and more desirable rocks are taken; the more lowly in society must always accept their position without complaining. As a modern editor wrote: 'The pages abound with errors and mistakes, and records accepted without discrimination, yet they charmed and delighted their readers.'[12] The work had the advantage of being almost the only work available at a modest price that had reasonably accurate, coloured plates. What the reader wanted was incident and amusement: the bizarre and the unusual rated as highly as the scientifically accurate. Comparisons can be made with the early naturalists (see chapter 2). Here is a tale told of a golden eagle from Sweden:

> A mother saw her child, which had been laid down at some distance from her in the fields, carried off by an Eagle, and heard its cries for some time in the air, till it was taken beyond her hearing and sight. She lost her reason, and became an inmate of a lunatic asylum – an asylum truly, for unless the mercy of Providence had shrouded her with the mantle of forgetfulness, had provided this anodyne for such heart-rending brief, surely the last cry of her child must ever have echoed in her ears.[13]

A tale of Gothic horror with every ingredient: it comes from a far country, contains hideous tragedy and gruesomeness, yet reveals, apparently, a moral truth. It is no surprise that Francis Orpen Morris' book went through a series of editions up until 1888.

He was an important node in an extensive network of correspondents and associates. Some game birds were not well covered in his *Natural History of British Birds*, probably because his younger brother, B. B. Morris was producing a companion publication entitled *British Game Birds and Waterfowl*, and a school-friend, the Reverend Richard Alington, Rector of Swinhope, prepared some of the working drawings.[14]

There are a number of points of comparison between the Reverend F. O. Morris, and the Revered C. A. Johns: both were extremely productive and popular writers of books on natural history. Morris wrote books on butterflies and moths (1852–1853) as well as the *British Birds* mentioned above, and the *Natural History of Nests and Eggs of British Birds* (1851–1853). Johns wrote *British Birds in their Haunts* in 1862, besides a string of other natural history titles. Yet another of the same genre was the Reverend J. G. Wood, whose *Common Objects of the Countryside* (1858) is said to have sold a hundred thousand copies in one week. He wrote a long string of well-illustrated books on birds, insects and flowers. Bridging the gap between ornithology and theology, but still very popular in character was Johns' *Bird Life and the Bible* (1887).[15] There was a boom in the publication of illustrated natural history books in the middle years of the nineteenth century, and clergy such as Morris, Wood, Johns and, to some extent Tristram, were amongst those who contributed to it.

From county bird monographs to scientific conservation

Popular though such works were – they served to awaken hundreds of thousands of urban dwellers to the interest of natural history – their scientific importance was less than those of a genre that had its heyday rather later in the century: the county bird monograph. Thus although a paper entitled 'Observations on the ornithology of Cambridgeshire' appeared in the *Journal of the Cambridge Philosophical Society* as early as 1827,[16] written by all-round natural historian and polymath the Reverend Leonard Jenyns, Rector of Swaffham Bulbeck, whose field observations on the meadow pipit are noted above, a series of impressive county volumes appeared later in the century. The Reverend Churchill Babington (1821–1889) published *The Birds of Suffolk*, 1884–1886. He was also able to make use of a wide network of clerical connections; he acknowledges the help of a dozen clergy in his search for records, including the Reverend W. H. M. M. Carthew, of Woodbridge, the Reverend A. Foster-Miller of Redgrave, the Reverend Dr Goodacre of Wilby, the Reverend Herbert Jones of Livermere, and so on. This was followed rather quickly by the much lesser known *Ornithology of Suffolk* (1891), written by the Reverend Julian George Tuck (1851–1933) of Tostock, one of the not inconsiderable number of naturalist clergy who was both squire and parson in his home parish. There was then something of a gap before the Reverend Norman F. Ticehurst's *History of the Birds of Suffolk*, published in 1932.[17] The story for many other English counties would be similar. The pattern was in many ways comparable to the production of county floras described in chapter 3.

Many of those who wrote county bird monographs were amateurs, proving that until well into this century it was possible for a country vicar or rector, without a formal connection with a university, to do important work. Sometimes a local organisation or a national scientific society provided a springboard. One such individual was the Reverend F. C. R. Jourdain, called by David Allen 'a notorious *pastor pugnax*', 'inexhaustible', 'formidable' and more besides. He had, if the simile is not too close to the bone, the energy of a poacher turned gamekeeper, or, perhaps more appropriate, one who has undergone a conversion experience. A country rector near Abingdon, he was particularly associated with the Oxford Ornithological Society. Originally a noted egg-collector, he later changed his approach. Traditionally records were not regarded as worth very much unless backed up by a specimen.[18] In the years following the First World War the emphasis changed. The Royal Society for the Protection of Birds and other conservation organisations became more influential, and it became clear that overhunting and other forms of persecution had reduced some species, and eliminated others from the British list, and the traditional approach was unsustainable. Jourdain, instead, where records for county bird reports or journals such as *British Birds* were in question, developed what amounted to a drill – the very careful recording of details, and the importance of high standards of 'rigour' in the acceptance of records of rarities. No longer was it necessary to shoot a bird or collect an egg to have a record accepted. The development of photography also contributed to this liberalization. Hard-working and productive, Jourdain was one of the co-authors of the massive *Handbook of British Birds* (1938–1941), a five-volume magnum opus that remained in print through its descendant *The Popular Handbook* until well into the 1970s.[19]

In fact this shift in emphasis simply marked an acceleration of a trend that was already identifiable towards the end of the nineteenth century. The Reverend F. O. Morris, reactionary Tory that he was in some ways, had little against the sporting shooting of game-birds in its place, but he was absolutely opposed to senseless slaughter. He disapproved of rows of dead birds of prey on gamekeepers gibbets, and indeed, although not opposed to game preserving per se, thought that gamekeepers should be taxed as a luxury (£20 per annum, he thought was appropriate). He deplored the destruction of owls and herons, believing their effects on coverts and fisheries respectively, were exaggerated. He wrote to *The Times* and petitioned the House of Commons about many such matters. Among his minor, partial successes was the formation of the Yorkshire

Association for the Protection of Sea Birds, so sickened was he by the wholesale destruction by shooting (by 'sportsmen') of the breeding seabirds on the cliffs of Bempton and Flamborough Head, near Scarborough. It has been suggested that this was the first British wildlife conservation organisation. The campaigning was responsible for the passing of the Sea-Birds Preservation Act by Parliament in 1869, the first such protective legislation passed in Britain. This was an important milestone, although, alas, it was not terribly successful, being difficult to enforce. It was followed by the Wild Birds Protection Act of 1880, and set the scene for a century of conservation legislation. The role of Francis Orpen Morris in much of this is now largely forgotten.[20]

In another of his numerous letters to *The Times*, entirely consistent with his other campaigns, Morris recommended that food be put out for birds. This failed to catch on, however, and it took two severe winters in the early 1890s for bird-feeding to become a British institution.

The transformation from passionate collector to concerned conservationist was by no means unusual. One wonders indeed, whether it can be the same Canon Tristram, at one time known as 'The Great Gun of Durham', who had collections of natural history specimens that included well over 20,000 specimens, including many great rarities, who supported, at the Edinburgh meeting of the British Association for the Advancement of Science (1873) the following motion:

> The Conference of Delegates, having heard of the threatened extermination of certain birds, as British breeding species, through the destruction of their eggs, deprecates the encouragement given to dealers by collectors through their demands for British-taken eggs, and trusts that the corresponding societies will do all that lies in their power to interest and influence naturalists, landowners and others in the preservation of such birds and their eggs.[21]

But such is the case. Already by 1889, however, 'The Great Gun' was conscious that great private collections were a thing of the past. In that year he wrote to a Canadian friend that 'Seebolm, Shelley and myself are about the only private collectors left in the country'. From the late 1860s onwards he was active in a number of North of England and national bird protection organisations, and indeed at the very end of his life was Vice-president of the Royal Society for the Protection of Birds (1904–1906). In a very real way he continued campaigns initiated by Morris. Perhaps (maybe correctly), *a propos* of his early destructive activities in the Middle East (page 73), he saw British species as more in need of protection than those elsewhere.

A colleague in some of these ventures was Canon E. Ponsonby

Knubley (1850–1931), for nineteen years Rector of Staveley in Yorkshire, and himself the son of a country parson. Canon Knubley was active in the Yorkshire Naturalists' Union for many years, and Chairman and Convenor of the Union's Wild Birds' Eggs Committee, and a member of the British Ornithologists Union. As a delegate representing these organisations he was present at the British Association meetings that were important influences in getting early conservation onto the statute book.[22]

In the twentieth century the involvement of clergymen with ornithology became increasingly associated with the conservation movement. The Reverend Peter H. T. Hartley (1909–1985), for example, was one of a relatively small number of parson-naturalists to have a university degree in a biological subject (First Class Honours in Zoology, University of London, 1933). He had an active ministry in East Anglia, becoming Archdeacon of Suffolk, 1970–1975. He was active in the Royal Society for the Protection of Birds, frequently writing for that organisation's journal, *Bird Notes*.

As shooting and egg-collecting became less politically correct, and indeed illegal, and as the broad outlines of the taxonomy and distribution of the British avifauna became clear, the emphasis was increasingly on studies of the ecology of birds (their relationships with their environments, food supplies, predators and the nature of their population dynamics), and their ethology (their behaviour – song and courtship, etc.). Needless to say there are important links between these: the behaviour of many species is closely linked to their environment and way of life.

Two modern Cambridge polymaths

Of the many naturalists that have been introduced so far in this book, many have had a variety of interests. Although often identified particularly with one area, or one biological group, parson-naturalists have often had varied interests and published on many aspects of natural history, as well as outside the subject. Many clergyman-naturalists have, of course, published on theology, as well as natural history. Perhaps coincidentally, this eclecticism of vision has been particularly shown by ornithologists. A couple of examples will have to suffice.

One of the most academically distinguished clergy of his day was the Reverend Professor Charles Earle Raven (1885–1964). Scholar and double first at Gonville and Caius College, Cambridge, he was later Dean and Fellow of Emmanuel College. He made a major contribution in both the arts and the sciences. A chaplain to the forces in the First

World War, he later became a pacifist, writing about pacifism and the theological aspects of war. He was for a while Rector of Bletchingley, Surrey. Besides writing extensively on theology, he also wrote several books on birds, including *In Praise of Birds* (1925) and *Bird Haunts and Behaviour* (1929).[23] One of his special enthusiasms was the study of the history of natural history. His *John Ray: Naturalist* (1942)[24] and *English Naturalists from Neckham to Ray* (1947)[25] are both masterly works of scholarship and extremely well-written. As one might have expected, Raven took an important part in discussions between science and religion, writing *The Creator Spirit* (1927), *Natural Religion and Christian Theology* (1953), and *Christianity and Science* (1955).[26] He was also, incidentally, one of the earliest Anglican proponents of the ordination of women.

The Reverend Edward Armstrong (1900–1978), an Ulsterman by birth, but who, with the exception of two years as Chaplain of St Andrew's, Kowloon, Hong Kong (1929–1930), spent all his ministry in England, was one of the authorities of his day on bird behaviour and bird song.[27] He also wrote books entitled *Shakespeare's Imagination*, *The Gospel Parables*, and *St Francis: Nature Mystic*. After a number of years in parishes in industrial cities in Yorkshire, he moved to the parish of St Mark's, on the outskirts of Cambridge, in 1943. He wrote:

> Darkness was falling on a November evening in 1943 and the bombers were roaring off into the gloom when, happening to look out of my study window, I saw a small bird alight on the trellis outside and then fly up into the ivy on the wall. A couple of evenings later the wren was there again. Evidently he came regularly to these sleeping quarters. My interest was again captured by a bird which had fascinated me as a boy. Here was a species about which I should like to know more. I had recently come to live in Cambridge after years spent in the centre of a great industrial area where there had been few opportunities to watch birds, but now, in war-time, if any observations were to be other than superficial I must accept sever limitations in their scope. War constrains some to be excessively peripatetic, others it limits to a very restricted orbit. I was in the latter category. Perhaps I could make the best use of my meagre opportunities if I were to concentrate on studying the 'life and conversation', as Gilbert White would have put it, of a single species.[28]

The observations were confined to the large suburban gardens on the outskirts of the city, and the woods and fields just beyond the city limits, within a mile of the vicarage garden, over a period of about ten years.

His monograph on *The Wren* appeared in 1955, and a stream of papers on the species followed. These studies of the wren were the basis of a great deal of his subsequent work. He showed how intimate were the connections between the behaviour, particularly the courtship and breeding behaviour, of a species, its form and colouration, and its environment, food-supply and ecology. He went on to apply these ideas to other species and to other environments. In the years following his studies of wren song and behaviour in the sheltered garden and woodland habitats of eastern England, he examined the patterns of behaviour of birds in the tundra environments of Iceland and Lapland, and on remote islands off the west coasts of Scotland and Ireland. Later still he ventured into the savanna and mountain environments of East Africa. Although a meticulous scientific observer, he retained a sense of wonder in the beauty and complexity of the natural world. His view was that by understanding the intricacy of the manner in which the living world worked, and the way in which the different parts fitted together, the observer could obtain a better insight into the mind of the Creator.

Such men appreciated the interconnections of knowledge. Raven knew his science, and knew his theology, and these helped him to document the life of John Ray. Edward Allworthy Armstrong, ornithologist, sought to find out what sort of naturalist was William Shakespeare. However, he found that birds were tokens – ideas that were the centres of image clusters in the mind of the Bard. Shakespeare knew little of birds, but like the mediaeval naturalists from whom he learned the little that he knew, he associated them with particular notions, such as love, hate, power, and death. It was this wellspring of images in his mind that contributed to Shakespeare's genius.

Like William Turner (see chapter 3), these modern clergy, and others of the same genre over the centuries, the idea of the unitary nature of knowledge had its appeal: 'The earth and all that is therein is the Lord's'. This appreciation of the interconnectedness of all things is not far removed from modern notions of ecology and the ecosystem.

Notes

1 Allen, D., *Naturalist in Britain: a Social History* (Harmondsworth, Penguin Books, 1978) p. 214.
2 *Ibid.*
3 Hinde, T., *A Field Guide to the English Country Parson* (London, Phoebe Phillips/Heinemann, 1983) p. 123.
4 Allen, D., 1978, *Ibid.*, p. 101.
5 Allen, D., 1978, *Ibid.*, pp. 141–142.
6 Tristram, H. B., *The Great Sahara* (London, Murray, 1860); *The Land of Israel*

(London, SPCK, 1866); *The Natural History of the Bible* (London, SPCK, 1867); *The Topography of the Holy Land* (London, SPCK, 1872).

7 Quoted in Bodenheimer, F. S., 'Canon H. B. Tristram 1822–1906', *Durham University Journal*, 49, 1957, pp. 95–97.

8 Slater, H. H., 'A winter visit to the Farne Islands', *Naturalist*, [10], 1884, pp. 89–91.

9 Emmet, J., 'In memoriam: John William Chaloner', *Naturalist*, [19], 1894, pp. 113–115.

10 Leonard Jenyns Diary: Newton Library, Cambridge.

11 Morris, F. O., *The History of British Birds* (London, Groombridge, 1850; redesigned ed. by Soper, T., London, Webb and Bower, 1981), p. 12.

12 *Ibid.*, Introduction to 1981 ed., p. 9.

13 *Ibid.*, p. 16. See also: Limbert, M., 'F. O. Morris's List of Yorkshire Birds', *Naturalist*, 117, 1992, pp. 113–125.

14 *Ibid.*, Introduction to 1981 ed., p. 8.

15 Johns, C. A., *Bird Life of the Bible* (London, Longmans Green, 1887).

16 Jenyns, L., 'Observations on the Ornithology of Cambridgeshire', *Transactions of the Cambridge Philosophical Society*, 2, 1827, pp. 287–384.

17 Ticehurst, N. F., *History of the Birds of Suffolk* (London, Gurney and Jackson, 1932).

18 Allen, D., 1978, op. cit., pp. 237, 253–254.

19 Hollom, P. A. D., *The Popular Handbook of British Birds* (London, Witherby, 1972).

20 Morris, F. O., 1981 [1850], op. cit.

21 Knubley, E. P., 'The protection of wild bird's eggs', *Naturalist*, [18], 1893, pp. 238–240. See also: Baker, R. A., 'The great gun of Durham—Canon Henry Baker Tristram, FRS (1822–1906). An outline of his life, collections and contribution to natural history', *Archives of Natural History*, 23, 1996, pp. 327–341.

22 *Ibid.*

23 Raven, C. E., *In Praise of Birds* (London, 1925), and *Bird Haunts and Behaviour*, (London, 1929).

24 Raven, C. E., *John Ray: Naturalist* (Cambridge University Press, 1942).

25 Raven, C. E., *English Naturalists from Neckham to Ray* (Cambridge University Press, 1947).

26 Raven, C. E., *The Creator Spirit* (London, Martin Hopkinson 1927); *Natural Religion and Christian Theology* (Cambridge University Press, 1953): *Christianity and Science* (London, Lutterworth, 1955).

27 Armstrong, E. A., *Bird Display and Behaviour* (Cambridge University Press, 1942); *Bird Song* (Oxford University Press 1963).

28 Armstrong, E. A., *The Wren* (London, Collins, 1955), p. 1.

Chapter Five

A draught of fishes . . . beasts and creeping things: vertebrates other than birds

They inclosed a great multitude of fishes (Luke 5. 6)
Every . . . creeping thing and beast of the earth after his kind (Genesis 1. 24)

Gilbert White on fishes and reptiles

We should remember that Gilbert White was undoubtedly one of the most successful popularizers of English natural history. Although the *Natural History of Selborne* is based upon genuine letters to Thomas Pennant, Esquire, and the Honourable Daines Barrington, many were specially written for the publication of the book in 1788 (the original manuscripts are in the British Library). An obvious example is the first, nominally to Thomas Pennant, but which is clearly contrived, as it introduces the parish, briefly summarizing its position, geography and principal physical features.

Letter 29, also to Pennant, bears the date 12 May 1770. It commences with comments on the late spring, with its 'cold turbulent weather... succession of frost, and snow, and hail, and tempest, that [caused] the regular migration or appearance of the summer birds . . . [to be] much interrupted.' This section closely follows the text of a real letter to Pennant. The published version, however, goes on to discuss the pairing of birds (the pair-bond as a modern ethologist would put it), mentioning a series of anecdotes based on his observations of house-sparrows, house martins and barn owls around his village, and the partridges of the fields nearby. The final section of the letter comments on house-cats' 'violent fondness for fish', contrasting this with the fact that 'of all quadrupeds cats are the least disposed towards water'. It may be thought a simple step from the swimming abilities of cats, to the habits and appearance of otters, and the last paragraph of Letter 29 reads:

> Quadrupeds that prey upon fish are amphibious: such is the otter, which by nature is so well formed for diving that it makes great havoc among the inhabitants of the waters. Not supposing that we had any of these beasts in our shallow brooks, I was much pleased to see a male otter brought to me, weighing twenty-one pounds, that had been shot on the bank of our stream below the Priory, where the rivulet divides the parish of Selborne from Harteley-wood.

Gilbert White is less at home with fishes, amphibians and reptiles than he is with birds and mammals, and he admits it in a letter to Thomas Pennant dated 18 June 1768 (letter 17). He expresses great satisfaction on hearing that his correspondent is pursuing studies of these groups with 'vigour', but goes on: 'The reptiles, few as they are, I am not acquainted with, so well as I could wish'. He states that there is a 'dubiousness and obscurity attending propagation of this class of animals' which he compares to the obscurity that exists in the manner of reproduction in the cryptograms in the plant kingdom. About these creatures old wives' tales abounded, and wherever possible, statements were made on the basis of his own careful observation or from what he regarded as authoritative sources. He was a great devotee of the works of John Ray, and quotes *The Wisdom of God in the Creation* in which there is an 'excellent account . . . concerning the migration of frogs from their breeding ponds'. This 'subverts' the 'foolish' notion that they dropped from the clouds in rain. 'It is from the grateful coolness and moisture of these showers that they are tempted to set out on their travels.' Writing in June he observes 'Frogs are as yet in their tadpole state; but in a few weeks, our lanes, paths and fields, will swarm for a few days with myriads of these emigrants, no larger than my little finger nail'.

The belief that toads are long-lived, however, Gilbert White believed to be true. He recounts, in the same letter:

> I have been informed . . . from undoubted authority that some ladies (ladies you will say of peculiar taste) took a fancy to a toad, which they nourished summer after summer for many years, till he grew to a monstrous size, with the maggots which turn to flesh flies. The reptile used to come forth every evening from an hole under the garden steps; and was taken up, after supper, on the table to be fed.

Eventually, however, the poor creature was attacked by a rook, which struck out an eye, and the toad languished for a while and died. As toads have been recorded to live more than 40 years in captivity, the tale undoubtedly has the ring of truth.

White correctly remarks that vipers 'are oviparous, yet they are viviparous also, hatching their young within their bellies and then bringing them forth'. Modern observers confirm that they produce a membranous egg at or before birth; occasionally the translucent egg is produced from which the young viper hatches after birth. He described the dissection of a female viper about 27 May: she was found 'filled with a chain of eleven eggs, about the size of those of a blackbird: but none of them were advanced so far towards a state of maturity as to contain any rudiments of young'. Again modern sources maintain the fertilization occurs in May, the young appearing in August, so the comment is almost certainly correct. He is doubtful of the suggestion, oft-quoted in the countryside, that vipers open their mouths to admit young down their throats if alarmed. The notion, that has been in the literature since the sixteenth century, is erroneous, but, in the wild, young snakes do occasionally disappear beneath the body of a female. 'Country people talk much of a water snake' he also notes, 'but I am pretty sure without any reason'. He believed, more correctly, that the 'common snake' (the grass snake) sometimes went into water 'perhaps with a view to procure frogs'.

Strange notions existed also concerning fish, such as that goldfish kept in a glass bowl could survive without food. Gilbert White demonstrated this to be the nonsense it obviously was, by careful observation, experiment and deduction:

> True it is that they will subsist for a long time without any apparent food but what they can collect from water that is frequently changed; yet they must draw support from animalcula, and other nourishment supplied by the water; because, though they seem to eat nothing, yet the consequences of eating often drop from them. That they are best pleased with such a jejune diet may easily be confuted, since if you toss them crumbs they will seize them with great readiness, not to say greediness: however bread should be given sparingly, lest, turning sour it corrupt the water. They will also feed on the water-plant called lemna (duck's meat) [duckweed] and also small fry.[1]

Detailed scrutiny of the evidence, careful appraisal of secondary sources, occasional experiments – these were parts of Gilbert White's *modus operandi*, and on the whole they served him well. Not surprisingly, however, we occasionally see what later became known as the 'natural theology' glinting through his writing. We have seen he was a devotee of John Ray, and obviously read and reread *The Wisdom of God*. The adaptation of any organism to its environment and way of life was seen as part of the Creator's providential concern for it, and in turn evidence for the existence of a Creator. Although he does not burden the reader excessively with such philosophical and theological concerns, when he considers the manner in which the tadpole's tail disappears as it moves from water to land, he cannot resist the temptation to elevate, as well as to inform:

> How wonderful is the oeconomy of Providence with regard to the limbs of so vile a reptile! While it is aquatic it has a fish-like tail, and no legs: as soon as the legs sprout, the tail drops off as useless, and the animal betakes itself to the land!

Fishermen: ecclesiastic

There have been other parson-naturalists with a scientific interest in fishes, but not very many. The first ecclesiastic to take an interest in such matters was the Venerable Bede (*c*.673–735), who wrote, in *The History of the English Church and People*, completed in 731, that Ely was 'an island surrounded by water and marshes, and it derives its name from the vast quantities of eels that are caught in the marshes'. The eels are still there. A number of parsons have been fishermen rather than naturalists *per se*, but have taken an intelligent interest in the natural history of the species they caught. Such was the Reverend John William Chaloner (1813–1894), who was, like many a nineteenth-century parson, born in the rectory in which he died (see chapter 1). John Chaloner was Rector of Newton Kyme, Yorkshire for over forty years, his father having been rector before him. (One obiturarist commented that the dedication of the church at Newton Kyme, was St Andrew, 'the grand old fisherman'.) An all-round naturalist, Chaloner was associated with the Yorkshire Naturalists' Union, publishing notes on natural history in its journal *The Naturalist*. Exuding bonhomie, and like many a fisherman, always an optimist, he was stated to have been fond of tobacco. He smoked an ounce of 'black shag' every day for 40 years. 'Did this account for his abounding health at 83?' wondered his obituary-writer? He was at the end of his life a Conservator of Salmon Fishery on the Wharfe. Another wrote: 'As a fly-fisher he was hard to beat; in fact, I have on many occasions heard him termed by practical men 'the best on the Wharfe'. Apparently the Easter Sunday afternoon service was for many years slightly shortened, for 'the rector had to drive to York to catch the express for Loch Awe' where he woke next day, rods and tackle at the ready, for the start of a fortnight's fishing.[2]

If there is one parson-naturalist of the nineteenth century who is asso-

1. John Ray (1627–1705)

2. Allegorical frontispiece from John Ray's
Methodum Flantarum Nova, 1682

THE

Wiſdom of God

Manifeſted in the

WORKS

OF THE

CREATION,

In Two Parts.

VIZ.

The Heavenly Bodies, Elements, Meteors, Foſſils, Vegetables, Animals, (Beaſts, Birds, Fiſhes, and Inſects) more particularly in the Body of the Earth, its Figure, Motion, and Conſiſtency, and in the admirable Structure of the Bodies of Man, and other Animals, as alſo in their Generation, *&c.*

By *JOHN RAY*,
Fellow of the *Royal Society*.

The Second Edition, very much enlarged.

LONDON:
Printed for *Samuel Smith*, at the *Princes Arms* in St. *Paul's* Church-yard. 1692.

3. Title page of John Ray's *Wisdom of God Manifested in the works of Creation*, 1692

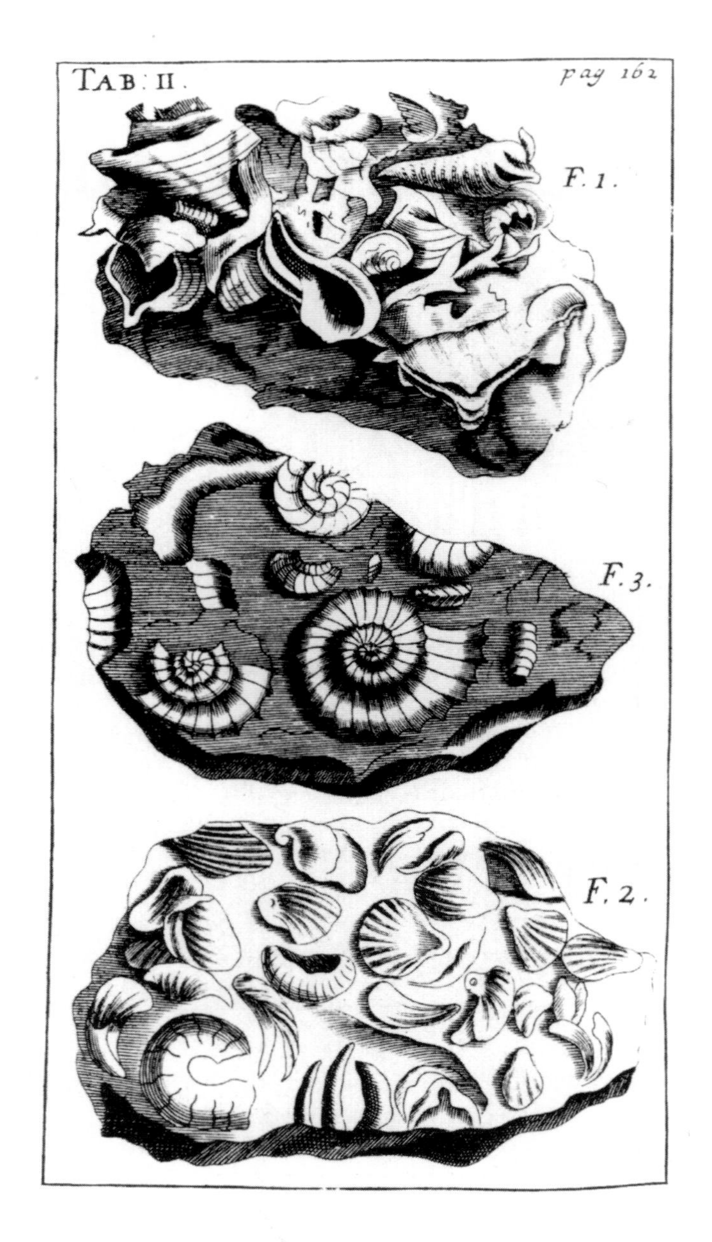

4. Illustrations of fossils from John Ray's *Observations, Topographical, Moral and Physiological*, 1673

5. The Reverend William Kirby (1759–1846)

6. The Reverend Professor John Stevens Henslow (1796–1861)

7. The Reverend Professor Adam Sedgwick (1785–1873)

8. William Buckland (1784–1856)

RELIQUIÆ DILUVIANÆ;

OR,

OBSERVATIONS

ON THE

ORGANIC REMAINS

CONTAINED IN

CAVES, FISSURES, AND DILUVIAL GRAVEL,

AND ON

OTHER GEOLOGICAL PHENOMENA,

ATTESTING THE ACTION OF AN

UNIVERSAL DELUGE.

BY THE REV. WILLIAM BUCKLAND, B. D. F. R. S. F. L. S.

MEMBER OF THE GEOLOGICAL SOCIETY OF LONDON; OF THE IMPERIAL SOCIETIES OF MINERALOGY AND NATURAL HISTORY AT PETERSBURG AND MOSCOW; OF THE NATURAL HISTORY SOCIETY IN THE UNIVERSITY OF BONN, ON THE RHINE; AND OF THE NATURAL HISTORY SOCIETY AT HALLE; HONORARY MEMBER OF THE AMERICAN GEOLOGICAL SOCIETY; CORRESPONDENT OF THE MUSEUM OF NATURAL HISTORY OF FRANCE; FELLOW OF C. C. C. AND PROFESSOR OF MINERALOGY AND GEOLOGY IN THE UNIVERSITY OF OXFORD.

SECOND EDITION.

LONDON:
JOHN MURRAY, ALBEMARLE-STREET.

MDCCCXXIV.

9. Title page of second edition of William Buckland's *Reliquiae Diluvianae*, 1824

10. The Reverend William Orpen Morris (1810–1893)

11. The Reverend Canon Charles Kingsley (1819–1875)

12. Father Julian Tenison Woods (1832–1889)

13. Canon Henry Baker Tristram (1822–1906)

14. The Reverend William Warde Fowler (1835–1912)

15. The Reverend Adrian Woodruffe Peacock (1858–1922)

16. The Reverend Edward Armstrong (1900–1978)

ciated with the study of fishes, together with other vertebrates such as mammals, reptiles and amphibians, it is the polymath Leonard Jenyns, who, incidentally, was introduced to the study of natural history (as were many thousands of others, clerical and lay) through a reading of Gilbert White's *Selborne*. It is recorded that while at Eton (where he was no good at games) he copied out whole sections of it, fearful that he would not come across a copy again. Later he edited an edition of White's Letters.

Darwin's fish man

Leonard Jenyns seems to have taken a special interest in fishes since his schooldays, but here he is in later life. An entry in his Diary for 22 May 1830 runs as follows:

> With the assistance of a couple of fishermen we dragged Reche [Reach] Lode this morning in several places between Reche & Upware. Our object was to ascertain what species of fish are produced in that water; – & the following is a list of the different kinds wh. we obtained.
>
> Sp. 1. Esox Lucius.- Pike.
> – 2. Gobis fluviatilis. – Gudgeon.
> – 3. Abramis Brama. Bream.
> – 4. Leuciscus rutilis. – Roach.
> – 5. _______ erythrophalmoa. Redeye.
> – 6. _______ Phoxinus. Minnow.
> – 7. Gobitis [sic Cobitis] Taenia. Groundling.
> – 8. Molva Lota. *Burbot* or Eelpout.
> – 9. Cernua fluviatilis. Ruffe or Pope.
> – 10. Perca fluviatalis. Perch.- [3]

The capitalization and spelling of the above follow the original as closely as possible. The extract provides an interesting insight to the method of investigation used.

Many of the fish species Jenyns records are still to be found in the rivers and drains of Cambridgeshire, although the burbot has not been recorded in the county since 1969 or in Britain since 1972, and is probably extinct. Jenyns gives very detailed descriptions of, and makes detailed comments on, some of the species. The taxonomy of British fishes was still rather insecure, and Jenyns comments on the remarks of another parson fish-expert, the Reverend Revett Sheppard, that there are, in the River Trent, two distinct species of bream, the carp [gold, bronze] and the white [silver] bream. 'I am inclined to think these are really two species, wh. we have compounded together, – & the specimens found in Reche Lode appear to be all of the white or small sort.' He was correct. Many of the common names for fish in use in Cambridgeshire were (and still are) a source of confusion, which Jenyns attempted to sort out, not always satisfactorily; for example, he mentions the 'Dare' which he describes as rough scaled, but otherwise identical with the roach: the term is sometimes used today for the dace (*Leuciscus leuciscus*). The names redeye, roach, rud[de] and shallow are sometimes used as alternative names for the same species, but are also sometimes applied to different species. This too caused uncertainty to Jenyns (as well as to more recent fisher-folk). The care with which Jenyns went about his enquiries can be shown by the following:

> (7. Groundling)
> Many years ago, I took 2 specimens of this fish in the pits by Cow Bridge, but never met with it again till the present occasion when we captured 5 more. They appear to keep much in the mud, & were only discovered by diligently turning over the refuse of the net. None appeared to be full grown. . . . [The common name spined loach is sometimes used in Cambridgeshire.][4]

He distinguished between this species, and the true loach, or 'stone' loach (*Noemacheilius barbatulus*) recognizing that the latter occurred in streams with stony or gravel beds. He also published on the fish of eastern England in *A Manual of British Vertebrate Animals* (Cambridge, 1835), *Observations in Natural History* (London, 1846), and also wrote up the fish specimens collected by Charles Darwin in his voyage round the world in volume 4 of *The Zoology of the Voyage of the Beagle* (1835).[5] This must have been an odd experience for him, for he had been offered the position that was later accepted by Darwin, but turned it down, feeling he could not leave his family and parish for the long period necessary. The invitation came through John Henslow, to whom he was related by marriage (see page 18); both Darwin and Jenyns were of course part of Henslow's coterie of naturalists.

By all accounts, Jenyns was orthodox and traditional in his theology and his churchmanship. Late in life he wrote a theological pamphlet entitled 'The Life of the World to Come' on what he felt the hereafter would be like.[6] He liked quiet decorum during the services he took (and got it). He read the offices of the church conscientiously and regularly: he told a story of how he gave a full service, 'throwing as much energy into my sermon as I was ever wont to do' and read the entire service one extremely cold, snowy day, when, apart from himself and the parish clerk, there was a congregation of but two. Orthodoxy, in Anglicanism, is the cousin of order, and in his short autobiography he is clear on the way he values order and propriety. This is perhaps the key to his natural history work. Much of it was in the area of taxonomy and nomenclature – the classification and naming of organisms. His interests included mammals, as well as fishes. He distinguished species of shrews and bats from each other ('Remarks on British shrews, including the distinguishing features of two species formerly compounded'), but also showed sometimes how two species formerly considered distinct were the same ('Some observations on the common bat of Pennant, showing its identity with the pipistrelle of French authors').[7] He was painstaking in his use of minute characters, such as those of the creatures' teeth in the taxonomy of animals ('On the dentition and other characters of British shrews . . .').[8]

A further insight into the importance he attached to order and system is to be found in his 'Report of the recent progress and present state of zoology', which he gave to the British Association for the Advancement of Science at its Edinburgh meeting in 1834. 'It is now generally acknowledged', he wrote, 'that the true and legitimate object of zoology is the attainment of the Natural System' – the 'natural' or true system of classifying the species and other taxa that make up the animal kingdom. He stated, as his objective:

> My intention, then, is principally to notice those researches which of late years have tended to elucidate the characters and affinities of the larger groups of animals, and thereby advance our knowledge of their natural arrangement. This will include a consideration of such systems as have been brought forward in illustration of this part of the subject.

This search for order in nature was very compatible with Paleyan 'natural theology': not only was each organism adapted precisely and intimately to its environment and way of life, through the Creator's ingenuity or 'Providence', but there existed a broader pattern or order, of which all organisms were a part.[9]

His desire for order was seen in every compartment of his life: in his autobiography he writes at some length of the 'laws of health' and the way in which he believed that health and happiness were to be attained in no small measure from adherence to a well-established routine of diet, exercise and daily pattern of activity. It is unsurprising therefore that as a relatively young man he was compiling the *Catalogue of Quadrupeds and Birds, in the Museum of the Cambridge Philosophical Society* (1836)[10] and his *Systematic Catalogue of British Vertebrate Animals*

(1835).[11] Some theoretical aspects of nomenclature and taxonomy he covered in a paper entitled 'Some remarks on genera and subgenera, and on the principles on which they should established'.[12] In 1856 – interestingly on the eve of the publication of *The Origin of Species* – he gave a paper to the British Association for the Advancement of Science 'On the variation of species'.[13] He was, of course, a devotee of Linnaeus: as a young man he wrote in his natural history diary:

> I am an enthusiastic admirer of that great man, and look upon the Systema Natura as one of the most elaborate perfect works of its kind. . . . It is a performance that will stand the test of ages.[14]

But his admiration was not slavish. He agreed that the work needed to be modified, updated and improved, for it was after all 'produced by a single individual'.

A love of order is often associated with an eye for detail: not only did he pay attention to the dentition of shrews in order to establish their exact taxonomic relationships, but he was also amongst the earliest naturalists to pay detailed attention to the parasites of organisms. On his list of publications are papers that deal with the parasites of slugs, humans, bats, mice and other mammals, birds and wheat. He hints, in one of these papers, but does not specifically state, that each species of vertebrate has its own parasite load: 'On three undescribed species of the genus *Climex* closely allied to the common bed-bug'.[15] He goes into fine detail on the characteristics of the different species, illustrating with detailed line drawings, the species that occurred on bats, pigeons and house martins. In his private diary he was more specific: he divided parasites into those that were fixed 'never found separate from the animals they inflict . . . are born upon them . . . pass the whole of their existence upon them' and the wandering, moving from individual to individual in the course of their life; the latter group 'frequent various situations, and lead a wandering life, accidentally attaching themselves to different animals that fall their way'. He continued:

> As far as I can ascertain, no fixed parasite ever inhabits more than one species of animal, whereas the wandering ditto will occasionally be found on several sorts.[16]

Although simplistic, these generalization displayed ecological and parasitological awareness of a high order, and were far ahead of their time.

There were other ecological excursions, particularly later in life. Perhaps because he was so frequently 'out and about', not only on fieldwork, but on parish business (he attached great importance to parish visiting) he was extremely interested in meteorological phenomena, and searched for pattern: after the 'unparalleled clemency' of the winter of 1821–1822, he looked for 'a long series of warm winters'. It was but a short step to considering the effects of weather on plants and animals. A very cold spell in late January 1823, when temperatures went down below 20°F (–7°C), and it not only 'froze even under men's beds' (presumably in chamber-pots) but occasioned the destruction of numbers of small birds. He carefully compared the date of appearance of a particular flower, or particular bird in song: in 1823, in contrast to 1822, he write 'the average difference will be found to be about a month'. Always he displayed the eye for detail, the search for pattern, the noting of the influence of one factor on another. In his life he wrote a total of eight papers on meteorology. This concern for the relationships between organisms and their environment is shown, for example in a paper 'On the turf [peat] of the Cambridgeshire Fens'[17] (1845) and on 'Local biology' after he had removed to Bath in 1873.[18]

Creation was a harmonious, but exceedingly complex, whole. The life and work of Leonard Jenyns (he took the name Blomefield while living in Bath, when he inherited property from that branch of his family) were characterized by order and integrity. In his aspiration to live a good Christian life, and in his parish work alike, we see the love of order and decorum, the search for pattern, and a delight in the complexity of relationships unravelling before him. In this he was remarkably like Gilbert White, who so influenced him, and whom he so often quoted in his note-books.

A mixed bag

Another naturalist with a strong regional focus, who was interested in vertebrates, was the Reverend Hugh Alexander Macpherson. He was a graduate of Oriel College Oxford (BA, 1881; MA, 1884), and served in the Carlisle Diocese (the nearest to Scotland, not entirely surprising in view of his strongly Scottish name) for a good deal of his ministry. From 1888 he was chaplain to H.M. Prison in Carlisle. In 1892 he published *A Vertebrate Fauna of Lakeland (including Cumberland and Westmorland with Lancashire North of the Sands)*.[19] describing in great detail the natural history mammals, birds, amphibians, reptiles and fishes of the district now known as Cumbria. This is an exhaustive work of some 600 close-packed pages, displaying a very detailed knowledge of the vertebrates of Lakeland, from both field and study. There are comparisons between the manner in which this regional memoir is compiled, and the 'County floras' mentioned in chapter 3. Like his botanical colleagues, Macpherson used his clerical colleagues in the Lake District counties as sources of information: for example, the Reverend T. P. Hartley is described as being 'intimately acquainted with Windermere', and as having described the 'Alpine Charr' (*Salmo alpinus*) from that lake, noting in detail the way in which the local people catch it. The Reverend R. Burn is said to have 'carefully examined' a Common Beaked Whale (*Hyperoodon rostratum*) washed ashore near Maryport in August 1887.

Again, as with the compilers of county floras, Mr Macpherson relied on the work of earlier studies by regional clerical naturalists for some of his material. He is, perhaps justifiably, a little condescending towards the Reverend Dr Robinson whose *Essay towards a Natural History of Westmorland and Cumberland* was published in two small volumes in 1709, and who, he says 'deserves all credit for having made an effort to touch the subject, however superficially'. The Reverend W. Richardson, of Ullswater, is mentioned as drawing up a 'quasi-scientific' paper of the district; he is treated little more generously, his study being described as 'meagre and sadly incomplete.' He is, however, credited with remarks about red deer (*Cervus elephas*) in Martindale in the 1780s and 1790s. Other clerical naturalists credited in this volume include the Reverend R. Lees, of the Church of St Andrew, Greystoke, for comments on the custom of granting a subsidy for the killing of foxes.

Despite his work on vertebrate biology, it might be considered inappropriate to include William Stukeley (1687–1765) in these pages, as although he could be considered a naturalist of sorts, and was a parson, he was not to any great extent a naturalist and a parson at the same time. He is also far better-remembered for his enquiries in fields other than natural history. He was, however, such an interesting, bizarre character that he is worthy of notice here. He qualified in medicine at Cambridge in January 1708 (Bennett or Corpus Christi College); he went 'a-simpling', collecting simples, plants used in medicine, and while an undergraduate used to steal dogs to dissect them. He knew Steven Hales, the pioneer plant physiologist (see page 50), and Sir Isaac Newton; he also made additions to John Ray's *Catalogus Plantarum circum Cantabrigiam* and started out as a doctor, practising at different times, in Boston, in Lincolnshire, and in London. He became a Fellow of the Royal Society on 20 March 1718. On the death of an elephant in London he, with his friend Sir Hans Sloane, dissected it in a Chelsea garden. The results of this research were published as *Essay towards the Anatomy of the Elephant*. He suggested that the creature's death had been hastened by 'the great quantity of ale' that spectators gave it. In the 1720s, natural history took a subservient place to archaeology, and he began to travel around many parts of Britain, examining antiquities, looking particularly at stone circles and henge monuments (like Stonehenge and Avebury, about which he wrote books, published in 1740 and 1743, respectively, maintaining that they were associated with 'the British druids').

In 1726 he returned to Lincolnshire, and married a couple of years later. He had been ordained, at the Archbishop's suggestion, in 1727, and obtained the living of All Saint's, Stamford. By rather extraordinary intellectual gymnastics he managed to reconcile 'druidism' with the Christian faith by arguing that the druids were derived from Phoenicians who arrived in England in Abraham's time; these folk were 'of Abraham's religion entirely', and thus differed little from Christians, indeed the Church of England. His excellent fieldwork was as one biographer put it 'entangled with the most curious mixture of Biblical and classical allusions and flights of the wildest . . . fancies'. Waterton, Bishop of Gloucester, who knew Stukeley well described him as an honest man but a strange mixture of 'simplicity, drollery, absurdity, ingenuity, superstition, and antiquarianism'. Another said he was 'mighty conceited'. Another example of his individuality was that he buried the product from his wife's miscarriage close to a Druidic temple he constructed in his garden. The Church of England has produced some eccentric clergy, but Parson Stukeley was a very odd ball indeed.[20]

Not all parson-naturalists were as bizarre as he. Most, like gentle Gilbert White or Leonard Jenyns saw their study of natural history as a logical part of their priestly duties. Fewer clergy studied the reptiles, amphibians, fishes or some of the inconspicuous mammals of the English countryside than were attracted by the brilliant flowers or the birds, but they had their devotees. Even the most humble, discomforting snake ('Upon thy belly shalt thou walk') was a part of Creation, and worthy of careful consideration. So too the insects and the other invertebrates to which we now turn.

Notes

1 Letter 54; in *The Natural History of Selborne*, the letter is undated, but was apparently published in the *Gentleman's Magazine* for 1786 (vol. 56, p. 488) under the date June 12, and with the signature of 'V'.
2 Emmet, J., 'In memoriam: John William Chaloner', *Naturalist*, [19], 1894, pp. 131–135.
3 Jenyns, J., Natural History Diary, Newton Library, Cambridge.
4 *Ibid*.
5 Jenyns, L., *The Zoology of the Voyage of the Beagle*, vol. iv, *Fish* (London, Smith Elder, 1842).
6 Blomefield, L. (formerly Jenyns), *The Life of the World to Come* (Bath, privately printed, no date, probably early 1890s).

7 Jenyns, L., 'Some observations on the common bat of Pennant, showing its identity with the pipistrelle of French authors', *Transactions of the Linnean Society of London*, 16, 1833, pp. 159–168.
8 Jenyns, L., 'On the dentition and other characters of British Shrews, with reference to M. Duverny's recent researches into the structure of this genus of animals' *Magazine of Zoology and Botany*, 2, 1837, pp. 24–42.
9 Modern taxonomists seek to arrange biological groups according to their evolutionary relationship; Jenyns was indeed prescient. Note also his paper: 'Some remarks on the study of zoology and the present state of the science', *Magazine of Zoology and Botany*, 1, 1836, pp. 1–31.
10 Jenyns, L., *Catalogue of Quadrupeds and Birds in the Museum of the Cambridge Philosophical Society* (1836).
11 Jenyns, L., *Systematic Catalogue of British Vertebrate Animals* (Cambridge, 1835).
12 Jenyns, L., 'Some Remarks on Genera and Sub-Genera, and on the Principles on which they should be established', *Magazine of Natural History*, 6, 1835, p. 385.
13 Jenyns, L., 'On the Variation of Species', *British Association for the Advancement of Science Report*, Cheltenham, p. 101.
14 Jenyns, J., Natural History Diary, Newton Library, Cambridge.
15 Jenyns, J., 'On Three Undescribed Species of the Genus *Climex*, Closely Allied to the Common Bed-bug', *Annals and Magazine of Natural History*, 3, 1839, pp. 241–244.
16 Jenyns, J., Natural History Diary, Newton Library, Cambridge, 30 November 1824.
17 Jenyns, L., 'On the turf of the Cambridgeshire Fens', *British Association for the Advancement of Science Report*, Cambridge, 1845, p. 75.
18 Jenyns, L., 'Local biology; followed by remarks on the fauna of Bath and Somerset', *Proceedings of the Bath Natural History and Field Club*, 2 (4) 1873.
19 Macpherson, A. H., *A vertebrate fauna of Lakeland (including Cumberland and Westmorland with Lancashire north of the Sands)* (Edinburgh, David Douglas, 1892; reprinted by Paul P. B. Minet, Chicheley, 1972).
20 Hinde, T., *A Field-guide to the English Country Parson* (London, Phoebe Phillips/Heinemann, 1983), pp. 107–108; Piggott, S., *William Stukeley*, 1950; *Dictionary of National Biography*, vol. 55. (London, Smith Elder, 1898), pp. 127–128.

Chapter Six

Go to the ant: insects and other invertebrates

. . . the beetle after his kind and the grasshopper after his kind . . .
(Leviticus 11. 22)

Bees and bee-keeping

Bees, ants and other insects have long been a source of allegory, and moralizing tales. 'Go to the ant, thou sluggard, consider her ways and be wise' directs Proverbs (6.6). And Samson's riddle based on the saying 'out of the strong came forth sweetness', inspired by his finding a bees' nest, dripping with honey in the carcass of a lion (Judges 14.14) has amused generations. It is always tempting to see allegories of human affairs in the social order of bees, ants and wasps, and thus it is unsurprising that clergy have taken a special interest in the colonial insects.

The Reverend Charles Butler (*c*.1560–1647) has been described as the 'Father of English bee-keeping'. He studied at Magdalen College, Oxford, from 1579 to 1587. In 1595 he had responsibility for the small parish of Nately Scures, and the Mastership of the Holy Ghost School, Basingstoke, Hampshire. He was, for the sum of £12 per annum, expected to take services in chapel, and 'instruct the young men of the town in religion and literature'. From this he paid 12 shillings per year to rent the hay from the cemetery. It was probably here that he first took an interest in bees. Perhaps he kept skeps in the same burial ground; he had earlier tried the commercial rearing of silk-worms. He gave up the Mastership in 1600, when he was appointed to the living of Wootton St Lawrence, Hampshire. Once established there, he took his observations on bees further, and wrote one of the first English books on insects, certainly one of the first written by a clerical naturalist, entitled *The Feminine Monarchie or Treatise Concerning Bees and the Due Ordering of Them*. Here for the first time rules for the 'ordering' of the bees were based on detailed personal observation and practical experience, and not on the precepts of Aristotle or other ancient authorities. He advised bee-keepers not to work with bees when 'smelling of sweat' or 'stinking' of 'leeks, onions or garlic'. Eventually Charles Butler is said to have profited sufficiently from bee-keeping, and the book, for him to give his daughter, his 'sweet honey-girl', a substantial dowry (£400).[1]

Gilbert White is said to have been his great-great-grandson (through the 'honey girl') and Gilbert wrote quite extensively about insects in his *Natural History and Antiquities of Selborne*. Indeed he had more than a passing interest in bees, describing how they swarmed on two very warm early spring days, 26 and 27 March 1777.[2] He also describes the dispersal of aphids for long distances by the wind,[3] and in one of his letters gives a charming, perceptive and modern account of the biology of the cricket, a detailed case study of an organism in relation to its environment and behaviour.[4] In another account, he describes some of the pests of his Hampshire parish, including mites and turnip flies. He strongly advocates, a century and a half before the development of scientific agricultural and medical entomology, the systematic study of pest species, with a view to their control and management:

> A full history of noxious insects hurtful in the field, garden, and house suggesting all the known and likely means of destroying them, would be allowed by the public to be a most useful and important work. What knowledge there is of this sort lies scattered, and wants to be collected; great improvements would soon follow of course. A knowledge of the properties, oeconomy, propagation and in short the life and conversation of these animals, is a necessary step to lead us to some method of preventing their depredations.[5]

Some clergy at least had a down-to earth, practical and utilitarian approach. As has already been shown (e.g. on page 65) many clergy adopted something of a humanitarian approach to natural history, believing that their enquiries should be useful, benefiting humankind.

Beautiful butterflies

John Ray's approach was different:

> You ask what is the use of butterflies? I reply to adorn the world and delight the eyes of men; to brighten the countryside like so many golden jewels. To contemplate their exquisite beauty and variety is to experience the truest pleasure. To gaze enquiringly at such elegance of colour and form designed by the ingenuity of nature and painted by her artist's pencil, is to acknowledge and adore the imprint of the art of God.

This translation, by Canon Raven, from John Ray's *Historia Insectorum*, published posthumously in 1710, summarises the way in which many parson-naturalists have regarded the living world. The passage certainly summarises Ray's theology neatly.[6] John Ray's ventures into the world of insects and invertebrates were attenuated. He had quite a number of observations on moths and butterflies, including in 1693, a mention of the technique of 'simbling' or assembling moths by confining a female in a container and waiting for males to come in from a distance around. Interestingly this record is one where the parson-naturalist was assisted by his wife: how often wives must have assisted in natural history observations.

The incident happened on 29 May 1693: it must have been a fine, early summer night.

> It emerged out of a stick-shaped geometer caterpillar: it was a female and came out from its chrysalis shut up in my cage: the windows were open in the room or closet where it was kept, and two male moths flying round were caught by my wife who by a lucky chance went into the room in the night: they were attracted, as it seems to me, by the scent of the female and came in from outside.[7]

We may note in passing that his daughters also seem to have helped him quite extensively: '. . . at the beginning of summer my little daughters caught many of this species [presumably with nets] flying at dusk in our garden'.[8] His youngest daughter, Jane, seems to have been the keenest collector, she took her first specimen in Ray's orchard when she was four-and-a-half (in July 1692), and she was still collecting as a teenager, eleven years later.

In his later years, when he was relatively infirm, he wrote a ten-page pamphlet *Methodus Insectorum* (published in 1705). He never completed his studies of invertebrates, and the *Historia*, edited by someone else, is somewhat imperfect. Nevertheless, it contains particulars of a number of species not previously described scientifically, and details of many creatures: butterflies, moths, beetles, bees, wasps, dragonflies, grasshoppers as well as worms, leeches, spiders, ticks and millipedes. Sometimes the book displays real originality and brilliance, in for example, his extremely detailed observation of the nest-building behaviour of a leaf-cutter bee, which Raven identifies as *Megachile willughbiella*.[9]

Not many decades later, however, gentility and refinement had set in, and some entomological writing, particularly on butterflies, was somewhat sentimental. The beauty of insects was quite rightly emphasized, but other aspects of the reality of nature were neglected. Women, it was felt, could find much to admire in nature, but their perceived gentle susceptibilities must be protected. A strange volume called *The Young Lady's Introduction to Natural History* appeared in 1766, and some of the beautifully illustrated volumes on butterflies and moths, not a few of them written by clergy during Victoria's reign, displayed something of the same sentiments. *The Natural History of British Butterflies* (1852–1853), by the evangelical fundamentalist, the Reverend F. O. Morris (1810–1893, see also pages 7, 74–78), provides an example. Later his publications included a stream of anti-evolution pamphlets, but *A Natural History of British Moths* appeared between 1859 and 1870. A lepidopterist of a slightly later vintage, a man of rather different scientific timbre, and an excellent recorder of plants as well as insects, was the Reverend Edwin Newson Bloomfield (1827–1914), who published the *Lepidoptera of Suffolk* in 1890.

Butterflies were widely collected: not only were they intensely beautiful, but they were relatively easy to identify, and with just a few dozen species in Britain, it was possible to make a reasonably complete collection. The all-round naturalist, the Reverend Leonard Jenyns was an enthusiast. Here are some notes, taken more-or-less at random from his natural history diary for 1825:

> May 14
> We captured on the Devil's Ditch today a new butterfly for Cambridgeshire, the Dingy Skipper, Hesperia tages of modern Entomologists; it was not very plentiful & only three specimens were taken: Lycana idas [chalkhill blue?] was in abundance.
>
> Aug 1
> Took a specimen of Argynnis paphia (the Silver Washed Fritillary of Collectors) on wing today in the Oakery near the Canal. –j It was much faded & torn, so that July is undoubtedly the proper month for these Insects.
>
> This is the first instance of my ever taking this species at Bottisham; though not new to Cambridgeshire, as I met with two specimens last year, in Whitewood, – Gamlingay.[10]

Alas, the butterfly fauna of Cambridgeshire is much depleted since his day.

Their intrinsic beauty attracted many to butterflies, and to a lesser extent, moths, and appealed to many who were collectors rather than naturalists and scientists. The Reverend Archdale Palmer Wickham (1855–1935) was such a person. He seems to have been something of an eccentric; as well as having a passion for Lepidoptera, he was a keen cricketer, playing for Marlborough, Oxford and the Norfolk XI before he joined the Somerset side in 1891, at the age of 36, keeping wicket regularly until 1907. He played with black-topped pads and grey cummerbund, with a stance behind the wicket 'so low that his Harlequin cap only just appeared above the bails'. He was Vicar of Martock during his cricket-playing days, but later moved to East Brent, in the north of the county. He collected in Shapwick and Loxley woods, and around Brent Knoll, his lantern being a familiar sight to his parishioners as he collected moths upon a summer night. This probably confirmed the impression of wild eccentricity. His collection was described as 'magnificent', and long after his death was presented to the British Museum (Natural History), now the Natural History Museum, London.[11]

Very different in character was the Reverend Charles Smith (1795–1862), born in Liverpool, and briefly articled to a solicitor before he entered Trinity College, Cambridge in 1818, becoming third wrangler in 1820 (see glossary). After curacies at Burghfield, near Reading, and Fawley, near Henley-on-Thames, he became Vicar of Gainsborough, Lincolnshire in 1843, a living to which was attached the prebendary stall (i.e. a canonry) in Lincoln Cathedral. As well as becoming Chancellor of the Lincoln Diocese (in 1859), he produced a stream of pamphlets advancing the Protestant cause, as he saw it. He is described as having been an 'ardent entomologist', but seems to have been an extremely pious and sensitive man and only collected insects, particularly Lepidoptera, when he had satisfied himself that they were almost devoid of feeling. His pious human nature is confirmed by the fact that he ministered 'assiduously and bravely' to his parishioners during a cholera epidemic. He wrote an excellent article in the *Entomologists Magazine* in August 1833, and was honoured by a colleague who named of a moth after him.[12]

Beetle-mania in the 1820s and 1830s

Gilbert White's life overlapped with that of the Reverend (later the Venerable) William Kirby (1759–1850), Vicar of Barham in Suffolk, who was a fine entomologist. He wrote a monograph on English bees (*Monographia Apium Angliae*, 1802); this provides a prime example of a parson-naturalist's success, achieved as the result of long familiarity with a limited location, for he collected 153 different wild bees from his own parish. He was associated with the parish of Barham for sixty-eight years, first as curate, then from 1797 as rector. As the result of this, he got into correspondence with William Spence, a business man from Yorkshire. They co-operated over the book entitled *Introduction to Entomology*, the first volume of which appeared in 1815. This very attractively written, semi-technical work for the beginner in the field of entomology has been described as capturing the spirit of the old collectors. It went through several editions before the final two volumes (III and IV) appeared in 1826.[13] The series hit the market at just the right moment. For some reason in the 1820s and 1830s, the collection of insects, particularly beetles, became fashionable. Leonard Jenyns wrote of Cambridge at the time:

> Never before ... was natural history so much in favour in the University; nor has it ever since held the position it then occupied ... So numerous were the Entomologists in particular ... that several persons among the lower classes derived a part of their livelihood during the summer months from collecting insects for sale ...[14]

Many parson-naturalists gained their initial interest in natural history in these frenetic times. One was the Reverend Churchill Babington (1821–1889) who acquired the nickname 'Beetles'. Another beetle-man in the Cambridge of the 1820s and 1830s was that clergyman manqué, Charles Darwin, who shared his enthusiasm for collecting beetles with his cousin, William Darwin Fox (1805–1880), who was later Rector of Delamere, Cheshire for 35 years (1838–1873). Fox and Darwin corresponded throughout their lives, Fox providing much information for Darwin's researches. In their student days, however, and immediately after, Darwin used to elicit his cousin's help in identification of beetles; 'remember I am your pupil' he wrote in June 1828, continuing by asking his cousin to 'write me a good long letter about yourself & all other insects'.[15] The two of them used to visit friends who were beetle-collectors. One north-country clerical family who seem to have been beetle-collectors for several generations, were the Heys: it appears that the young Darwin and Fox visited the Reverend Samuel Hey of Ockbrook, Derbyshire in 1829, while they were still Cambridge undergraduates. Samuel Hey wrote to his Archdeacon son on 16 September 1829:

> Mr Fox brought over a relative of his, Mr Darwin, to see my collection. They both pronounced it a very fine collection for so small a one, and discovered in it several very rare insects, such as they had

> never before seen. Mr Darwin, indeed both of them, were captivated by the Snowdon beauties. Mr Darwin wants to know on what part of Snowdon you took the *Chrysomela cerealis*, and on what plant, as he means to go there on purpose to search for it. This he can readily do, as he lives at Shrewsbury. He named a great many insects for me. I gave them one of my three specimens of *Epaphius*, and he and Mr Fox were to toss up for it.[16]

In 1909, the Reverend W. C. Hey (son of the Archdeacon, and grandson of Samuel), described what seems to have been a later occasion, quoting a letter to the Archdeacon from another relative:

> A Mr Darwin has been to see your father's insects. He seemed a very intelligent man.[17]

Canon William Warde Fowler (1835–1912) was a beetle-man of a slightly later vintage. Like Darwin, he was an undergraduate at Christ's College, but was born while Darwin was still aboard the *Beagle*. Vicar of Liversedge for over 40 years, he was a distinguished botanist as well as entomologist, but his magnum opus was *Coleoptera of the British Isles*, in five volumes, plus a supplementary volume, published between 1887 and 1913, a work that remains a standard work a century later.[18] As was often the case, with parson-naturalists specializing in the taxonomy of a particular group, he depended heavily on a network of correspondents, many of them clerical acquaintances, for material. One was the Reverend Hugh A. Stowell (1829–1886), who in his day probably knew more about the insects of the Isle of Man than any other person. Although of Manx parentage (he came from a distinguished Manx clerical family), he was born at Pendleton, near Manchester. He was chaplain of Christ Church, Maughold, Isle of Man 1858–1863, and of Dhoon 1858–1859, and was an extremely active beetle collector throughout that time. He contributed a paper on Manx Coleoptera to the *Zoologist* in 1862, in which he mentioned that he captured 406 species in the neighbourhood of his parish of Maughold, although he enumerates only 82 by name. He also contributed a chapter to Thwaite's *Directory of the Isle of Man* (1863), in which he mentions a few other species, bringing the total up to 100, the total number of captures claimed then reaching 504.[19] Unfortunately his entire collection seems to have been destroyed or lost around the time of his removal, around 1866, to a living at Beardsall, near Derby (where he spent the latter part of his ministry). Both Hugh (Senior's) sons were clergy: the Reverend Ernest G. C. Stowell was a master at Kirkby Steven Grammar School, and Hugh F. L. Stowell was Rector of Ovington, Arlesford, Hampshire.

Neither were distinguished naturalists, but both seem to have assisted their father in his studies of Coleoptera (and later of Lepidoptera).[20]

The Dorset spider man

There are in fact a number of points of comparison between the lives of Charles Darwin and Octavius Pickard-Cambridge (1828–1917). Like Charles Darwin, who, as we have already noted on a couple of occasions was very much part of the network to which many parson-naturalists belonged, Octavius had a false start in life, doing two years of training for the bar (Darwin did, and hated, two years of medical training in Edinburgh, before being sent to Cambridge to train to be a clergyman.) Like, Darwin, too, Octavius had been a traveller in early manhood, for while Darwin had circumnavigated in the *Beagle*, the young Pickard-Cambridge had travelled extensively in the Middle East. Both were enthusiastic collectors of insects as young lads. But while Charles Darwin had abandoned his plans for a career in the Church before he went ashore from the *Beagle*, Octavius Pickard-Cambridge, after a couple of curacies, in 1868 became successor to his father as Rector of Bloxworth in Dorset. Interestingly, Octavius had gone to Durham University, and not to either Oxford or Cambridge. Durham in 1857 was a very young university, and although it already had a strong clerical tradition, it made an effort to teach modern science. Pickard-Cambridge, although he did not study science formally at Durham, almost certainly would have had contact with the Reverend Professor Temple Chevalier (1793–1873), Professor of Mathematics and Astronomy from 1835 until his death, and also a pioneer meteorologist. Chevalier taught Hebrew, as well as science, and thus had contact with many young ordinands. Octavius Pickard-Cambridge wrote his first paper before going up to Durham (in the *Zoologist* in 1852), and his second, his first foray on spiders, in the same journal in 1859. There followed some eighty scientific papers on spiders, which he enthusiastically collected from the Dorset heaths; sometimes he bicycled around the county in his researches. As with Canon Fowler and his beetles, spider specimens were sent to Octavius from all over the world.

Although traditional in some of his views–the Pickard-Cambridges were squires of Bloxworth as well as rectors, and Octavius was an 'Old Tory', active in the Primrose League[21] – in some ways he was quite liberal theologically. He accepted much of Darwin's argument, and corresponded quite extensively with the author of the *Origin*, providing details on the taxonomy of certain groups of spiders. They differed in some of the finer points of sexual selection.

Pickard-Cambridge found Darwin's ideas helpful in his taxonomic work on spiders. He named 115 species new to science. His authoritative *Spiders of Dorset* appeared in two volumes, published in 1879 and 1881. The list of Dorset species led the way, but the tomes included all the British species then known, those species not occurring in the county being given less prominence. The arrangement was not popular, but nevertheless, the work stood the test of time for nigh on a century (like Fowler's *Coleoptera*). More is known of the spiders of Britain than any other country, largely because of the work of the Reverend Octavius Pickard-Cambridge, FRS. He was the archetypal naturalist of the Victorian Age, diligently accumulating masses of facts in order to name and classify hundreds, thousands of organisms. As a taxonomist, most of his work was with dead museum specimens; with the organism in its environment and behaviour he was less at home, although he did write a few pioneering papers on behaviour.[22]

Sponges and spiders: the Durham connection

There were others of the Victorian period of the same type, devoting much of their lives to establishing the taxonomy of a limited, specialised group of organisms. An example was the Reverend Alfred Merle Norman (1831–1918), the County Durham clergyman (he held curacies and livings at Sedgefield, Houghton-le-Spring and Burnmoor), with strong links to the University of Durham (he was awarded a DCL in 1883). As well as being Honorary Secretary of the Durham Diocesan Conference (1882–1896) and an Honorary Canon of Durham Cathedral, he made a special study of sponges (Porifera). He wrote dozens of papers on the group, many of them beautifully illustrated, and in 1890 received an FRS for his work in marine biology.[23]

It is interesting to follow chains of influence in the development of natural history amongst the clergy. The influence of Canon Norman on another devotee of the spiders can be clearly traced. Norman had published work on other marine groups besides the sponges; by 1873 he had published on sea spiders (Pycnogonida), a group related to the arachnids, and had encouraged the Reverend John Edward Hull (1863–1960), while the latter was Vice-Principal of Durham Training College (later the College of the Venerable Bede, later still the College of St Hild and Bede), to pursue the study of spiders and their allies. Hull wrote in 1911 that he had turned his attention to the difficult and little-known group, the Acari, the mites. He commented to a colleague in 1918: 'I am still slogging away at the mites . . . and my table is full of packages, already I hardly know where to begin'. Hull also wrote for advice on the classification of these tiny creatures to Octavius Pickard-Cambridge; the circle of clerical naturalists interested in spiders and mites was indeed a compact one, for both were Durham graduates.[24]

John Hull had been born in Northumberland, but brought up in Chester-le-Street, County Durham; he went to the Durham Training College, and later to Hatfield Hall (BA, 1888; MA, 1891). He was ordained in 1889, spending much of his ministry in the Diocese of Newcastle. Curacies in Northumberland and Durham (including North Shields, 1895–1896 and Haltwhistle, 1896–1901) were interrupted by his time as Vice-Principal in Durham (1891–1895). He then held livings at Nenthead (1901–1905), Ninebanks (1905–1922) and Belford (1922–1944). While at Ninebanks (his most productive period, scientifically) he also had responsibility for the parish of Carr Shield in West Allendale; the total stipend, in 1915 was £230. These parishes were large, thinly populated and remote: Nenthead church is at nearly 2000 feet (around 600m) and is thus the highest church in England. He seems to have been a lonely man, and travelled across the beautiful but often bleak moorlands of northern England by bicycle.

Hull was awarded a Durham DSc for his scientific work in 1933, and Professor Heslop Harrison, who presented him for the degree, said:

> The study of the minute and the difficult has always had its attraction for the keen naturalist and no country had a prouder record than ours. But what was more important to northcountrymen, no counties could surpass those which that University represented in the long line of enthusiastic workers they had produced.

This enthusiasm for the small and the obscure is also reflected in a piece he wrote for the *Vasculum*, a natural history journal for Northumberland and Durham that he edited from 1915 to 1940. In the first issue he pleaded: 'The study of the Acari or mites may be commended to anyone fairly familiar with the microscope and anxious to get off the beaten track'.[25] The attempt to work in a difficult and little-known group was seen as a challenge. Just as some clergyman-botanists delighted in the study of groups such as lichens, fungi or mosses, so there have been parson-naturalists who have seen the detailed study of an obscure group such as the spiders, mites or land-snails (see below) a part of their tribute to the diversity of Creation.

Hull, like Pickard-Cambridge, discovered and named many species new to science, but alas, many of his type-specimens, the original specimens (preserved in spirit) on which his descriptions and names were based, were destroyed when he was unable to obtain supplies of methylated spirits during the Second World War. Many of his specimens deteriorated through neglect. His work has been criticized in other ways too. Many of his published diagrams were too small to be useful for identification (they have been called 'Hull's miniatures') and some of his descriptions too brief. He seems to have been rather a disorganized worker. R. A. Baker, who wrote an account of his life and work, reported:

> Sometimes the contents of a notebook are chaotic – drawings of mites, integral calculus, solid geometry, pressed flowers, notes on Psocidae and British Odonata, all in the same book.[26]

He also displayed a keen interest in cricket (like Archdale Wickham, mentioned above), and made a special study of (and indeed published in the fields of) local history and north country place names. He seems to have been well-loved. He was a one-off, and yet displays a number of characteristics typical of the parson-naturalist: extraordinary dedication to a single biological group, despite being something of a polymath, long association with a small area, strongly linked to a network of clerical colleagues interested in the same and related fields, and at least some minor eccentricity.

Mollusca: the beginnings of the ecological approach

Another parson-naturalist with a concern for some of the 'by-ways' of invertebrate taxonomy was the Reverend Leonard Jenyns, who we met earlier; he is usually associated with the taxonomy of vertebrates, particularly fishes (chapter 5). However, in 1832 he published A *Monograph on the British species of Cyclas and Pisidium*, two genera of freshwater bivalves (two-shelled molluscs). He is at pains to point out the difficulties in the taxonomy of the group:

> . . . [I]t is an absolutely requisite to caution conchologists against drawing any conclusions with respect to the specific distinction of these animals from a mere inspection of the shell alone. This is so liable to vary from age, peculiarity of situation, and probably from other causes, that it becomes necessary in some cases to compare a large number of specimens, collected from different sources, in order to determine the characters of a single species with any degree of precision. Occasionally the shell becomes exceedingly ventricose at the expense of its height, which is thereby considerably diminished. . . . Neither can sculpture be relied upon, the striae varying exceedingly in number and distinctness according to the

> nature of the water in which the shell is found ... Age likewise produces great changes.[27]

Jenyns gave minutely detailed descriptions, based upon both the hard and soft parts of these organisms, of twelve species in the two genera, illustrating them with detailed line drawings. He also distinguished several different forms of some species, noting that different localities produced subtly different forms. A number of the taxa described in this monograph were new to science. Once again, no detail of the Creator's diversity and complexity was to be missed.

The next century was the century of ecology, when creatures were considered in relation to their surroundings and way of life. We may contrast the extraordinarily detailed taxonomic work of Pickard-Cambridge on spiders, with that of the Reverend C. E. V. Kendall, focusing on mollusca, and which had a broader, ecological approach. The term ecology was only coined in Germany in 1866, and its introduction to Britain can be pin-pointed to a paper by A. G. (later Professor Sir Arthur) Tansley in 1904. In 1909, as the result of work done in his spare time from his duties as a Lancashire curate, C. E. Kendall, with a couple of colleagues (J. Davy Dean and W. Munn Rankin) devised a scheme for classifying the vegetation communities of South Lonsdale in the Pennines: he used the term 'biological associations' or 'life-associations' and showed the close correlation between plant communities and the mollusca (freshwater and land snails).[28]

> Thus regarding a particular area broadly from the view of an ecologist to whom the life conditions of a species are of interest not second to the taxonomic rank of the form, there is a closed patchwork of wide habitats showing among themselves much diversity, but within an almost uniformity of conditions, upon which the presence of living forms depends.

The paper continued:

> The many plant associations of first importance which have been recognized as life-associations are made to serve for a preliminary molluscan survey. It appears to us that the loan of the results obtained in one field of natural science to problems in another is amply justified in the present treatment, as well as in the hope for future work on new lines.[29]

Kendall subsequently moved to Oundle, where he undertook a further six years work and applied the same techniques to a limited number of types of woodland, grassland and freshwater communities in the Nene Valley of Northamptonshire. His area included a number of fragments of the ancient Forest of Rockingham. He identified 95 species of molluscs as present in the region, correlating the molluscan associations closely with the plant communities, pointing out that these creatures are often more spot-bound than plants. 'By means of careful search and comparison it is possible to define the association of species which may be found living together in any particular habitat.'[30] Later still, in a summary paper, published after another ten years of research, he applied his idea of associations of molluscs being tightly linked to plant communities over the greater part of Britain. Kendall really was preparing the way for future ecological research when he ended this paper:

> One would like to see what a combination of forces could do; the results of the observations made in one area by botanist, lepidopterist, coleopterist etc., all working together. This combination of observers could produce a perfect picture of life, animal and vegetable, in their locality, and linking it up with the observations made in other areas we might be able to arrive at conclusions of real value.[31]

A remarkably holistic statement this, and an entirely appropriate one for a clerical ecologist who saw glory in the complexity of the living world.

A delight in 'small things'

We may perhaps appropriately conclude this brief survey of clergyman-entomologists and others devoted to invertebrates with another quotation from the natural history diary of Leonard Jenyns; on 2 August 1825 he mused:

> Entomology has long been my favourite pursuit more particularly than the other branches of Zoology; indeed the more attention I pay to it, the more entertainment and variety I find in it; the subject is inexhaustible. So great is are the numbers of this tribe of beings that are to be met with in almost every situation throughout the year. Nor can I see that in any respect does the study of Insects merit that contempt & disdain which some of our moderns behold them, when we consider, the real advantages which we have certainly derived from some with whose history we are acquainted, and the probability of there being of equal use, as yet unknown. –

> Who shall dare to say, that from a closer application to this branch of Nature's Works we may not some day discern insects capable of adding as much to our comforts as the Silkworm . . . and the Hive bee. – Perhaps the greatest benefit to be looked for from the study of Insects, is such a knowledge of their history, manners & habits, as shall enable us to destroy or at least keep within bounds those species which either directly or indirectly injure our person or our substance.
>
> As yet Entomology is in its infancy; if then we have already derived so much, how much more may be expected, as our information on the subject extends? The cause of the contempt for insects with a great many persons is their diminutive size, to which they add that they are the least important and most imperfect of the works of Nature. – But what pride and arrogance it surely is, to deny the uses and importance of beings, because they are not adapted to our vision. We measure their defects by our own imperfect sight, forgetting that great and small are relative terms to us, that entirely vanish in our idea of the Almighty, to whom size is nothing, & who [h]as been equally concerned in the making of a flea & an elephant. – Every part of the Creation demands his care and our own attention:– to the thoughtful Observer there is nothing so minute, but what proclaims the power, the wisdom & the goodness of its first cause. – The smallest Insect displays the skill of Providence, in its adaptation to those purposes for which it was made, and the end it was intended to answer. – [32]

Jenyns, it seems, had been reading Paley's *Natural Theology*. Yet the words show remarkable prescience, written as they were almost a century before the development of medical entomology and notions of biological control.

Notes

1 Vernon, F., *Hogs at the Honeypot: Bee Books Old and New*, quoted in Francis, L., *The Country Parson* (Leominster, Fowler Wright, 1989), p. 177.
2 22 November 1777. Letter 36, to the Honourable Daines Barrington.
3 Letter 53, to the Honourable Daines Barrington (undated).
4 Letter 48, to the Honourable Daines Barrington (undated).
5 30 March 1771, Letter 34, to Thomas Pennant, Esquire.
6 Raven, C. E., *John Ray, Naturalist* (Cambridge University Press, 1942), p. 407.
7 *Ibid.*, p. 395, quoting *Historia Insectorum*, p. 177.
8 *Ibid.*, p. 394, quoting *Historia Insectorum*, p. 182. Raven identifies the insect as the Burnished Brass, *Plusia chrysitis*.
9 *Ibid.*, p, 396, quoting *Historia Insectorum*, p. 245.

10 Jenyns, J., Natural History Diary, Newton Library, Cambridge.
11 Strong, G., 'A bat for the bishop', *This England*, 30(2), 1997, pp. 22–23.
12 *Dictionary of National Biography*, vol. 5, pp. 71–72.
13 Allen, D. E., *The Naturalist in Britain: a Social History* (Harmondsworth, Penguin, 1978), p. 102.
14 *Ibid.*, p. 103.
15 Letter C. R. Darwin to W. D. Fox, 12 June 1828 (Christ's College Library, Cambridge), published in Burkhardt, F. and Smith, S., eds., *Correspondence of Charles Darwin* (vol. 1, Cambridge University Press, 1985), p. 57.
16 Hey, W. C., '"A" Mr Darwin', *Naturalist*, [34], 1909, p. 142.
17 *Ibid.*
18 Woodruffe-Peacock, E. A., 'In memoriam: William Fowler', *Naturalist*, [37], 1912, pp. 121–123. Watling, R., 'The British Mycological Society: the Yorkshire connection', *Naturalist*, 107, 1982, pp. 121–129.
19 Stowell, H. A., 'Notes on the entomology of the Isle of Man (embracing the orders of Lepidoptera and Coleoptera'), in *Thwaite's History and Directory of the Isle of Man*, 1863, p. 85. Some further information is in: Gelling, J., *A History of the Manx Church* (Douglas, Manx Heritage Foundation, 1998), pp. 138, 240.
20 Some of the Reverend Hugh Stowell's letters on the subject are in the Archives of the Manx Museum, Isle of Man.
21 The Primrose League was a political association formed in 1883 to support the principles of Conservatism as represented by Benjamin Disraeli, Earl of Beaconsfield, who died on 19 April, 1881, a date which became known as 'Primrose Day'.
22 Armstrong, P. H., 'Three parson-naturalists from Durham' *Naturalist,* 120, 1995, pp. 65–75). Pickard-Cambridge, A. W., *Memoir of the Reverend Octavius Pickard-Cambridge, MA, FRS, by his son* (Oxford, privately printed, 1918).
23 Baker, R. A., 'The Durham connection in the History of Arachnology in Britain (1850–1959)', *Archives of Natural History*, 18(2), pp. 221–230.
24 *Ibid.*
25 *Ibid.*
26 *Ibid.*
27 Jenyns, L., 'A monograph on the British species of *Cyclas* and *Pisidium*', *Transactions of the Cambridge Philosophical Society*, 42(2), 1832, pp. 289–311.
28 Kendall, C. E., Dean, J. D. and Rankin, W. M., 'On the geographical distribution of Mollusca in South Lonsdale', *Naturalist*, [34], 1909, pp. 314–319, 354–359, 378–381, 435–437.
29 *Ibid.*
30 Kendall, C. E., 'The Mollusca of Oundle', *Journal of Conchology*, 16(7–8), 1921–1922, pp. 220–244, 248–251.
31 Kendall, C. E., 'Ecology of the British Land Molluscs', *Naturalist*, [54], 1929, pp. 247–250, 273–276.
32 Jenyns, J., Natural History Diary, Newton Library, Cambridge.

Chapter Seven

Clergyman geologists: curates searching for evidence of the Flood?

He putteth forth his hand upon the rock

(Job 28. 9)

In the preceding chapters we have seen how ideas such as those set out in John Ray's *Wisdom of God* and William Paley's *Natural Theology* – notions that the complexity and diversity of the living world provided evidence for the existence of God – gave inspiration to clerical students of natural history for several centuries. Whether a man was investigating marine algae or mites, fungi or freshwater fish, he frequently saw the created beings in front of him as providing an approach to the glory of the Creator.

Some clergy naturalists seem to have been pious aesthetes, some were bluff sporting men. Some defended Darwin, some deplored him. Most rejoiced in the beauty of flower, butterfly or bird as a manifestation of divine power. The challenges provided by the enquiries of clerical geologists were sometimes a little different.

Divines, dining, catastrophism and uniformitarianism

It is not widely appreciated that modern British geology was to a considerable extent established as a discipline by those ordained into the Holy Orders of the Church of England.

To take the example of the senior institution, the Geological Society of London, of the 55 members elected in the year of its foundation (1807), no fewer than eight were clergymen. They included, as one might have expected, the Reverend John Huitson, FRS, Woodwardian Professor of Geology in the University of Cambridge, and the Reverend Professor John Josias Conybeare, from Oxford, but also other less notable figures, ordinary country parsons, from various parts of the country. Their companions were a distinguished group: over half the original members were, or became fellows of the Royal Society. There were a couple of MPs, Sir Humphrey Davy, the Secretary of the Royal Society, a bevy of medical men and a few industrialists. The composition of the tranche of members elected in 1808 was similar, with the addition of several military and naval officers, and a sprinkling of peers and baronets; this time there were seven clergy, including the Very Reverend Samuel Goodenough, FRS, Bishop of Carlisle. Five more were elected in the next three years. Two of the first dozen Presidents of the Society were in Holy Orders, four of the first twenty. These were: the Reverend William Buckland, FRS, DD, Professor of Geology at Oxford (1824–1826), the Reverend Adam Sedgwick, Woodwardian Professor at Cambridge (1829–1831), the Reverend William Whewell, Professor of Moral Philosophy at Cambridge (1837–1839), and then the second presidency of William Buckland (1839–1841). There was then something of a gap, before, in 1884, the Reverend Thomas George Bonney, FRS, Professor of Geology at University College, London, took up the reins. He had previously been Secretary of the Society for the years 1878–1884. Immediately before him the Reverend Thomas Wiltshire had been Secretary. And so it went.[1]

It is true that some of the clergy at that time, the first few decades of the nineteenth century, formed part of the same social network as many doctors, academics, military officers and landowners, and might have been expected to have been drawn into such an enterprise through the normal network of social contacts: indeed the society evolved out of a rather exclusive dining club, the meal costing 15s (the pre-decimal equivalent of 75p, at a time when many received less than £1.00 a week). This 'high cost of belonging' wrote David Allen, 'despite the fact that most of the founder-members were under forty, indicates a high average social rank'.[2] But perhaps a clue lies in the fact that the society was outward-looking, and not London-centred. A booklet *Geological Inquiries*, prepared in 1808, was sent round the country by the first president, George Bellas Greenough (1778–1855), an extremely affluent MP. Greenough then went to visit many informants, no doubt attracting many who were not already members to join. The clergy of the Church of England, with its dispersed, rural, parochial ministry, were natural local informants. Moreover, many of them had a real concern for the land and agriculture, since these influenced the welfare of their parishioners, and through their own landed interests. Many clergy had glebe land, and traditionally part of their income came from tithes of agricultural produce. Many, too, having long associations with a particular area, were able to devote a lengthy period to the study of a single locality. Such was the Reverend J. G. Cumming, Vice-Principal of King

William's College, Isle of Man, who in the *Proceedings of the Geological Society* in 1846, published an exhaustively detailed paper 'On the geology of the Isle of Man', a model (for its day) of a local geological monograph.[3]

It might be considered, particularly after the publication of Charles Lyell's *Principles of Geology*, 1830–1833 and Darwin's *Origin of Species* in 1859, that many clergy might have felt that the conclusions reached by geological science were at odds with traditional biblical teaching, or at least with the accounts of the Creation and early earth history given in the book of Genesis. In fact, for several decades there was a countervailing tendency: many clergy saw in geology a possible vehicle for demonstrating the accuracy of the biblical accounts, and sought to tie together the chronology of the earth as revealed from the Old Testament and the history of the earth as revealed through stratigraphy. The picture of the country curate poking around in quarries, seeking evidence of 'Noah's Flood' in the rocks is not entirely a mythical one.

One of the men among the first 55 members of the Geological Society was the Reverend Joseph Townsend from Pewsey in Wiltshire. The claim has been made that his sole reason for membership of the Society was that he assisted in the publication of the work of William 'Strata' Smith (1769–1839), an engineer with the Somerset Coal Canal Company, whose task it was to make a study of the network of canals then being constructed. He worked out not only that strata were arranged in a more or less orderly series of layers across England 'like pieces of bread and butter', but also that each stratum could be distinguished on the basis of the fossils it contained. He produced a series of stratigraphic maps, and eventually published his findings in *Strata Identified by Organised Fossils* in 1816 and *Stratigraphical System of Organised Fossils* in 1819, but not before he had communicated his material to a few of his clerical friends, some of whom published it with their particular gloss, for example that of the 'scriptural geologist'. Thus, as early as 1799, Smith communicated to his friends the Reverend Benjamin Richardson of Farleigh, Hungerford and Joseph Townsend (at that time of Bath) his 'Tabular view of the order of strata in the vicinity of Bath, with their respective organic remains'. Some of this material, it seems, appeared in the Reverend Richard Warner's *History of Bath* (1801). Townsend embodied Smith's findings (with acknowledgement) in his imposing work *The Character of Moses Established for Veracity as an Historian* in 1813, which attempted to demonstrate the congruence of the geological record and Genesis, the 'First Book of Moses'. This matter will be returned to.[4]

It is perhaps worthy of notice that amongst the geologists of the nineteenth century, the *catastrophist* view of geology was in competition with the doctrine of *actualism* or *uniformitarianism*. The latter, espoused in James Hutton's *Theory of the Earth*, published in 1785, maintained that the history of the earth could be understood in terms of the long-continued, extremely gradual action of processes that could be observed today – the action of the wind, rivers and streams, the waves: 'no vestige of a beginning, no prospect of an end'. Some considered such views heretical, but its image of long, dimly-lit corridors of time stretching into an inconceivably ancient past and into an unknown future was in keeping with the spirit of Romanticism that penetrated much of the writing of the age. The catastrophic view was, however, ostensibly more compatible with the Biblical view of history: the earth had been subjected to a series of sudden dramatic changes. The Deluge, the destruction of Sodom and Gomorrah, the collapse of the walls of Jericho, the rolling back of the waters of the Red Sea, were thus incidents in the history of the earth for which it might be possible to find geological evidence. It is therefore unsurprising that many geologists, clerical and lay, should show a fascination with catastrophic events like earthquakes, volcanic eruptions and tidal waves.

The Reverend John Mitchell – catastrophist?

One distinguished clerical geologist who to some extent fits this description, but from an era many decades before the Geological Society was founded, was the Reverend John Mitchell. He was probably born in Nottingham in 1724, and was admitted to Queens' College, Cambridge on 17 June 1742, the commencement of an association that lasted twenty-one years. As an undergraduate he was Bible Clerk, reading the Bible aloud in Hall for a shilling a week. He initially studied mathematics and was fourth wrangler in the second year of wranglerships, 1748. He took an MA in 1752 and a BD in 1761. He held a series of college posts: praelector in arithmetic (1751), college tutor (1751–1763), censor in theology (1752–1754) and senior bursar (1756–1758). His stipend seems to have been despondently low: in 1753 he received £9 per annum for his fellowship, £8 for the censorship and another £2 for examining. Perhaps partly for this reason he became Rector of St Botolph's, Cambridge, a stone's throw from his college, on 28 March 1760. In 1762 he was appointed Woodwardian Professor of Geology in the University, but gave 'few, if any, lectures'.[5]

Nevertheless, he was extremely active in geology. In the spring of 1760 he read a paper to the Royal Society (which, until the formation of the Geological Society was the main vehicle for the publication of this type of enquiry) with the title 'Conjectures concerning the cause, and observations upon the phenomena of earthquakes, particularly of that great earthquake of the first of November 1755 which proved to be fatal to the City of Lisbon, and whose effects were felt as far as Africa and more or less throughout almost all Europe'.[6]

This paper, which has been described as 'epoch-making', attempted to give a natural cause to, and to explain, seismic movements. In it can be detected the lines of reasoning of the wrangler (mathematician), but also traces of the catastrophic approach. Mitchell suggested the existence of subterranean fires, the percolation of water from above producing vapour, the 'quantity and elastic force of which' produced earthquakes. Volcanoes, he argued, were connected with the same subterranean fires; their vents marked weak portions of the earth's outer shell, from which vapour and molten material were able to escape.

> The motion of the earth is partly tremulous, and partly propagated by waves which succeed one another, sometimes at larger, sometimes at smaller distances, and this latter motion is generally projected much further than the former . . .
>
> Compression [in the earth's crust] must be propagated on account of the elasticity of the earth in the same manner as a pulse is propagated through the air.

Modern geophysicists would have little difficulty with much of this.

Mitchell went on to suggest that the focus from which an earthquake is propagated might be ascertained; first, from observations of different directions from which shock waves arrived at several distant places: 'If lines be drawn in these directions, the place of their common intersection must be nearly the place sought'. Second, from the times of arrival, and third, from successive arrivals of 'the great sea-wave'. He argued that the greatest degree of exactness was obtainable

> . . . in those cases where earthquakes have a source under the ocean for the proportionate distance of different places from that source may be very nearly ascertained by the interval between the earthquake and the succeeding wave; and this is much more to be depended on, as people are much less likely to be mistaken in the time between two events which follow each other at a small interval, than in observing the precise time of some single event.

Using these methods, he calculated the focus of the Lisbon earthquake as under the Atlantic Ocean, one degree from Lisbon and one-and-a-half degrees from Oporto. He also thought that the foci of earthquakes were not deep-seated, perhaps one-and-a half miles in depth, 'although data were wanting'.

Maybe of even greater importance, because the information was of immediate practical relevance, was his section on the upper crust of the earth:

> [The earth] is not composed of heaps of matter casually thrown together, but of regular and uniform strata. These strata, though they frequently do not exceed a few feet, or perhaps a few inches, in thickness, yet often extend in length and breadth for many miles, and this without varying their thickness considerably. The same stratum also preserves uniform character throughout, though the strata immediately next to each other are very often totally different, Thus for instance we shall have perhaps, a stratum of potter's clay; above that a stratum of coal; then another stratum of clay; next a sharp grit sandstone; then clay again; and coal again above that, and it frequently happens that none of these exceeds a few yards in thickness.

Next he gave a detailed account of 'perpendicular fissures' or joints, and went on to show that he understood the principles of structural geology, of folding, and of the erosion of uplifted strata.

He continued:

> [W]e ought to meet with the same kinds of earths, stones and minerals, appearing at the surface in long narrow strips, and lying parallel to the greatest rise of the mountains: and so in fact we find them.

For this brilliant paper, which has a strongly catastrophist thrust, but yet in which some elements of uniformitarianism can be detected, John Mitchell was elected a Fellow of the Royal Society in June 1762. It must have seemed, with his elevation to the Woodwardian Chair and to the Royal Society in quick succession, that he had a formidable geological career ahead of him. It must thus have been a surprise to many of his colleagues when this 'little short man, of black complexion, and fat' as one contemporary diarist put it, a confirmed bachelor of over forty, gave up his Chair, as was required, to marry a Miss Williamson in 1764. With his new bride 'a young lady of considerable fortune', as the *Cambridge Chronicle* described her, he became Rector of Compton, in the valley of the Itchen, near Winchester. Shortly after he was collated to Havant, in Hampshire, but within a few months his young wife died.

Perhaps to get away from memories, perhaps to be a little closer to his roots in Nottinghamshire, and maybe relatives, he moved north, and on 3 October 1767, he was instituted as Rector of Thornhill, near Dewsbury, Yorkshire. Here he married again, although little is known of his second wife, except that her Christian name was Ann, and that she survived him by 25 years, dying on 6 November 1818. There seems to have been at least one daughter, although whether from the first or the second marriage is not clear.

In his Yorkshire rectory, in addition to experiments on magnetism, vision and on light, he was something of an astronomer, he built a telescope, and applied probability theory to astronomy. He knew, and corresponded with, Herschel, also with Henry Cavendish (1731–1810), the pioneer in the fields of electricity and magnetism, his letters showing that he had gone much further than in his 1760 paper in working out the stratigraphy of England, for on his regular visits to Royal Society meetings in London he travelled by horse or carriage, using several different routes, and losing no chance to examine quarries, pits and other excavations. A letter to Henry Cavendish, dated 11 August 1788, and other notes, show that he had an unsurpassed knowledge of the stratigraphy of southern England, having been the first to establish the main subdivisions of the English Mesozoic formations. Alas, perhaps through modesty, he published none of this material, although, as he lived in the heart of the expanding Yorkshire coalfield, his knowledge could have been of inestimable value. Thus despite his distinguished Cambridge career, the holding of the Woodwardian Chair, the FRS, and his brilliant, eclectic mind, John Mitchell remains something of a 'might have been' and perhaps with the sudden loss of his young first wife, something of a tragic figure. His parishioners did not see things so, as the following epitaph shows:

> In the chancel of this church are deposited the remains of the Reverend Jn Mitchell, B.D., F.R.S., and 26 years Rector of this Parish. Eminently distinguished as the Philosopher and the Scholar, he had a just claim to the character of the real Christian, in the relative and social duties of life. The tender Husband, the indulgent Father, the affectionate Brother and the sincere Friend were prominent features of a Character uniformly amiable. His charities were not of Ostentation, but of feeling; His strict discharge of his Professional duties, that of principle, not form. As he lived in possession of the esteem of his Parishioners, so he has carried with him to the grave their regret. He died the 21st April 1793, in the 69th year of his age.

The Conybeares

Among the members of the Geological Society elected in its first year, was the Reverend John Josias Conybeare (1779–1824), Professor of Anglo-Saxon, and later of Poetry, and Vicar of Bothestan, and himself the son of a Rectory. He did in fact write several useful papers on geology. Scientifically, however, he was overshadowed by his younger brother, William Daniel Conybeare, who was put up for membership on 19 April 1811, and was on the council of the society for many years, serving as vice-president 1826–1828 and 1831–1833. (The Conybeares, incidentally, provide a good example of the importance of the family connection in parsonic natural history. They were related by blood and by marriage to a whole series of distinguished naturalists, including the Babingtons: the Reverend Churchill Babington, for example, as well as holding the Chair of Archaeology at Cambridge was a most competent all-round naturalist, and the author of *Catalogue of the Birds of Suffolk* [1884–86], see chapter 4.)[7]

William Conybeare seems to have been a precocious child; before the age of twelve he 'had written a novel, a play and sundry poems', the only copies of which, preserved by an old aunt, 'luckily fell into my hand at the age of sixteen', as he later wrote, and were burned. His father had a little country house at Bexley, Kent, and it was there that the young William became interested in the chalk, and the Eocene beds above it (revealed by shafts sunk in the neighbourhood), and the fossils they contained. Later he was one of the mainstays of a splinter-group of the Geological Society, which each Whitsun in the company of notables from London undertook fieldwork in the region. He was to some extent a behind-the-scenes worker, collaborating with others, providing them with information, and drawing diagrams. When Greenough prepared his Geological Map of England in 1820, he acknowledged Conybeare's input. He was a diluvialist, believing that the surface of the earth had been transformed by one or two great deluges, and after one paper he gave in 1829 it was said '[Conybeare] admits three deluges before the Noachian'. It may have been partly through his influence that 'drift' (glacial till or boulder clay, for example) was described as diluvial. He was, however, a versatile geologist. In 1821 he described the *Pleisiosaurus* found by Mary Anning in the Jurassic rocks of Lyme Regis, Dorset, and he also made an important study of the coalfields of Somerset. He co-authored, with William Phillips, the *Outline of the Geology of England and Wales*, 1822. Of this it was remarked:

> Conybeare . . . so amplified and enriched the work by his original observations, that it became a standard geological companion, and

> did more than any other independent work to advance the study of geology in this country.[8]

It had been suggested that Conybeare and Sedgwick (another parson-geologist, of whom more below) should co-operate on a further edition of the work, and Conybeare did in fact draw up a plan. Perhaps his clerical duties, and his growing family, absorbed more and more of his time, but the scheme was never completed. He was then the Vicar of Sully, Glamorgan; in 1836, he became Vicar of Axminster, and in 1845 Dean of Llandaff. Nevertheless his influence on geology was profound.

The eccentric Buckland

Another member of this coterie was the Reverend William Buckland (1784–1856); a larger-than-life figure in the history of science, he was appointed Reader in Mineralogy at Oxford in 1813, and a little later to the Chair of Geology. He was one of the chief protagonists of diluvial geology, attempting to establish that the drifts deposits (sands, gravels, tills) were the product of the Flood. His *Reliquiae Diluvianae; or, Observations on the Organic Remains Contained in the Caves, Fissures and Diluvial Gravel, and on Other Geological Phenomena, Atesting to the Action of a Universal Deluge* was published in 1826, dedicated to Dr Shute Barrington, the Bishop of Durham, and was a classic of the genre[9] (see Plate 9). He was twice President of the Geological Society, 1824–1826 and 1839–1841. An energetic man, he published widely on geology, and was an enthusiastic field worker. He excavated bones from a cave at Kirkdale in Yorkshire, producing them at a dinner of the society. He described the first pterodactyl found by Mary Anning in 1828. When the same young woman found fossil cephalopods (belemnites) with their ink-sacks preserved, he persuaded the Royal Academician Sir Frank Chantry to use them to draw an *Ichthyosaurus* with the ink. He was an earnest debater, vigorously defending his scientific position. Charles Lyell's diary entry for 14 December 1831 is instructive:

> Dined at the Geological Society Club . . . a pleasant club – Stokes, Greenough, Buckland, Lord Cole . . . and a few more. Murchison was pheasant-shooting in the country, but cut in for the meeting. A short paper on Springs, and other by Mr Hutton on the Whin Sill of Yorkshire, drew up Buckland, Greenough, Murchison and De La Beche, and they seemed much disposed to go on for ever, Buckland speaking five times, but not once too often. I was glad to sit quiet.[10]

Buckland also seems to have appreciated the finer things of life. For many years the Geological Society's meetings were over dinners, and William Buckland, it is recorded, 'when he journeyed to London to attend the meeting of the Society, was accustomed to stay at the Salopian Coffee House and Tavern, Charing Cross, a house noted for good dinners and wines.'

Some of his gastronomic tastes were more individual: Canon Buckland claimed to have eaten his way through the animal kingdom. Crocodile was from time to time served to visitors, so too were mice, cooked in batter. He claimed that the most disagreeable creature he ever ate was mole, the next bluebottle. He is alleged to have once eaten the heart of a French king, shown to him as a curio at a country house.

He had an extremely histrionic method of teaching. Charles Lyell wrote that he 'would keep his audience in roars of laughter, as he imitated what he thought to be the movements of the *Iguanodon* or *Megatherium*, or seizing the ends of his clerical coat-tails would leap about to show how a pterodactyl flew.' (See Plate 8.)

The audiences loved it, no less in the field than in the lecture hall. He would say: 'The next lecture will take place in the fields above the quarry at Stonesfield' or 'at the top of Shotover Hill'. The lectures were sometimes conducted on horseback as 'geological rides'. At the Birmingham meeting of the British Association for the Advancement of Science in 1839 he attracted several thousand to a lecture at Dudley Caverns, illuminated by thousands of candles for the occasion. After the discussion of the geology of the area, he allowed himself to be carried away on a stream of patriotic fervour: the mineral wealth of the region was no accident; it showed that Providence had intended, by these gifts, for Britain to be the richest and most powerful nation. 'And with these words the great crowd, with Buckland at its head, returned towards the light of day, thundering out, with one accord, "God save the Queen."'[11]

The picture must have been all the more extraordinary, as he habitually conducted fieldwork in the most incongruous formal clothing: he would set off into the countryside wearing black frock coat, dark suit and top hat, carrying an umbrella and a most ridiculous dark blue bag, from which he was wont to produce specimens, like a conjuror. He had his carriage ostentatiously strengthened for loads of rocks and fossils, with a small furnace in order to assay specimens in the field.

The way he lived at home was equally eccentric; one visitor to Christ Church, Oxford, recorded how 'from a low plain Gothic wall, in the quad at an ordinary door opens

> and you behold a very wide and short staircase, almost covered with

> fragments of rock, specimens of fossil remains, an immense tortoise, and a stuffed wolf. In the breakfast-room are a series of piles of books, boxes, papers . . . all blended together in one mass of confusion, which, I was informed, had not been invaded by the dust cloth for the last five years.[12]

Living animals of various species roamed the household. His lively wife once attempted to have 'the dust and rubbish' cleaned up, 'but found it so disturbed the doctor, that she determined never again to risk her matrimonial felicity in such a cause'. Amongst Canon Buckland's many other oddities was his habit of concealing his geological hammer, particularly when geologizing in sabbatarian Scotland on Sundays.

He must have been an inspiring, if eccentric teacher. His performances in the field and lecture-hall captured the imagination of students and amateur geologists alike, at Oxford and his occasional open performances at meetings of the British Association. But some found his posturing graceless. Charles Darwin, perhaps a little oddly for one who had endured many extremely dull lectures at both Edinburgh and Cambridge, regarded him as 'a vulgar and almost coarse man', and as one driven 'more by a craving for notoriety, which sometimes made him behave like a buffoon, than by a love of science'.

Sedgwick's legacy

Darwin had in fact been something of a guinea-pig in the development of the outdoor method of teaching by the Reverend Professor Adam Sedgwick, who held the Woodwardian Chair of Geology at Cambridge from 1818 until his death in 1873 (see Plate 7). As Darwin records:

> As I had first come up to Cambridge at Christmas, I was forced to keep two terms after passing my final examination, at the commencement of 1831; and Henslow then persuaded me to begin the study of geology. Therefore on my return to Shropshire I examined sections and coloured a map of parts around Shrewsbury. Professor Sedgwick in the beginning of August intended to visit North Wales to pursue his famous geological investigation amongst the older rocks, and Henslow asked him to allow me to accompany him. Accordingly he came and slept at my Father's house . . .
>
> Next morning we started for Llangollen, Conway, Bangor and Capel Curig. This tour was of decided use in teaching me a little how to make out the geology of a country. Sedgwick often sent me

on a line parallel to his, telling me to bring back specimens, and mark the stratigraphy on a map. I have little doubt that he did this for my good, as I was too ignorant to have aided him . . . At Capel Curig I left Sedgwick and went by straight line by compass and map across the mountains to Barmouth, never following a track unless it coincided with my course.[13]

Darwin used in his geological researches during the *Beagle* voyage – in South America, the Falklands, in Australia – almost every aspect of what Sedgwick had taught him that summer in Wales: the direct line of transect across country, the inspection of sections or exposures, the marking of stratification on a map, the collection of rock specimens, and the careful use of a compass.

Later, after Darwin's student days, perhaps partly inspired by Buckland's performances, perhaps adapting the teaching technique to work with groups rather than individual instruction:

In 1835 . . . Sedgwick started the practice of giving lectures out-of-doors, on horseback, which at once proved extremely popular. Parties of up to seventy mounted students would regularly turn out and go cantering across the Fens, to listen in the course of the day to five different lectures – the last of which, on fen-drainage, was traditionally delivered from that matchless point of vantage, the cathedral roof at Ely.[14]

Although the idea of a cavalry regiment of galloping geologists careering across the Cambridgeshire countryside to al fresco lectures captures the imagination, Sedgwick's onetime student and later assistant, the Reverend T. G. Bonney (1833–1923, later Professor of Geology at University College, London) records that it was not all that usual for undergraduates to possess or have access to horses, most simply could not afford the expense, and thus some would be excluded from these excitements. One who did take part, however, was the lifelong naturalist and student of geology, Charles Kingsley (1819–1875), later Canon of Chester, and later still Canon of Westminster, to whom the invention of the phrase 'muscular Christianity' has been attributed. (He had acquired some skill as a horseman foxhunting in Devon.)

Adam Sedgwick, however, was a towering figure in the history of British geology. He came from Dent, on the borders between Westmorland (later Cumbria) and Yorkshire, gaining a scholarship to Trinity College, Cambridge to study mathematics and theology. He became a fellow in 1810, taking priest's orders eight years later, around the time he became Professor of Geology. Later he became a Canon of

Norwich Cathedral. Extraordinarily, he held few qualifications for the Chair: he declaimed at the time 'Hitherto I have never turned a stone, now I shall leave no stone unturned'. And neither did he. Coming from northwest England he was drawn to the investigation of the rocks of the neighbouring Lake District. The sedimentary rocks there are, for the most part, older and more complex in their arrangement than those of the Midlands and East Anglia: they have been contorted by folding, fractured by faulting, pierced by volcanic vents and intruded by igneous rocks. Sedgwick rejoiced in unravelling these complexities through detailed mapping and observation. Sometimes, as befitted a person of his station in life, he employed a 'miner's boy' to do the more vigorous hammering. Later he turned to North Wales, the enterprise in which Darwin joined him in 1831. By 1835 he had worked out the stratigraphic succession in the area, naming the oldest of the strata the Cambrian (Cambria – Wales). He also worked in south-west England, identifying the Devonian system there, as well as in Scotland and the Alps.

One of his best-known works was *British Palaeozoic Fossils* (1854). Sedgwick used the technique, developed by William Smith a few years earlier, of identifying strata by the fossils they contained, and described the oldest fossil assemblages then known in the British Isles from the Cambrian. Like diluvialist Buckland in the earlier part of his career, Adam Sedgwick was a catastrophist: perhaps the notions were more compatible with his theological views, perhaps it was the effect of his early field studies in the geologically complex Lake District, with its evidence of great foldings of the rocks and outpourings of lava in the past. While the uniformitarians followed Lyell in emphasising that geological processes had operated uniformly and slowly over immensely long periods of time, with minimal importance being attached to sudden, forceful events ('parsimony of force, prodigality of time') catastrophists such as Sedgwick invoked a greater amount of violent upheaval, and shorter corridors of time. While he believed that the extinction of fossil species was the result of catastrophic events, he felt that new species were ushered into existence by Divine acts of Creation. Not surprisingly he was opposed to Darwin's ideas on evolution through natural selection, expounded in the *Origin of Species* in 1859, writing off that book as 'false and mischievous' and claiming that when he read it, he laughed until his sides ached.

As the history of the foldings of the rocks, and of the earth's sedimentary sequences were worked out, there were of course speculations as to the reason for some of the more spectacular of the fold-systems. Some argued that contraction of the earth was the reason for the rucking-up of sedimentary rocks into fold-mountains. Another Cambridge cleric, also a former wrangler, the Reverend Osmond Fisher, Fellow of

Jesus College Cambridge, and Rector of Harlton, calculated in *The Physics of the Earth's Crust* [15] that any contraction of the earth was too small to account for the high mountains, and the large distances that rock formations appeared to have been thrust, as for example, in the cases of Scandinavia and the Alps. Instead he postulated convectional currents, rising in the mid-oceans and sweeping downwards beneath the continents, in doing so citing the volcanic islands in the oceans and the occurrence of earthquakes along the coast of Japan and in the Aleutians. In this he anticipated notions of plate-tectonics, a concept that to some extent reconciled catastrophic and uniformitarian approaches, by around eighty years.

An approximate contemporary of many of the above in the heroic age of geology, was J. Clifton Ward (1843–1880), who was also active in the north of England; he was an associate of Thomas George Bonney (see below) and made important contributions to the microscopic study of rocks, publishing a paper entitled 'Comparative microscopic structure of some ancient and modern volcanic rocks' in the *Quarterly Journal of the Geological Society* in 1875 and a paper on 'Granitic, granitoid, and associated metamorphic rocks of the Lake District'. Clifton Ward was one of the comparatively few professional scientists who took Holy Orders after establishing themselves in their subject. Originally with the Geological Survey, he left in 1878 to become curate of St John's, Keswick, and two years later became, for a brief period, Vicar of Rydal.[16]

Galloway: an extreme scriptural geologist

There might be some question as to whether William Brown Galloway (1811–1903) should truly be described as a geologist, or indeed any sort of naturalist, as the amount of fieldwork he did seems to have been limited, but his writings on what might be considered geological topics were so prolific and so typical of a particular genre, that he is taken as a case study here. He was a close contemporary of many of the figures that have been introduced above, but was one of the very first products of Durham University, going up in 1839. He seems to have been competent academically, taking the junior Hebrew prize in 1840, and the senior prize in 1841. He was granted a Licentiate in Theology after passing his examinations, on 23 June 1841.[17]

William Galloway was curate at Barnard Castle, not far from Durham, from 1841 to 1845, thereafter taking two further London curacies, at Holy Trinity, Bromley, 1845–1847, and then at St Pancras, 1847–1849. Later he was Vicar of St Mark's, Regent's Park for nearly

40 years (1849–1888). He seems to have thrived on city life, and made numerous contacts in London. He died on 20 March 1903.

Theologically and philosophically William Brown Galloway was something of a fundamentalist, and as one person put it after his death: 'His great aim in life was the defence of Scripture.'[18] This defence began in 1842, not many months after his leaving Durham, and continued until close to the time of his death, and constituted a stream of books and pamphlets aimed at demonstrating the literal truth of Scripture. His early writings were predominantly theological in tone, for example: *The Chain of Ages Traced in its Prominent Links, by Holy Scripture from the Creation of Adam to the Close of the First Century of the Christian Era*.[19] These clearly demonstrate a conservative, literalist approach, and a concern for the Bible as a source of historical information. This concern with time runs through much that Galloway wrote.

Later he attempted, with more and more vigour, to show how the biblical record could be linked to the evidence of science in every respect. In particular he was at pains to demonstrate 'scientifically' that the Flood described in Genesis had occurred: he was a 'diluvialist'. He published *Physical Facts and the Scriptural Record* (1872), *Science and Geology in Relation to the Universal Deluge* (1888) and *Testimony of Science to the Deluge* (no date, *c.*1895).[20]

His speculations were fairly florid. A single example must suffice. The Cretaceous chalk, with its nodules of flints, that underlies much of East Anglia, parts of Lincolnshire, and east Yorkshire, he felt, was meteoritic in origin, having formed on dry land.

> I am prepared to show many objects of the dry land in flint, which could not have been formed under water ... These consist of portions of decayed tree roots in flint, with the bark in places where the wood had fallen away ... [P]ortions also of other and larger trees from the chalk district of Yorkshire ... hallow stalks of cabbage ... also pods of beans ... all of flint ... gourds or other vegetable fruits ... roots of turnip and specimens of fungus, all of flint.
>
> ... [C]onsidering the vast extent of the chalk and flint formation, it is manifest that had it all fallen upon the earth at one time, it might have materially affected the earth's balance. But, coming by degrees at successive periods, the balance might adjust itself by the flow of waters of the sea to the opposite side of the globe where the weight had to be counterbalanced .. [T]he gradual accumulation of a vast mass of compensating waters on the opposite side of the world, might, by its superincumbent weight, ... break down the underlying strata there.[21]

These movements altered the equilibrium of the earth: 'a change of axis would demonstrably result . . . [and] such a change of axis would produce a universal deluge'.[22] The origin of the Flood described in the book of Genesis is thus explained.

Although there was not much evidence of fieldwork in his writings, beyond perhaps occasional brief descriptions of rocks or landscapes and some photographs of some curiously-shaped flints, all this was backed-up by numerous quotations from scripture and other ancient writings.

William Galloway produced many publications of similar character, some of them going into several editions, and the last written when he was over ninety. He seems to have been a determined and a somewhat stubborn man. Often his speculations were supported by pages of mathematics, and careful selections from contemporary geological and other scientific authors. The method is somewhat reminiscent of some late twentieth-century 'creation science' writers (also often rather extreme evangelicals): tiny snippets from worthy authorities are quoted quite out of context. Nevertheless, despite the wry amusement with which such ideas are received in scientific circles today, Galloway was typical of many scriptural geologists, but few of them were quite as prolific as he.

The rise and fall of the Flood

The geological notion that the Earth's surface had been overwhelmed by one or more great deluges which had transformed the landscape and even the structure of the earth's crust, is almost as old as geology itself. There were numerous variants. One proponent of the idea was the Reverend Thomas Burnet (1635–1715), who was, both in his views and in his activities, something of a maverick, an individualist. He was much involved in some of the religious controversies of his troubled days, and it may be that his eccentricity cost him preferment in the Church. Despite this reputation, Thomas Burnet was an extremely literate man, writing both Latin and English of the greatest elegance. Born at Croft, in Yorkshire, after schooling at Northallerton, he entered Clare Hall, Cambridge on 26 June 1654, later moving to Christ's College, where he became a Fellow in 1657. In due course he became Master of Charterhouse, where he attracted complaints, for although in priest's orders, he wore a 'lay habit'.

He discussed the notion in the context of the suitability of the earth as a home for humanity in his *Sacred Theory of the Earth*, published first in Latin in 1681, but translated into English and expanded in 1684. He believed that the earth had originally been created by divine action in a state of perfection, flat and smooth, and that the present landscape was the result of degeneration. He compared the original perfect form to that of a gigantic egg, the shell of which cracked in the Deluge, causing internal waters to burst out. Fragments of shell becoming mountains. The same catastrophe caused the equator, originally coincident with the plane of the ecliptic (the plane in which the earth revolves around the sun) to shift to its present position. The Noachian Flood, therefore, was directly or indirectly responsible for the arrangement of mountains and valleys, the regularities and irregularities in stratification, the nature and distribution of fossils. He argued using the latest available mathematical methods, thus attempting to explain Biblical events in terms of physical laws and thereby developing a 'sacred physics'. He was also a strong advocate of empirical observation and investigation, rather than the 'dry philosophy' of Aristotle.[23]

In 1692 he published another work which attempted even more strongly to reconcile geological ideas with Genesis. He offered a non-literal interpretation, and included a purported conversation between Eve and the serpent in the Garden of Eden which caused the gravest offence, and eventually Burnet had to publish a letter of apology. Indeed he asked his bookseller to withdraw the book. Later in life he published two more books containing unorthodox religious views – one of which amounted to a rejection of the doctrine of original sin. But he was so concerned that his ideas might be judged heretical, that numbers circulated were kept very small. That of course, just attracted interest, although much of it after his death on 27 September 1715.

There were, however, among his contemporaries, those who were not so sure about the use of the Noachian Flood as an explanatory mechanism. John Ray, another staunch supporter of fieldwork and careful individual field investigation, made a careful study of fossils and their distribution. Indeed some of his descriptions were faultless. Here he is on the subject of ammonites, which he had collected from Whitby, on the Yorkshire coast:

> They likewise some of them retained all along the surface of them [a] very pretty kind of Sutures, such as are observed in the Skulls of several kinds of living creatures, which Sutures were most curiously shaped in the manner of Leaves and every one in the same Shell exactly like one another . . . All these Sutures I found by breaking one of the Stones to be the Termini or bounding of certain Diaphragms or partitions, which seemed to divide the Cavity of the Shell into a multitude of very proportionate and regular Cells or Caverns . . . [24]

John Ray noticed that many fossils found in the rocks were quite different from living creatures still existing: these forms were 'lost out of this world', i.e. extinct. '[T]hat is a supposition which Philosophers hitherto have been unwilling to admit.' In his most careful collection and examination of fossils, his appreciation of the phenomenon of extinction, and his understanding that fossil assemblages did not resemble those of living organism, John Ray was far ahead of his day, just as he was in the fields of botany and zoology (see Plate 4).

He did not like the idea that fossils were the result of the Flood described in Genesis. If that had been the case:

> First it will hence follow that all the Earth was once covered by the Sea, and that for a considerable time: for there being found of those shells [i.e. fossils] in the middle of Germany, at least 200 miles distant from the Sea, as myself can witness, nay, upon the highest Mountains of Europe, even the Alps themselves, the Sea must needs have covered them, and consequently, the water, keeping its level, all Europe and the World besides. Now that ever the Water should have covered the Earth to that height as to exceed the tops of the highest Mountains, and for a considerable time abode there, is hard to believe, nor can such Opinion be easily reconciled with the Scripture. If it be said that these Shells were brought in by the universal Deluge in the time of Noah, when the Mountains were covered, I answer that that Deluge proceeded from the Rain, which was more likely to carry Shells down to the Sea, than bring any up from it.[25]

The logic is hard to fault.

Nevertheless the Flood idea stuck, reinforced by influences from the continent, such as the work of Georges Cuvier (1769–1832) who in 1812 had published a book *Discourse Préliminair*e on fossil vertebrates, which took a strong Diluvialist position. Cuvier accepted the accuracy of the Genesis version, but maintained that the Noachian Flood was but the last of many such events. There must have been:

> repeated irruptions and retreats of the sea . . .; most of the catastrophes which have occasioned them must have been sudden. . . . Life, therefore, has been often disturbed on this earth by terrible events – calamities which . . . have perhaps moved and overturned to a great depth the entire outer crust of the globe . . . Numberless living beings have been victims of these catastrophes; some have been destroyed by sudden inundations, others have been laid dry in consequence of the bottom of the seas being instantaneously elevated. Their races even have become extinct, and have left no

> memorial . . . except some small fragment which the naturalist can scarcely recognise.[26]

The translation is that of Robert Jameson, dated 1817, the Professor of Natural History at Edinburgh, whose lectures were thought by the young Charles Darwin to be exceedingly dull, very different from those of the Reverend William Buckland.

The central thesis of Buckland's inaugural lecture was that the facts of geology were in accord with Scripture, but with reservations, for he eschewed a literal interpretation of the Genesis accounts of the Creation and the Flood. Not days, but substantial periods of time might have elapsed between successive acts of Creation. He noted the presence throughout large areas of central and southern England of 'gravel and loam' at relatively high levels in the landscape, where they were unlikely to have been deposited by rivers or streams. This 'diluvium', according to Buckland, was to be distinguished from the alluvium that lined river valleys. He attributed its origin to a universal flooding that had occurred during Cuvier's most recent episode. About ten years later what appeared to be proof of Buckland's views was found. In 1821 men working in a quarry revealed the opening to Kirkdale Cavern in Yorkshire; numerous bones were found within. Buckland visited the site, conducting an examination of the remains. Beneath a layer of mud on the cavern floor he discovered the fossil remains of 23 species of animals, including hyenas, tigers, mastodons and hippopotami. Buckland found teeth marks on some of the bones, and concluded that the cave had been a den of hyenas in antediluvian (pre-Flood) times. The layer of fine material overlying the animal remains was interpreted as sediment deposited during the Flood.

> [T]he phenomena of this cave seem referable to the period immediately antecedent to the last inundation of the Earth, and in which the world was inhabited by animals, almost all bearing a . . . resemblance to those that now exist; but so completely has the violence of that tremendous convulsion . . . remodelled the from of the antediluvian surface, that it is only in caverns that have been protected from its ravages that we may hope to find undisturbed evidence of events in the period immediately preceding it.[27]

The publication of the Kirkdale cave conclusions in 1822 resulted in William Buckland being awarded the Royal Society's Copley Medal. Buckland, however, had got the bit between his teeth and in the months that followed he investigated over 20 cave sites in England and Europe in his search for antediluvian fossils. He published his findings late in

1823 in the book with that formidable title the *Reliquae Diluvianae* . . . (see page 118).

William Buckland's descriptions of the fossil vertebrates were extremely careful and accurate: he made detailed comparisons of the fossil material with analogous present-day material, comparing, for example, the bones from Kirkdale with those from a modern hyena. The book also captured the imagination, and remained popular and influential for nearly two decades. The notion that the rhinoceros, hippopotamus and hyena had roamed England in the recent geological past was an inspiring one.

Meanwhile, once again, new ideas were drifting across the Channel. A number of thinkers, in Britain and on the continent had hinted that erratic boulders – apparently far-travelled masses of rock, quite different from the rocks around them – had been moved to their present position by glaciers. Two Swiss engineers, Jean de Charpentier (1786–1855) and Ignace Venetz (1788–1859), published strong evidence that the Alpine glaciers had formerly been far more extensive. Louis Agassiz (1807–1878) visited them and immediately attempted to apply their ideas to his own Jura region of Switzerland. In 1837 he expounded, in vivid, almost extravagant terms, his view of a recent ice-age, 'the greatest catastrophe which has ever modified the face of the earth'. Three years later, in much more measured terms, he developed his ideas in *Études sur les glaciers*. Not long after, he toured the British Isles collecting evidence for glaciation, sometimes accompanied by Buckland. Buckland was entirely convinced, and abandoned the diluvial hypothesis, becoming an enthusiastic proponent of the glacial theory, much to the chagrin of some his brother clergymen-geologists. Scriptural geologist Galloway, for example wrote:

> It was only from about the year 1838 that the Glacial Theory began to be accepted by geologists in England, in opposition to the previous philosophical views of the ever-illustrious Cuvier . . . Even Buckland, the author of *Reliquiae Diluvianae* and of the Bridgewater Treatise on Geology, professed himself a convert to the theoretical conclusions of Agassiz in the year 1840. But his own sounder judgment is to be found in his earlier works.[28]

In the years after the publication of Lyell's *Principles of Geology,* acceptance of the literal truth of the book of Genesis, as a guide to Earth history became more and more difficult, and the intellectual gymnastics involved in 'harmonizing' the Book of Nature and the Book of Scripture, more and more convoluted. For a few decades the 'day-age' hypothesis, hinted at by Buckland, had its devotees, as noted above.

Advocates of this idea postulated that a 'day' in the Creation story represented a long period of geological time. Such was the notion of the Reverend Samuel Kinns, Curate of All Saints. Langham Place, London (1890–1908), later Vicar of Holy Trinity, Minories, who amongst his other distinctions held a PhD from Jena, was a fellow of the Royal Astronomical Society, and a member of the Society of Biblical Archaeology. His book *Moses and Geology; or, the Harmony of the Bible with Science*,[29] appeared first in 1882, and went through thirteen printings between that date and 1892. At an early point in the work he expresses his objective as being to demonstrate the truth of the statement: 'Upon a careful study of the sublime truths of the Bible they will be found to harmonize with Science.'[30] Kinns attempts to show that 'fifteen creative events as given by Moses' ie in the Biblical account, occurred in exactly the same order as in the geological record ('as taught by science').

> I. Moses: *'In the beginning God created the Heaven and the Earth.'*
> Science: Astronomical facts go to prove other worlds were created before our own. It is therefore in the right order to mention 'The Heaven' first.
> . . .
> V. Moses: 'And God said, Let the earth bring forth grass.'
> *The literal translation is: 'Let the earth sprout forth herbage.'*
> Notice, seeds are not mentioned.
> Science: The earliest forms of vegetable life were *not*, grass, but Cryptogams, such as algae, lichens, ferns, &c., which are propagated by spores and not by seeds. Dawson and Hooker have found such land plants in the Upper Silurian.
> . . .
> XI. Moses: *'And God created great whales.'*
> (Should have been translated 'sea monsters')
> Science: In the succeeding strata of the Lias, monster marine Saurians, such as Ichthyosaurus and Pleisiosaurus are found.[31]
> . . .

Thus, each of the fifteen events, including the creation of Man, in Genesis are described in scientific terms, in detail in a chapter of the book. Kinns argues that the probability of the fifteen creative events appearing in exactly the same order in the geological record as in the Mosaic record in Genesis is indescribably tiny: '*hundreds of millions* against' (his italics). Thus are the two records considered harmonized. Kinns considered that he had demonstrated a harmony with astronomy, as well as with the geological record.

By the 1870s the diluvialists and scriptural geologists were in retreat. In 1889 the conservative Reverend William Purchas wrote a *Flora of Herefordshire*. He persuaded his clerical colleague Reverend W. E. Symonds, FGS, Rector of Pendock (formerly of Wadham College, Oxford), to write notes on the geology of the county. These provide a straightforward review of the stratigraphy and palaeontology of each area, with brief comments on matters such as the way in which erosion had developed different landscapes from different lithologies. The account is thus an entirely conventional summary, in terms of the state of geology in England some five decades after the publication of Charles Lyell's *Principles of Geology*. There is an attempt, for example, at a correlation of the Old Red Sandstone rocks of Herefordshire with the Devonian and Old Red Sandstone of other parts of the British Isles. The association of particular fossils such as the primitive fish *Cephalaspis* and *Pteraspis*, with particular strata is mentioned, as are the effects on the landscape of the Woolhope Dome (a major upfold in the layered rocks of the region) of 'the long ages of denudation'.

Symonds had excavated some of the caves near Whitchurch over the period 1870–1872, and describes finding the bones of several extinct mammals in them (including the mammoth and bison). He wrote: 'Prehistoric Man also must have sought them as a refuge, as his chipped flints and fractured pebbles were found associated with the bones of extinct mammalia'. He is clearly a disciple of Lyell, and quite possibly Darwin, for he seems to accept the notion that humanity is extremely ancient and that the techniques of geology and palaeontology are appropriate to the study of its antiquity.[32]

It seems that in commissioning Symonds to write the introductory geology section to his *Flora*, William Purchas got something a little different from what he expected, for in the front of the copy he presented to Durham University Library is a quite lengthy, hand-written statement:

> In reference to some of the notes of the Geology of Herefordshire and certain conclusions advanced therein which seem incapable of reconciliation with the Mosaic account of the Creation I should wish to say that while it may be quite true that these conclusions may seem to be legitimate deductions now, or to be now demanded by the facts at present known to Geologists, it is equally true that in a science such as Geology which is still youthful, new and important facts may any day be brought to light which may demand considerable modification of views now widely and very positively maintained, and that while we do not at present see how the testimony of Genesis & that of the rocks are to be harmonized, we may

best [be] satisfied that a fuller understanding of the matter will shew there to be substantial accord.

I regret that this note was not printed at the end of the Preface.[33]

William Henry Purchas

Thomas Bonney: polymath and Darwinist

Thomas George Bonney (1833–1923) has been described as one of the last links with the nineteenth-century 'heroic age' of geology: the age of Sedgwick, Buckland and the Conybeares. The son and grandson of clergy, in some ways he typifies the nineteenth-century parson-naturalist: the phrase 'Victorian polymath' comes to mind to describe such men, for Bonney was distinguished in a number of fields, of which mathematics, geology, geography, architecture and theology are but some. Even this statement fails to give a true impression of the breadth of his enthusiasm: he had a feel for the unity of knowledge, and was a great integrator. He was a well-known climber, and president of the Alpine Club for a while, having first visited the Alps in 1856. He traversed glaciers, and ascended high peaks; he once ate a marmot (shades of Buckland). He understood the way in which various factors interacted. In *The Building of the Alps* (1912),[34] written when he was nearing eighty, he included sections on Alpine meteorology, vegetation and 'the Alps in relation to man'. The vegetation chapter shows an appreciation of the manner in which the interplay of altitude, aspect, substratum and microclimate influences the distribution of plant species. He frequently wrote of the way in which human activities and the physical background of a region maintained a dialogue with one another. Here he is, in a very different type of environment:

> [The Fenland is] a wide-spread tract of perfectly flat land extending to the sea, and scarcely above its level; once an ague-haunted marsh, flooded in great part for many months of the year, and rich alone in fish and wild fowl; now intersected with ditches, a light, dry black soil, green in spring time with sprouting blade, golden in in autumn with the dense ears of grain. It is a strange solemn land, silent even yet, with houses few and far between, except where they have for centuries clustered on some bank of Jurassic clay, which rises like a shoal not many feet above the plain.[35]

Thomas Bonney came from a family, originally of Huguenot origin, of noted teachers and clergy. He was the eldest of ten children of the Reverend Thomas Bonney (senior), headmaster of Rugeley Grammar

School, in central England. His father and mother were both keen naturalists, but his early interest is said to have been kindled by the gift of a set of geological specimens by a lady relative, 'a friend of Buckland, Sedgwick and others of that generation'. He went to school at Uppingham, and then entered St John's College, Cambridge to read mathematics, graduating in 1856 as Twelfth Wrangler (twelfth amongst those awarded first class degrees). He also took second class in classics, and was only prevented by illness from taking the examinations for Honours in theology. He then taught mathematics for five years at Westminster School, being ordained deacon in the Church of England in 1857 and priest in 1858. He returned to his old college in 1861 as junior dean, becoming tutor in 1868, as well as college lecturer in natural science. His responsibilities were primarily in geology, a field which like Sedgwick, he had largely taught himself. Thomas Bonney had responsibilities for teaching the subject throughout Cambridge University, for by this time Professor Sedgwick was well over eighty. He was an enthusiastic advocate of field and practical work for students.

Despite shouldering a good deal of his teaching during his later years, Bonney was not elected to succeed Professor Sedgwick when he died in 1873, and there are grounds for suspecting that there may have been some slight tension with T. McKenney Hughes who was appointed to the Woodwardian Professorship.

It is no surprise therefore that in 1877 Bonney accepted the Chair of Geology at University College, London. From this base he played a leading role in the administration of British science, serving for many years on the Council of the Geological Society, receiving the Wollaston Medal in 1889. He was also president of the Mineralogical Society, elected FRS in 1878, and took a leading role in the management of the British Association, especially the Geological Section: he was president of the 'British Ass' in 1910. He was chairman of the Royal Society's Coral Reef Committee which organised the deep-drilling of Funafuti Atoll in the Pacific, which led to the substantial proof of the Darwin-Dana theory on the origin of coral reefs (that the thick layers of coral had accumulated during the gradual submergence of a volcanic islet, or rise in sea-level, or both).[36]

Despite these honours and a frenetic round of scientific activities, his clerical career continued. He was made an Honorary Canon of Manchester Cathedral in 1887, was preacher at the Chapel Royal and select preacher to the University of Cambridge. He published volumes of sermons.

His lack of training in geology was no more of an impediment than it was to Lyell, Darwin or Sedgwick: perhaps it contributed to his independent outlook. Maybe also his mathematical background was the basis of his demand for rigour. He would not accept a theory until it was 'exhaustively proved'. He once opined: 'Fine phrases unsupported by facts prove to be no better than cheques without a balance at the bank'.[37]

From the days of his first visit to the Alps in 1856, Thomas Bonney had an interest in glaciers, glacial action and glaciated landscapes. Ice action was the subject of his second paper (in 1866), of his Presidential Address to the British Association over 40 years later (1912), and of two of his books.

After many years of fieldwork in the Swiss Alps and in the glaciated valleys of upland Britain he remained sceptical of the efficacy of ice as an agent for wide scale erosion. While small mountain lakes and tarns might be formed by ice scraping, he did not accept glacial action as an originating cause of large lake basins. Of Alpine glaciers he wrote:

> The glacier appears often to have been impotent as an excavatory agent during the greater part of its course, and reserved itself for one final effort at or near the end of the point of emergence from the mountains. Even in Greenland, where the great glaciers ... have exposed rock beneath, this is not excavated, but is only brought to a level surface by the great ice-rasp.[38]

There are geomorphologists today who would substantially agree, arguing that frost-shattering was the main agent, the glaciers themselves merely serving to carry material away. Also, Bonney had the greatest reluctance in accepting that ice from Scandinavia impinged on the eastern part of Great Britain. Modern geologists and geomorphologists have little difficulty in imagining a continental ice-sheet extending from Scandinavia across the North Sea to eastern England, but Bonney was scathing in a letter to Thomas Mallard Reade (5 April 1906), about the idea of a 'Dogger Bank ice-sheet'. He admitted: 'Scandinavian rocks are not rare in this part of Cambridgeshire' but went on 'how land ice is to bring them across the general southerly drift of erratics, I fail to see.' He firmly believed that material could be moved long distances by 'sea ice' (icebergs and floes). Thomas Bonney's letters are littered with sarcastic remarks about those with whom he disagreed – the 'extreme glacialists'. He refers to: 'ice madness', 'faithful followers of ice sheets ... talking more like clericals than scientific men', 'divorced from reason', 'crank', 'bosh', 'evidence which killed the glacier pig at the end of his rooting', 'fungus growth of nonsense'.

Although he was more outspoken in the privacy of a personal letter than in print, he seems in some respects to be something of a stubborn man. Thus in a letter in 1905 he wrote: 'I prefer not to read too much literature when I go to study a district which has been the subject of controversy'.[39] In the preface to one of his books: 'I generally abstain from looking at any book which appears while I am writing, if it is likely to take a line similar to my own; for I find that to know what others have just been saying hampers more than it helps me'.[40] In other ways he was remarkably open. He was a devotee of the the gradualist or uniformitarian views of Lyell and Darwin, writing at one stage that 'Mineralogy still needs its Darwin'. Yet he accepted the importance of ice action within a few years of the ice age theory being promulgated, and he worked extensively on the igneous and metamorphic rocks of upland Britain, and understood that the conditions under which they formed were very different from those now existing.

With the likes of the Reverend Professor Thomas Bonney the catastrophism-uniformitarian debate had run its course: it was appreciated that both sets of concepts had something to contribute. The ice age was here to stay: the questions now to be addressed emphasised the mechanisms and processes at work. The scriptural geologists were in retreat, and a new understanding between religion and science was sought. This, in 1913 Bonney tried to provide in his *Present Relations between Science and Religion*,[41] a masterly synthesis (for its day) of scientific and theological ideas. This was firmly in the Paleyan mould, seeing order and pattern in physical science and also in the living world, and arguing that 'the reign of law' cannot 'exist apart from a Supreme Intelligence and Power, which we can only designate as a Lawgiver'. Yet he put an evolutionary gloss on the argument seeing the evolutionary development of life throughout geological time – 'this regular and orderly process, the result of a purposeful intention, design, or law' – as something of an analogue for the directionality of the sweep of the Old Testament, culminating in the Revelation. He wrote:

> We must frankly admit that at the present day no geologist of any repute would accept the narrative of the Deluge or that of the episodes of Creation, as actual and literal history.[42]

Yet he saw no conflict between this view and the Theistic position. Towards the end of his book he concluded:

> [R]eligion and science will not and cannot dwell together in unity, until it is frankly recognized that each has a different province. The boundary between these is not always accurately defined. There is a borderland, and the zone is sometimes a wide one, over which each has rights, but when once an aggressive spirit is banned and natural good-will prevails, the difficulties are capable of adjustment.[43]

Conclusion

Although the Mosaic legacy lingered, strenuous efforts were being made to accommodate new ideas; for example, as late as September 1881 the Reverend B. W. Savile was writing from Shillingford Rectory, Exeter, to Charles Darwin:

> Though it seems difficult to reconcile 'Evolution' with the Mosaic record of man being a separate act of creative power, I do not think that it necessarily invokes 'Infidel' principles. – I have learnt by the experience of many years' study how differently sincere men interpret various passages of scripture, and I think we often misunderstand one another from not endeavouring clearly to understand what each one clearly means.[44]

For over two centuries debates had raged over the manner in which the 'evidence of the Mosaic record' could be reconciled with the evidence of field geology, before it ran itself, if one may use the expression, into the ground. It was natural that clergy with their concern for both origins and for eschatology should have been significant protagonists in the debate. As catastrophism vied with gradualism, and the diluvialists disputed with early glacialists, clergy were not, however, exclusively identified with a particular party. Evangelicals tended to be associated with the catastrophic and diluvialist stance, while what would now be identified as 'broad church liberals' tended to embrace uniformitarianism sooner. But it was not quite so straightforward as this; there were waverers, and some, like Buckland, changed sides.

As in the case of other branches of natural history, however, the notion of the network remains important in the understanding of the debates of the eighteenth and nineteenth centuries. The participants in the great disputations were personally well known to one another, corresponded frequently, sometimes conducting discussions at dinners of the Geological Society, meetings of the Royal Society or of the British Association for the Advancement of Science. Some of the clerical figures, particularly of nineteenth-century geology – Buckland, Sedgwick, Bonney – were larger than life characters, their influence extending for many decades. Personal contacts were all important, and in this respect the clergy, already linked by their clerical profession, and often by the bonds of kinship and marriage, had a unique advantage, and played a crucial role in the development of the natural sciences.

Notes

1 Woodward, H. H., *History of Geological Society of London* (London, Geological Society of London, 1907).
2 Allen, D. E., *The Naturalist in Britain: a Social History* (Harmondsworth, Penguin Books, 1978), p. 66.
3 Cumming, J. G., 'On the Geology of the Isle of Man', *Proceedings of the Geological Society*, 2 (1), 1848, pp. 317–347.
4 Gillispie, C.C., *Genesis and Geology* (Cambridge, Mass., Harvard University Press, 1951).
5 Geikie, A., *A Memoir of John Mitchell* (Cambridge University Press, 1918).
6 Mitchell, T., 'Conjectures concerning the cause, and observations upon the phenomena of earthquakes, particularly of that great earthquake of the first of November 1755 which proved to be fatal to the City of Lisbon, and whose effects were felt as far as Africa and more or less throughout almost all Europe', *Philosophical Transactions of the Royal Society*, 1760, pp. 566–634.
7 Allen, D. E., 1978, op. cit., pp. 60, 90.
8 Gillispie, C. C., 1951, op. cit.
9 Buckland, W., *Reliquiae Diluvianae; or, Observations on the Organic Remains Contained in the Caves, Fissures and Diluvial Gravel, and on other Geological Phenomena, Attesting to the Action of a Universal Deluge* (London, John Murray, 1826).
10 Woodward, H. H., 1907, p. 97.
11 Allen, 1978, op. cit., p. 65; Gillispie, C.C., 1951, op. cit., pp. 200–201.
12 Gillispie, C. C., 1951, op. cit.
13 Barlow, N., *The Autobiography of Charles Darwin* (London, Collins, 1958).
14 Allen, 1978, op. cit., p. 65.
15 Fisher. O., *The Physics of the Earth's Crust* (Cambridge University Press, 2nd ed., 1889)
16 Woodward, H. H., 1907, op. cit., p.122.
17 Durham University Calendars; Durham Alumni Records; Armstrong, P.H., 'Three parson-naturalists from Durham' *The Naturalist,* 120, 1995, pp. 65–75.
18 Durham Alumni Records.
19 Galloway, W. B., *The Chain of Ages Traced in its Prominent Links, by Holy Scripture from the Creation of Adam to the Close of the First Century of the Christian Era* (London, Samson Low, c.1880).
20 Galloway, W. B., *Physical Facts and the Scriptural Record* (London, Rivingtons, 1872); *Science and Geology in relation to the Universal Deluge* (London, Samson Low, 1888) and *Testimony of Science to the Deluge* (London, Samson Low, n.d. *c.*1895).
21 Galloway, 1888, op. cit., p. 3.
22 Galloway, 1888, op. cit., p. 41.
23 Livingstone, D., *The Geographical Tradition* (Oxford, Blackwell, 1992) pp. 107–108.
24 Ray, J., *Observations Topographical, Moral and Physiological*, 1673, p. 122.
25 *Observations*, p. 125.
26 Cuvier, G., *Essay on the Theory of the Earth with Mineralogical Notes and an Account of Cuvier's Geological Discoveries,* by Professor Jameson (Edinburgh, Blackwood, 3rd ed., 1817).
27 Buckland, W., 1824, *Reliquiae Diluvianae* ... op. cit., p. 42.
28 Galloway, W. B., n.d., p. 15.

29 Kinns, S., *Moses and Geology; or, the Harmony of the Bible with Science* (London, Cassell, 1892).
30 *Ibid*. p. 1
31 *Ibid*. pp.13–15.
32 Symonds, W. S., 'Notes on geology' in Purchas, W. H. and Ley, A., *Flora of Herefordshire* (Hereford, Jakeman and Carver, 1889).
33 Letter bound with copy of Purchas' *Flora of Herefordshire*, *Ibid*., Durham University Library.
34 Bonney, T. G., *The Building of the Alps* (London, Fisher Unwin, 1912).
35 Bonney, T. G., *Cambridgeshire Geology* (Cambridge, Deighton Bell, 1875) pp. 7–8.
36 Darwin, C. R., *The Structure and Distribution of Coral Reefs* (London, Smith Elder, 1842). The first draft of the 'Coral Atoll Theory' is in manuscript in the Cambridge University Library Darwin Archive, at DAR 41.
37 Letters T. G. Bonney to T. M. Reade, 22 August 1892 and 5 April 1906, Sydney Jones Library, Liverpool.
38 Bonney, T. G., *Ice-work Past and Present* (London, Kegan Paul 1896), pp. 89–90.
39 Letters held in the Sydney Jones Library, Liverpool.
40 Bonney, T. G., 1896, op. cit.
41 Bonney, T., *Present Relations between Science and Religion* (London, Robert Scott, 1913).
42 *Ibid*., Chapter 4, p. 120.
43 *Ibid*., Chapter 7, p. 205.
44 Cambridge University Library Darwin Archive, at DAR 177 S(i).

Chapter Eight

Natural history societies, museums and the conservation movement

Canon Charles Kingsley at Chester: a case study

Charles Kingsley (1810–1875) provides an example of a nineteenth-century parson-naturalist, who illustrates the themes both of polymath diversity and of eccentricity, or at least complexity of personality (see Plate 11). Although brought up in Devon, he was curate at Eversley, on the border between Surrey and Hampshire, in 1844, later becoming rector. He was a youthful enthusiast for natural history, studied with Sedgwick at Cambridge, and was an early advocate of Darwin's views. He was also a social reformer, novelist, poet and controversialist. He developed a sort of hearty Anglicanism for which he coined the term 'muscular Christianity'. Less well known is the fact that the saying 'religion is the opium of the people' was also his invention. He intended the phrase to illustrate the benign effect of religion, but the phrase was later given a quite different twist by Karl Marx. Besides several volumes of sermons, he wrote *The Water Babies*, dashed off for one of his children in 1862, and intended in part as a protest against the use of child labour in sweeping chimneys.

He enjoyed foxhunting, and would abandon work in his study to join the hunt. He kept a register of the foxes in the country around his village arguing that they, as well as the human villagers, were his parishioners.

He had a severe stutter, and probably suffered from depression. He was devoted to his wife Fanny, but their courtship was unorthodox. He expressed his passionate sexual desire for his intended by fantasizing religious humiliations in which they both participated, naked. He sent her explicit drawings of these: in one Charles and his beloved Fanny are making love, lashed to a cross being thrown about by a stormy sea. Always a sensuous individual, at one stage he declared to Fanny that he believed that in the hereafter, they would remain in permanent copulatory bliss. One of the pictures shows them, more-or-less disposed in this way, ascending to heaven. Charles has angel's wings – in fact the wings of a bird, every feather of which is drawn in exquisite detail (he was ever a naturalist). The text over the drawing is 'He is not dead but sleepeth.' After their marriage, it is alleged that Fanny was extremely extravagant, and part of Charles Kingsley's hyperactive lifestyle can be interpreted as attempting to earn sufficient income to support her.[1]

A nadir in his career was when he attempted to confront Cardinal Newman in print: he lost the argument, some theologians of the day stating he was 'cut to pieces and scattered around the theological battlefield'. His venture into academia was not too successful either. He briefly held the position of Professor of History at Cambridge, but some of his lectures were said to be more like 'historical fiction' than what was required, although he did tutor the future King Edward VII. On the other hand, a high point was his appointment to a canonry at Chester Cathedral; he lived in the city for several months a year, and got on well in the community. He founded the local natural history society, as did so many parson-naturalists of his generation.

It has to be admitted that the amount of serious scientific work that Charles Kingsley published was small. He was extremely enthusiastic and knowledgeable, and sometimes showed real flashes of insight. Here is an extract from an address he gave at, of all places, the Royal Artillery Institution at Woolwich, in late 1871. He shows a remarkable appreciation of an integrated, ecological approach to the science of living things:

> As the marvellous interdependence of all natural objects and forces unfolds itself yet more and more, so the once separate sciences, which treated of different classes of natural objects, are forced to interpenetrate (as it were) and supplement themselves by knowledge borrowed from each other. Thus . . . no man can now be a first-rate botanist unless he is also a meteorologist, no mean geologist, and, as Mr Darwin has shown in his extraordinary discoveries about the fertilization of plants – no mean entomologist . . .[2]

He was well-connected, and cooperated with many other naturalists (clerical and otherwise) in sending them information and specimens; for example, while living in Torquay in the 1850s, he regularly sent hampers full of specimens from Devonshire beaches, to the geologist and biologist Philip Gosse (whose book on sea-shore life had led to the denudation of the rock pools along some parts of the British coast). Charles Kingsley himself was another great popularizer of science, like the man who taught him at Helston Grammar School (the Reverend C. A. Johns) and with whom he exchanged letters and specimens until Johns died in 1874. Kingsley himself wrote a book on seashore life (*Glaucus, or the Wonders of the Shore*, 1855) – delightfully written, and full of allusions to how the exquisite living world was a manifestation of the glory of God.

This gives something of a clue to the rationale behind Kingsley's founding of the the Chester Society of Natural Science, Literature and Art. The purpose was moral, as well as scientific. When he first arrived in Chester in May 1870 he was invited to give a series of lectures on botany. He alternated the lecture-hall with the fields, and used his friend C. A. Johns' *Flowers of the Field* as text.[3] The lectures included references to geology and natural history generally and touched on evolution . . . and morality. Women were not allowed at the first series of botanical lectures, lest they distract the 'middle class young men'. The following year he ran a series of lectures on geology, again with associated field excursions, although this time ladies were allowed to join the class. The venture, once again was a great success, and the talks eventually appeared in print as a book called *Town Geology*.[4]

It was thus on 12 June 1871 (Charles Kingsley's fifty-second birthday) that at a meeting in his house in Abbey Square, near the Cathedral, a committee was formed and the Chester Society of Natural Science was brought into being. It had long been an ambition for him to do something along these lines, and he seems to have enjoyed every minute of the association, writing to some of his scientific associates to encourage them to become honorary members, thereby giving the society a certain kudos, and convincing the members that they were part of the scientific community. Lyell, Huxley and Hooker were amongst a number of notables who had pressure put on them in this way. Here is a part of his letter to geologist Sir Charles Lyell, written a few days after the meeting in Abbey Square:

> Chester, June 22, 1871
>
> I have a great favour to ask. Whether you decline or not, I am sure you will not be angry with me for asking. I have just started here a Natural Science Society – the dream of years. And I believe it will 'march.' But I want a few great scientific names as honorary members. That will give my plebs, who are of all ranks and creeds of course, self-respect; the feeling that they are initiated into the great freemasonry of science, and that such men as you acknowledge them as their pupils.
>
> I have put into the hands of my geological class, numbering about sixty, your new 'Students' Elements.' . . . These good fellows,

> knowing your name, and using your book, would have a fresh incentive to work if they but felt you were conscious of their existence.
>
> Let me then beg for your name, to be proposed by me as an honorary member. I ask nothing more; but to give that would be not only to help them, but to help me, who already feel the drag of the collar (having to do all myself as far as teaching and inspiring go) very heavy . . .
>
> Your most faithful and loyal pupil, C. Kingsley.[5]

The field trips seem to have been particularly memorable, and very well organised. One participant recalled:

> . . . the bright sunshine and sweet fresh air of the hill top; and the Canon stretching out his chest and breathing it in, and bidding us do likewise, and thank God for it all, and get rid of some of the stuffiness of . . . Chester. . . Then tea at the village school, and the Canon's delightful review of all we had seen; the comparing of the finds, fossil and fresh . . . all this to an audience of beginners, to whom all was new and wonderful. . . . The gates of a new and beautiful world were opened to us on this and other days, and we were invited to enter freely into it, and rejoice and be thankful.[6]

Hundreds of people attended some of these events: Fanny described the Canon's enthusiasm at being at their head, geological hammer and botanical specimen bag in hand. Here we can see a good deal of what Kingsley and other clergymen of his generation were about when they founded natural history societies and field clubs. Fresh air, the outdoor world, vigorous activity, the education of the general populace, a delight in 'God's world' – natural theology. Here too was a version of muscular Christianity. It is no coincidence that the early development of the Chester Society of Natural Science, Literature and Art coincided with another of Kingsley's social campaigns: his attack, in speech, sermon and pamphlet, on betting and gambling. Although he enjoyed riding and indeed watching fine horses, he utterly deplored any sort of gambling. Outdoor activities such as field botany and geology were much to be preferred: they uplifted the community. Another innovation was the annual Conversazione. The first was held in July 1872, when some two hundred society members and friends were attracted to an exhibition of shells, insects and fossils, and etchings and drawings of natural history, along with a demonstration of microscopy. The event is credited with having 'rejuvenated the intellectual climate of the entire city'.[7] The Chester Conversazione became a regular event, and the concept was adopted by other natural history societies. The tradition proved a lasting one, and I can recall my own interest in natural history being encouraged by such events held by the Cambridge Natural History Society in the 1940s and 1950s.

Canon Kingsley's third and last conversazione in Chester was in July 1873, for in that year he took up a canonry at Westminster. In his final speech he made a plea for the society to get the young people of the city 'to worship nature that they might worship God.' A few days before he had led his last field excursion with the Chester Society, to Shropshire. Such was the network of personal links, that members of the Caradoc Field Club were at the station at Church Stretton to greet two hundred members from Chester. A natural history ramble of 'eight or nine miles up the glorious Longmynd and Lightspout Valley' followed.[8]

Societies

The role of Canon Kingsley in the Chester Society was entirely typical. Many examples could be found, from all parts of the country, of nineteenth-century clergy who were the prime movers in the formation of a natural history society or field club, who nurtured the organisation through its early years, held offices, gave lectures, and provided exhibits for conversaziones. The Southport [Lancashire] Society of Natural Science, for example, had its first meeting on 23 October 1890. Amongst those 'few gentlemen' associated with its formation were: the Reverend J. Williams, MA, the Reverend C. T. Porter, DD, LLD, and the Reverend T. T. Smith. The last of these, the records show, gave a talk to the society entitled: 'Apples and pears: their origin, history and uses', a few months later. It should be remembered the the title of the organisation was the Society of Natural Science, and astronomy, anthropology and chemistry came within its purview, as well as geology and natural history *per se*. The fairly liberal interpretation of the club's responsibilities is further emphasised when it is noted that at a conversazione held on 13 January 1898, the Reverend Thomas Wakefield, FRGS, presented an exhibit of 'Curios from Africa'. The Reverend J. C. Draville, joined the council of the society for 1893–1894, and there were three clergy (i.e. those who used the style Reverend, not necessarily all Church of England) amongst the 85 members during the first few years of the society's existence.[9] The proportion was four out of 125 members in 1898–1899. In 1905–1906, the Reverend Robert Killip, a methodist minister appears on the scene, he was amongst his other interests, an amateur astronomer. So too was the Reverend A. L. Cortie, SJ, FRAS, of Stonyhurst College, who gave a talk on 'New stars' on 12 December 1901. He later became an honorary member, and maintained a link with the society for over 20 years.

Across the country, and a few years previously, the Goole Scientific Society, Yorkshire, had been formed, in 1875. Among the first four recorders of the society were, quite typically, a schoolmaster, a medical doctor (in fact the medical officer of health for Goole, Dr H. F. Parsons) and the Reverend R. D. Maxwell, the recorder for conchology (shells). Mr Maxwell was Goole's Congregational minister from about 1868 to 1879.[10]

In fact, the local natural history society might be one of the few venues where clergy of different denominations might meet on common ground. Church of England clergy predominated, but some free-churchmen made an important contribution. Catholic clergy, in the nineteenth century, were much rarer, but definitely were represented. Although they might differ passionately on theological matters, and indeed on quasi-political matters such as the establishment of the Church of England, or the role of denominational schools, clergy of different denominations sometimes co-operated 'for science' at the local level. Here is D. E. Allen's account of the situation in Northampton:

> Northampton in the [eighteen] seventies, like many other towns at this period was a warren of separate social groups and sub-groups each riven in turn by political and religious differences held with an intensity that is today barely comprehensible. The last, in particular, were such a powerful divisive force that when the idea of forming a local natural history society was broached, it was recognized that it stood no chance of attracting a truly representative membership unless the backing of the local churches could be secured. This problem . . . [the founder] overcame by deliberately recruiting . . . the clerical headmaster of the Grammar School, a Baptist and two Congregational ministers and a Roman Catholic priest. At a special preliminary meeting it was . . . formally laid down in the Rules that the Society should be conducted on a strictly non-sectarian basis.[11]

It was a success. But this cooperation was not always the rule. The Reverend Henry Hugh Higgins (1814–1893), MA (Cambridge), an all-round naturalist, but especially interested in fungi, was a founder of the Liverpool Naturalists' Field Club in 1860, becoming its second president, holding that position from 1862 until his death 31 years later. He is said to have 'dominated' the society and to have been arrogant and difficult, being intolerant of those who were not members of the established church. One commentator said 'because he was Church of

England, he felt he had the right to the chairmanship of everything'. He certainly was influential in a number of organisations, as well as the Naturalist's Field Club, including, the Liverpool Literary and Philosophical Society, the Liverpool Microscopical Society, and the Lancashire and Cheshire Entomological Society, It was said that entomologists would not join the Liverpool Naturalists because of his arrogant attitude!

He was, however, also a great enthusiast, even if it might be felt that his zeal was occasionally misdirected. The Field Club, under Higgins' leadership, had over 700 members, in 1867, and on one excursion to the Great Orme, in North Wales, there were 350 participants. Sometimes a steamer was chartered for these excursions. Anxiety was expressed, however, at these armies invading the countryside, particularly as prizes were given for the greatest number of plants collected. In 1890 prizes were offered for the greatest number collected, the greatest number named, a ladies prize for the best bouquet (imagine how that would go down on a scientific field trip today), and the solution of a 'botanical enigma'. This last was a description of a species likely to be found on the excursion: it had to be identified from the account. All of which makes the modern conservation-minded biologist squirm. He is said to have been a friend of Charles Kingsley, and maybe he got some of his ideas for field excursions from him, but he also trained with Sedgwick, so perhaps we can trace influence there.[12]

The theme was a common one: all over the country clergy were taking a leading role in the formation of natural history societies. On 18 February 1855, Leonard Blomefield (formerly Jenyns) founded the Bath Field Club. Interestingly he was a relative of the Reverend W. S. Symonds who founded the Malvern Field Club: the links of family and marriage were always important in the spread of ideas. The movement started in the middle years of the nineteenth century, expanding rapidly; by 1873 there were at least 169 local scientific societies in Great Britain and Ireland (104 were described as 'field clubs'), with a total membership of over 50,000.[13]

Data from the membership lists of the Lincolnshire Naturalists illustrate the continuing importance of the clergy (again defined as anyone who styled themselves as Reverend, not just Church of England clergy, although these predominated) into the early twentieth century. In 1909 membership was 97, of whom 20 were in holy orders (20 per cent); by 1913 the figure was 18 out of 92 (19.6 per cent). By 1927 membership was up to 114, of whom 19 were clergy of some sort (16.66 percent). These trends continued: membership was up to 147 by 1931, with 15 'Reverends' (10.2 per cent), In 1936 it was 12 out of 201 (6 per cent), and by 1940 the figures were 7 out of 209 (3.3 per cent). As membership climbed, clergy membership, and probably influence, declined. If this is typical, and it may well have been, clergy went from having a dominating, highly influential position in natural history societies in the latter part of the nineteenth century and the early decades of the twentieth, to constituting a small minority of members by the Second World War.[14]

Museums

It is appropriate that there is a Charles Kingsley Room in the Grosvenor Museum in Chester, a display devoted to natural history, and the history of its study, for the founding and support of museums was another important activity of the nineteenth-century clergy such as Charles Kingsley. Again we may take the Reverend Hugh Higgins as an exemplar. His original appointment to Liverpool, in 1843, was as Inspector of Church of England Schools in the Diocese. He also held a succession of curacies, and subsequently was chaplain of Rainhill Asylum, and he would have seen his work in museums as an extension of his educational mission. He is first noted as being interested in Liverpool's museums in 1859, when the Committee's report thanks him for procuring and identifying specimens. He was co-opted onto the Committee in 1860, and was Chairman from 1877 until his death (see page 144, above). He assisted in the arranging of some of the collections (especially the invertebrates) and wrote a descriptive catalogue. He was determined to make the Museum appeal to the 'man in the street'. He wrote a popular guide with the title *Museum Talk about Animals which have No Bones*. He was active in the Museums Association, serving as the first President, and constantly attempted to make exhibits interesting and innovative. He convinced captains of ships plying from Liverpool to bring back specimens, and in 1876 actually mounted an expedition to the Atlantic Islands, the Caribbean and South America to collect material. He also secured fossil specimens when railway cuttings were made in 1870 on the Liverpool to St Helens line.[15]

John Henslow was another parson-naturalist who was convinced of the educational value of museums. While a young lad he assisted one of his schoolmasters with the arrangement of some of the exhibits at the British Museum. Later he assisted Adam Sedgwick with geological exhibits in the Woodwardian Museum in Cambridge, he developed a zoology museum, and was active in a campaign to upgrade the Botanic Gardens as part of a move to strengthen the teaching of science in the University. Yet another set of exhibits with which he was associated was that of Kew. In an obituary of him in 1861, his kinsman and clerical and scientific colleague Leonard Jenyns wrote as follows:

> It was Henslow's patient devotion to zoology which enabled him to form an excellent Museum, long the only zoological Museum in the University, and the legitimate parent of that larger family of museums which have grown up and are still growing up in the Botanic Garden.[16]

When he moved to the parish of Hitcham in Suffolk, Henslow became involved with the Ipswich Museum, with which he had a long association: he became the museum's chairman in 1850. Incidentally his predecessor as chairman was another Suffolk parson-botanist-entomologist, William Kirby.

Henslow was always committed to the ideal that the prime purpose of a museum should be educational, Museums should be a focus of learning, rather than simple amusement or distraction. He felt that many provincial museums were not well run, lacking a clear focus and sometimes little more than curiosity shops. He attempted to put these principles into practice in Ipswich, and also in the temporary marquee museums that he set up as part of the village shows each summer in his parish of Hitcham. Dozens of exhibits would be arranged, and he would circulate through them giving a mini-lecture of a few minutes each: long experience of teaching, both to undergraduates and in the village school, had taught him that many in his audience had a limited span of attention.[17] The fame of those summer temporary museums obviously spread; Henslow being well-connected in the way he was, donations were received from many notables, including Sir William Hooker, of Kew, and Charles Darwin, Henslow's former student. Charles wrote from his home in Upper Gower Street, London, offering trophies that he had collected in South America on the *Beagle* voyage:

> September 16 [1842]
>
> My dear Henslow.
> I bequest your Museum a Parcel of Paints with which the Fuegian [ie the natives of Tierra del Fuego] colour their bodies. Two spears with which they spear Porpoises, Fish, Otters and Guaraco etc. – and a Pacific Dolphin Hook Ever yours, C. Darwin[18]

Conservation

The saying 'Cleanliness is next to Godliness' is an oft-quoted one, and in the case of the career of Canon Charles Kingsley, it has some meaning. Amongst his many campaigns was one for sanitary reform, within which he included making available clean air, clean water, efficient drainage and improved housing for all. At the time, hundreds of thousands of people living in slums in the cities, where sewerage systems were, to say the least, basic. He advocated giving instruction in basic human physiology and the science of health. The serious illness of the Prince of Wales attracted attention to his message: two hundred thousand people in the kingdom had died of 'preventable fever' since the death of Prince Albert, he declaimed in 1872. Purity has frequently been seen as a pious Christian attribute, and he spoke on the 'moral influence' of pure water. Shortly after leaving Chester he wrote a popular article 'Pure water; or a substitute for Latin verbs'.[19] He also seconded a motion at a meeting calling for the establishment of a society with the aim of preventing the pollution of the River Dee which ran through Chester: Kingsley enjoyed salmon fishing, so perhaps this was not entirely altruistic. Nevertheless it was this sort of activity that eventually led to Parliament passing the Rivers (Prevention of Pollution) Act, 1876, and Parliament's concern for the environment and the development of environmental law generally.

The 'conversion' of some of the great sportsmen and bird-slaughterers of the late nineteenth and early twentieth century, such as Tristram and Jourdain, has already been mentioned. It seems odd in a way that clergy should take so long to become actively associated with the conservation movement. *The Natural History of Selborne,* 1789, inspired a whole generation of parsons: to so many an understanding of nature was a path towards the understanding of the works of God. It would seem a simple step from delighting in nature to wanting to protect and conserve it. However, is was not until the 1860s that the Reverend F. Orpen Morris campaigned to protect seabirds – his letters to *The Times*, his lobbying of Parliament – began to have any real effect. He noted that not far from his parish, the colonies of seabirds along the cliffs of Scarborough and Bridlington were ruthlessly destroyed by parties of shooting 'gentlemen' who hired boats to take them to the bases of the cliff. The same thing was happening to colonies in other parts of the British Isles, such as the Bass Rock, the Isle of May, Pembrokeshire and the Scottish islands. An association was formed in 1869 and a Seabirds Act passed by Parliament. This was not entirely successful, and made way for the Wild Birds Protection Act of 1880, which endured until the 1950s. He was also partly instrumental in the formation of the Society for the Protection of Birds. The RSPB, as it became after being granted its royal charter in 1904, has its immediate origins in the so-called 'Fur and Feather Group', a group of influential women who were appalled by the destruction of birds for the plume trade, in particular the use of feathers and indeed whole birds in millinery. (Thus the primary motivation was was sentimental, rather than scientific.) It was well on into the twentieth century that the organisation became more scientific in its direction, emphasising the protection of habitats as well as the birds themselves. Clergymen were from time to time important in the running of that society, one of the most notable being the Reverend Peter H. T. Hartley (1909–1985) (page 79).

The passing of statutes to protect fauna, birds first, and later other organisms such as insects and other invertebrates, reptiles and amphibians (first in the Conservation of Wild Creatures and Wild Plants Act, 1975, now incorporated in the Wildlife and Countryside Act of 1981) is only part of the story. Rare and interesting plants and animals, however carefully protected by law, will not survive if they have nowhere to live. The conservation of habitats, of ecosystems, of entire landscapes is just as important. This approach also dates from the late nineteenth century, and again we find that clergy were actively involved. The early motivation was aesthetic.

Canon Rawnsley and the foundation of the National Trust

Canon Hardwick Drummond Rawnsley (1851–1920) was a leading figure in the late nineteenth- and early twentieth-century conservation movement. His background was conventional and familiar. He was the son of a parson – the fourth of ten children of the Reverend Robert Drummond Burrell Rawnsley, Rector of Shiplake. A scholarship to Uppingham School was followed by Balliol College, Oxford. Atypically he took a degree in natural sciences, but John Ruskin was amongst his circle of acquaintances. Perhaps he spent too much time in athletics and rowing, for he did well in these at both school and at Oxford, but achieved only a third class degree. He was ordained deacon in 1875, and became chaplain of the Clifton College Mission. It is claimed that his success in winning the confidence of Bristol's poorest people was a factor in getting him dismissed. Perhaps this contributed to his campaigning spirit.

He was priested in 1877, and went to Wray in Windermere; thereafter he was a vigorous defender of the Lake District and its landscapes, being active in the founding of the Lake District Defence Society. He spearheaded a campaigning against the building of railways through the Vale of Newland (Derwent Water) and Ennerdale. Another early campaign was against Manchester Corporation's plan to build a dam, to increase the size of Thirlmere to provide water for the city of Manchester. He was appointed Rector of Crosthwaite in 1883, and became Rural Dean of Keswick. His wife was artistically talented, and with her he founded Keswick High School, notable in its day for being co-educational, and emphasising music and dance. He was elected to Cumberland County Council in 1888, continuing his campaign for the preservation of the Lake District, but his opposition to liquor made him enemies amongst certain vested interests, and he was not re-elected in 1895. He was appointed an honorary canon of Carlisle Cathedral, but later declined the Bishopric of Madagascar. Canon Rawnsley wrote some 40 books, and dozens of articles about the Lake District.

He was described as 'impulsive, eloquent, irascible and mercurial, with a stocky figure and a bristling beard. He was at once gentle, compassionate and amusing, as at home with a fell shepherd as with royalty' – he was appointed chaplain to King George V in 1912. He was very much a 'whole environment' man, seeing the Lake District (and of course other places, but the Lake country remained his real love) in terms of the landscape, the plants, animals and the people that made the environment function. In a similar, integrational way he believed in the importance of the welfare of the whole person – body, mind and spirit – a legacy of his youthful sporting days, and a view that he carried into his educational work.

On 16 November 1893, Canon Rawnsley, Sir Robert Hunter (a solicitor) and Octavia Hill, two people whom he had met in the 1880s in campaigning for open access to upland country in the Lake District, met at the offices of the Commons Preservation Society. They discussed what became a few months later the National Trust, for the conservation of 'places of historic interest and natural beauty'. The Trust was registered on 12 January 1895, and given its own act of parliament, the National Trust Act, in 1907. Rawnsley later worked extensively on behalf of the Trust with Beatrix Potter, the authoress of children's books: it has been asserted that he may have had something of a crush on her. The National Trust ultimately became one of the most influential and important conservation organisations in Britain, being major landowners, and by the late 1990s having well over 2 million members.[20]

The conservation and management of churchyards

The study of the ecology of churchyards themselves has its devotees, although the Mr Addington mentioned in chapter 3 (page 60) is one of a relatively small number of clergy who have specialized in the study of this specialized but interesting ecosystem. Many clergy have appreciated the natural beauty and interest of churchyards in a rather less scientific way. One was the clergyman diarist, the Reverend Francis Kilvert (1840–1879), who in some ways stands in the nineteenth century in a similar position to Gilbert White in the eighteenth, in his lively, charming and perceptive analysis of rural life. His background was entirely typical. He was the son of the Reverend Robert Kilvert, Rector of Hardenhuish, and later of the nearby parish of Langley Burrell, in Wiltshire. One of Francis' sisters married a clergyman, another became a Clewer sister. There were a host of other clergy in the extended family and network of acquaintances. He studied at Oxford, was ordained, and for a while acted as curate to his father. Then for seven years (1865–1872) he was curate in Clyro, Radnorshire, before another spell as curate to his father. In 1878 he was presented to the living of St Harmon, north Radnorshire, moving a year later to Bredwardine, Herefordshire. He used to walk long distances around his parishes, documenting the life, times and countryside in his diaries in perceptive detail. He seems to have had an extreme, but doubtless entirely innocent, susceptibility to the beauty of young women and girls, and some quite sensual descriptions are found in his diary. In August 1879 he married Elizabeth Anne Rowland (1848–1911), but he died a month later. His wife found the notebooks in which his diaries were written, and perhaps because of the descriptions of female beauty within them, perhaps because of an account of their own courtship, burnt most of them.

Francis Kilvert was very much an amateur naturalist, but certainly seems to have appreciated the tranquility, beauty and interest of churchyards. Here he is in the churchyard of Langley Burrell on 'the first fine Sunday in May . . . the trees at their most exquisite and perfect loveliness'

> Sunday, 7 May [1871]
> I went into the churchyard under the feathering larch which sweeps over the gate. The ivy-grown old church with its noble tower stood beautiful and silent amongst the elms with its graves at its feet. No one was about or moving and the only sound was the singing of the birds. The place was all in a charm of singing, full of peace and quiet sunshine. It seemed to be given up to the birds and their morning hymns. It was the bird church, the church among the birds. I wandered round the church among the dewy grass graves and picturesque ivy- and moss-hung tombstones. Round one grave grew a bed of primroses. Upon another tall cowslips hung their heads.[21]

Churchyards frequently contain relict ecosystems, with fragments of grassland, shrub and even woodland surviving in the sanctuaries they provide where these communities have been largely destroyed in the impoverished arable landscapes or suburbs that surround them. Churchyard conservation and management is now a significant issue, involving vigorous debates (e.g. conservation versus management: should that patch of nettles, *Urtica dioica*, be allowed to remain as a habitat for tortoiseshell caterpillars, or be 'tidied up'?). Clergy, through their parochial church councils, contribute to these discussions, and it is entirely appropriate that they write about the issues involved. The Reverend Canon Henry Stapleton, edited *The Churchyard Handbook* describing the management of the churchyard environment.[22] Although it represents something of a digression from the theme of this book, I cannot forbear from including a mention of Francesca Greenoak's charmingly written and illustrated *God's Acre* on the natural history, ecology and conservation of of churchyards.[23]

The preceding chapters have concentrated almost entirely on the English clergy, although we have occasionally glanced over our shoulders towards their brethren in other parts of the British Isles. The English clergy, however, have been great travellers, and the contribution they made to more distant lands will be discussed next.

Notes

1 Remarkable details of the Kingsley's courtship and intimate life have been revealed in Chitty, S., *The Beast and the Monk: a Life of Charles Kingsley* (London, Hodder and Stoughton, 1974). Also relevant is: Thorpe, M. T, *Charles Kingsley, 1819–1875* (Princeton University Press, 1937, reprinted in 1967 by Octagon Books, New York).

2 Kingsley, F., *Charles Kingsley: his Letters and Memories of his Life, edited by his wife,* vol 2. (London, Henry S. King, 1877), p. 371. Charles Darwin's *The Fertilisation of Orchids* was published in 1862.

3 See chapter 2

4 Kingsley, C., *Town Geology* (London, Strahan, 1872).

5 Letter, Charles Kingsley to Sir Charles Lyell, quoted in F. Kingsley, 1877, op. cit., pp. 231–251.

6 Siddall, J., *The Formation of the Chester Society of Literature, and Art ...* (Chester, privately printed, 1911).

7 Colloms, B., *Charles Kingsley: the Lion of Eversley* (London, Constable, 1975), pp. 326–327.

8 Colloms, 1973, op. cit., p. 339.

9 Records at Southport Library, Merseyside.

10 Lambert, M., 'First recorders of the Goole Scientific Society', *Naturalist,* 114, 1989, pp. 93–97.

11 Allen, D. E., *The Naturalist in Britain: a Social History* (Harmondsworth, Penguin Books, 1978), p. 166.

12 Dallman, A. A. and Wood, M. H., 1909, 'A biographical list of deceased Lancashire botanists', *Transactions of the Liverpool Botanical Society*, pp. 4–59;

Ford, W. K., 1952, 'The Rev. Henry Hugh Higgins, M.A.: a Liverpool biologist', *Liverpool Libraries, Museums and Arts Committee Bulletin,* 1(2), pp. 67–79; Eric Hardy, Liverpool, personal communication.

13 Blomefield, L. (formerly Jenyns), *Chapters in My Life* (Bath, privately printed, 1888), p. 105; Allen, D. E., 1978, op. cit., pp. 162, 170.

14 I thank Mark Seaward, University of Bradford, for assisting with these figures.

15 Ford, W. K., 1952, op. cit.

16 Jenyns, L., *Memoir of the Reverend John Stevens Henslow,* Cambridge Philosophical Society, 1862, p. 207.

17 Russell-Gebbett, J., *Henslow of Hitcham* (Lavenham, Terence Dalton, 1977), pp. 99–100.

18 Cambridge University Library Darwin Archive, DAR 93.7. Published in Burkhardt, F. and Smith, S., *The Correspondence of Charles Darwin*, vol. 2 (Cambridge University Press, 1986), p. 333.

19 Kingsley, C., 'Pure water; or a substitute for Latin verbs', *Health and Education, Good Words*, March 1874.

20 Nicholls, C.S., ed., *Dictionary of National Biography: Missing Persons* (Oxford University Press, 1993); Evans, D., *The History of Nature Conservation in Britain*, 2nd ed., (London, Routledge, 1997), pp. 41–45.

21 Plomer, W., *Kilvert's Diary, 1870–1879* (Harmondsworth, Penguin Books, 1977). The description of the churchyard is on p.128. The biographical details are from the Introduction, pp. 5–6.

22 Stapleton, H., ed., *The Churchyard Handbook* (London, Church Information Office Publishing, 1976).

23 Greenoak, F. *God's Acre*, (Orbis, London, 1985). Churchyard ecology, natural history and management now has quite an extensive literature; for example Baker, G. M. A., *Wildlife Conservation in the Care of Churches and churchyards* (London, Church Information Office, 1972) (foreword by the Bishop of Leicester). Maycock, R., 'Oxfordshire churchyard survey', *British Ecological Society Bulletin,* 22(2), 1991, pp. 123–125. Other publications are produced by the Rural Theology Association and the Society for the Promotion of Nature Reserves. Specialist publications have appeared on the ecology, management and conservation of yew-trees, bats, lichens and ferns in churches and churchyards.

Chapter Nine

To the uttermost parts of the earth

Go ye into all the world, and preach the gospel to every creature
(Mark 16, 15)

Since the days of the Apostles there have been those who have responded to this exhortation, and seen it as their duty to go to 'the uttermost parts of the earth' (Psalm 2, 8) to spread the Christian Faith. Not a few English clergy who went as missionaries to the Colonies, for it was generally (but by no means always) to parts of the the British Empire that they went, were naturalists. From time to time, then, collecting gear was packed with the stole and communion set, and natural history reference books crated along with theological texts.

Spreading the Word has, indeed, very often been a part of the colonization process. Some colonization ventures were at least partly theologically inspired; the Pilgrim Fathers who arrived in America in 1620 (although the title is comparatively modern) provide one example. Christchurch, New Zealand was founded by a group of Anglicans in 1850. Even when things were quite otherwise, it was often official policy to include clergy amongst the colonizing group, the hope being expressed that their presence might exert a beneficial moral influence. The Reverend Richard Johnson was sent with the first group of convicts and soldiers to New South Wales, in January 1788.

An important group of expatriate parson-naturalists in the eighteenth century were those attached to the forces as chaplains. Gilbert White's brother John (1727–1780), for example, was Chaplain of the Garrison at Gibraltar from 1756 to 1771. It has to be said that, as was not unusual, John was dispatched into exile because he had been a source of worry and irritation to his family. He had been expelled from Corpus Christi College, Oxford (albeit after taking his degree, apparently for entertaining women in his college rooms in an inappropriate manner), and a few years later had got rather disastrously into debt. Gilbert encouraged him to take an interest in natural history, perhaps partly because he thought it would be beneficial to him. As was typical of colonial parsons, he proved a useful source of information for his more distinguished naturalist brother Gilbert. In response to queries from his brother on birds, insects and local customs, John sent a good deal of information back to Gilbert. He also sent specimens: in those days, when preservation methods were not very efficient, they must have been in a fairly unsavoury state on arrival. A dead vulture ran into problems with the quarantine authorities. John wrote a book on the natural history of Gibraltar *Fauna Calpensis*, but it was not published until more than a century after his death. An idea that Gilbert and John collaborate in the publication of a book of letters came to nothing either, but it did encourage Gilbert in his own literary ventures, and led to *The Natural History of Selborne*, eventually published in 1789.[1]

By the nineteenth century, the trickle of English clergy going overseas had become a flood. Hundreds of clergy, many of them employed by missionary societies,[2] set out for Africa, the Caribbean, South America, the Far East, Australia and the Pacific. They sent back specimens to Kew and the British Museum (Natural History), they opened up the taxonomy of unfamiliar tropical groups of plants and animals. They travelled and explored, for often their beat included many widely scattered small churches that they visited intermittently. As the century wore on, sometimes they had wives who were teachers, and in the twentieth century occasionally, doctors, and the ministry would thus be a cooperative one. A very few combined the roles of doctor and priest: one such seems to have been the Reverend William Cooper Thomson (dates uncertain, died before 1880) who was a missionary in Calobar, 1849–1865. When he returned to England, he practised medicine in Liverpool for a few years. He wrote a paper on the ferns of Calobar.[3] Missionary families existed; sometimes several generations of the children of missionaries returned to the mission field. This was so much the case, that the British Nationality Act, 1981, contained provisions that allowed persons born outside the UK while their parents were employed by missionary associations, to acquire British nationality, even when the the parents themselves were born outside Britain.

As local clergy were trained, however, and as countries obtained their independence and the governments that replaced colonial rule were in some cases unsympathetic to Christian missionaries, numbers declined.

Away from the intellectual stimulation and support of colleagues, sometimes working in remote areas for up to ten years at a time, these were exceptional men indeed. They had to be self-reliant, capable of tackling any task, and sometimes extremely physically courageous.

Norman Cruttwell: taxonomist of tropical orchids

Canon Norman E. G. Cruttwell (1916–1995) is in some ways typical of the missionary-naturalist genre and will serve as an exemplar. He came from a clerical family, and was born in Minehead, but while he was still a child (in 1924) the family moved to the parish of Christchurch, Radlett, in St Albans Diocese. Academically extremely able, he won a scholarship to Lancing College, and then took First Class Honours at Oxford. Relatively unusually for a parson-naturalist, his degree was in a biological science – botany. He was offered a research fellowship, but declined, having decided to go to Cuddeston Theological College (a college with a relatively 'high' or Catholic theology). He was ordained deacon towards the end of 1940, in the Winchester Diocese, working first in Basingstoke.

In 1945, Father John Bodger visited England, preaching on the desperate need for priests to come to New Guinea to replace those killed by the Japanese. Norman Cruttwell met him, and offered himself for five years – five years that extended into most of a lifetime. He sailed for New Guinea in 1946. He was sent to Menapi 60 miles (about 100 km) along the coast from Dogura, not far from the southern tip of the mainland of New Guinea. He remained there as priest-in-charge until 1966. In 1948 he commenced long patrols into the Daga Mountains, taking Bishop David Hand with him in 1952 to choose suitable sites for new mission stations: these were eventually established at Biman, Agaun and Agupon. In 1966 he moved to Agaun, which by then had an airstrip. Norman never married, but for part of his ministry in New Guinea his mother assisted him, and in 1956 his sister Rosemary came to Dogura: her husband was mission doctor there for ten years. In 1976 he handed over his position to a local priest, and from then until 1982 he was rector of St Francis' parish (how appropriate) in Goroka. As well as being a keen naturalist, he was something of a linguist, and worked on the Wedau bible. Anecdotes about him abound. He was once mildly rebuked in Synod by Sir Philip Strong, Archbishop of New Guinea. Norman was almost as enthusiastic about the brilliant tropical butterflies of Papua New Guinea as he was about orchids, and on one occasion was waxing lyrical about some remote region into which he had trekked, giving excited descriptions of what he had seen. Sir Philip eventually interrupted him with 'But Norman, did you see any *people*?'

While on patrol, visiting the mission churches in remote areas, Norman Cruttwell collected and pressed plant specimens: his special interest was orchids and rhododendrons, sending them both to the New Guinea National Herbarium at Lae, and to that at Kew. Because of his experience, after his retirement in 1982, he was engaged as curator of the Lipizauga Botanical Sanctuary in the Gahavisuka Provincial Park conservation project. He managed its development, and the training of local people until ill-health compelled him to retire to England, aged well over seventy, in 1991. He continued to work on the taxonomy of Papua New Guinea's orchids until shortly before his death. He saw the beauty of the orchids and other flowering plants of the tropics as a joyous part of God's creation, and perceived his task as attempting to understand their diversity. He had high standards in his scientific work, as in his personal life, and looked for similar standards in others, appearing grieved when he did not always find them. He was something of an individualist.[4]

W. B. Clarke: father of Australian geology

The saintly Norman Cruttwell stands in marked contrast to another colonial clergyman of over a century earlier, although there are a few points of comparison: as we have seen parson-naturalists tend to have certain similarities in their background. William Bramwhite Clarke (1798–1878) was much more a 'man of the world', and at times positively courted controversy. He was born at East Bergholt in Suffolk, where his clergyman father was headmaster, and where he received his early education, He proceeded to Jesus College, Cambridge in 1817, taking a BA in 1821, and MA in 1824. He was profoundly influenced, as were so many parson-naturalists of his generation, by the Reverend Professor Adam Sedgwick, and learnt his geology, and his enthusiasm for fieldwork, from him (chapter 7). He was ordained priest in 1823. After some years in English parishes (and what has been described as 'a tumultuous affair of the heart' in 1830–1831) he emigrated with his young family to Sydney in 1839, at least partly because he felt that his prospects and income, and those of his family, would be better.

Clarke was forty-one when he arrived in New South Wales. He was already well-published in the fields of geology and natural history. He had, for example, published substantial papers on meteorology and the geology of Dorset in the *Magazine of Natural History*.[5] He was something of an authority of the crag deposits of East Anglia. A special enthusiasm was that geology, along with other branches of science should be applied to practical problems, and should be seen to be useful. An early concern, after his arrival in New South Wales, therefore, was with the coal deposits along the coast, at Newcastle, northward of Sydney. In 1850–1851 he undertook geological surveys of the Australian goldfields. With the exception of Charles Darwin (whose training in geology had been limited to couple of weeks in North Wales with Sedgwick in the summer of 1831 (see pages 120–121), and who paid very brief visits to New South Wales, Tasmania and the south-west of Western Australia in 1836), the Reverend William Clarke was the first university-trained geologist in Australia, and thus indeed has claims to be the Father of Australian Geology.

An early, fortuitous meeting, just a few months after Clarke arrived in Sydney, was with the brilliant American geologist, James Dwight Dana, who was a scientist attached to the United States Exploring Expedition, which anchored in Sydney Harbour at the very end of 1839. Clarke and Dana travelled quite extensively together in New South Wales, and included a visit to the valleys of the Blue Mountains. They were important influences on each other, and maintained a lifelong correspondence.[7] Dana's description of Clarke in a letter to a colleague is of particular interest:

> . . . He is a strange man for a clergyman. Geology certainly comes first with him; next theology . . . He is very enthusiastic in his geological pursuits and intends to give the geological world an account of the rocks of New South Wales . . . I find he has been a very voluminous writer, having edited a religious magazine, besides attending to his theological duties, his geological observation, and all his various speculations on various subjects which have tired many a reader of London.[8]

There was perhaps something of a theological imperative behind some of Clarke's work. He firmly believed in the role of science to improve the lot of his fellow men. Hence his emphasis on 'applied' geology; and, for example, an early, and passionately argued piece on the importance of the conservation of Australia's forests, 'Effects of forest vegetation on climate', a paper read to the Royal Society of New South Wales on 1 November 1876.[9]

William Clarke, however, was an enigmatic and complex man. One biographer described him perceptively in these terms:

> Publicly he enjoyed the image of a kindly Anglican parson, well liked by his parishioners, and was generally perceived to be a scientist of note . . . Privately he was constantly torn between duty to church and family, and an overwhelming desire to promote and expand the frontiers of colonial science. However he was also human – his health was fragile; he was passionate, easily provoked . . . he liked a nip or two of wine.[10]

He was an energetic and scientifically very productive man: he was the first person to identify Silurian fossils in Australia. He was eventually, partly through the lobbying by English scientific colleagues with who he remained in close contact, rewarded with an FRS. Yet, despite his successes, as the analysis above implies, he seems to have been, at times a difficult man, and one who carried the problems with which he was presented on life's journey rather heavily. A scandal in the 1840s, during a short spell of schoolmastering, about the misappropriation of school funds took a long time to shake off. He was always chronically short of money: amongst other things this meant he sometimes had difficulties in publishing his researches. His wife Maria was extremely homesick, and four years after arrival in the colony, returned to England with their children to give them the education that, it was felt, could not be provided in New South Wales. They did not return to Australia for fifteen years. Deprived of their companionship and support, Clarke nevertheless had to support them in England. The separation might have been even longer, but for the fact that in 1856 he had a mild stroke, and his parishioners provided funds for their return to Australia.

Throughout his time in New South Wales, he acted as a passionate advocate and publicist for science in the colony. He was sometimes a tad outspoken. Perhaps influenced by his days with Dana, and other members of the Exploring Expedition, he compared the intellectual development of Australia unfavourably with that of America. In 1847 he published an (unsigned) article in the *Sydney Morning Herald* with the title 'The Intellectual Barrenness of New South Wales'. In reviewing a book on the geology of gold on one occasion he described it as 'an immense collection of apocryphal and half-invented statements', and its author 'a pretender and a rogue'. Here is another sarcastic gem:

> So far as the growth of wool, or the production of tallow, or the increase of illicit spirits may go – so far as the consumption of tobacco and brandy and rum may be taken as items in the history of our advancement, no doubt New South Wales exhibits remarkable development and indefatigable perseverance.

Such comments did not always go down well in the limited, closed society of New South Wales in the 1840s and 1850s (it is sometimes argued that the custom of anonymity, common at the time was a necessary protection in such a community). It may be that, from time to time, in hiding behind an unsigned or cryptically signed letter to the editor or some other example of his massive journalistic endeavour (many hundreds have been identified) in a personal attack on an individual he overstepped the mark of propriety.

Geology was of course his forte, but he also wrote on many other aspects of natural history, meteorology, astronomy, poetry, Australian exploration, and of course theology and religion. He was a defender of the rights of the Church of England in the colony, in the management of schools, and in other spheres. William Clarke died at St Leonard's, Sydney on 16 June 1878. He was much lamented.[11]

No doubt his character had flaws, but he had a good deal to put up with. Nevertheless, he did establish geology in New South Wales, and was an indefatigable proponent of science: he was one of the founders of the Royal Society of New South Wales, serving as vice-president and president from 1867 to 1876. Australian science owes him a lot, and indeed a Clarke Memorial Medal is awarded by the Society to a leading contributor to Australian science.

Julian Tenison Woods: theistic evolutionist

In fact, there are a number of clerical geologists associated with Australia. A particularly interesting example is the Catholic priest, Julian Tenison Woods (1832–1889). It has been emphasised before that there have been rather few Catholic clergyman naturalists – Tenison Woods is the splendid exception. Perhaps part of the key to understanding him is that he had a number of Anglican and indeed 'establishment' characteristics. He was born in London, his father, a keen amateur naturalist, being a journalist on *The Times*. Tenison Woods seems to have been well-connected socially, and indeed is said to have been a distant relative of one of the Archbishops of Canterbury and a Bishop of Ossory in Ireland. Originally a somewhat lukewarm member of the Church of England, he converted to Catholicism during the Catholic Revival associated with John Henry Newman's (1801–1890) embracing the Catholic faith in 1845. Tenison Woods himself dated his conversion to late 1848, when he was sixteen. He was briefly a member of the strict Passionist order, but left while still a novice. He moved to Tasmania, where he taught for a while, before a chance meeting with Bishop Murphy led him to seek ordination. He trained with the German Jesuits at Sevenhills, near Clare, South Australia. A man of immense faith, he was responsible for the foundation of several religious orders, including, with Mary McKillop (who was to become Australia's first saint), the Josephite Sisters.

He was ordained in 1857, and his first parish covered some 14,000 sq miles (about 40,000 sq km) of South Australia and adjacent parts of Victoria. Despite the difficulties of carrying books and rock and fossil specimens long distances as he visited his flock, he was constantly collecting and recording as he travelled. His first book, *Geological Observations in South Australia*, was published in London by Longmans in 1862, and was part of a stream of some 180 important papers and books. He was the first palaeontologist to work in Australia, making a special study of fossil molluscs, corals and bryozoans. He compared fossil molluscs with living forms, collecting and studying those from the intertidal zone of Australia's shorelines. He also attempted to place fossils in their stratigraphical context (the arrangement and nature of the rocks that include them), making a special study of the rocks of the Sydney area. He was one of the first to apply the 'glacial hypothesis' – the idea that the earth had been affected by an Ice Age – to Australasia, showing that while New Zealand had been profoundly influenced by ice action, these processes were unimportant in Australia. He was also something of a botanist. Above all else he was an integrator, seeing, like many polymath nineteenth-century scientists and naturalists, knowledge as a seamless whole. There are interesting comparisons with William Clarke: in a colonial environment where educated men were rare, and scientific expertise was even rarer, he was often called on by governments for advice. He wrote reports on fisheries for the governments of the colonies of New South Wales and New Zealand, and carried out geological investigations (particularly into coal resources) for the authorities in Queensland, New Guinea, the Straits Settlements and Borneo (now parts of Malaysia). He was also a great publicist for education, adult education, as well as that for children, both on behalf of his church and more generally. He was an effective communicator, writing dozens of newspaper articles, including an important series for the *Australasian* in the 1860s and 1870s.

Like many of his Anglican parson-naturalists brethren, he saw his scientific work as an extension of his work as a priest: it was part of his duty to reveal the glorious details of God's entire creation. As a missionary priest in vast areas of scientifically unexplored country in Australia (and to some extent elsewhere) he was able to do this extremely well. 'Science was part of Faith.' While he might not have gone the entire way with him, Tenison Woods was a supporter of Charles Darwin's evolutionary views. Darwin was 'a careful and methodical scientist', he wrote in 1862. After reading Charles Darwin's account of the geology of coral reefs he referred to him as 'that great geologist'. He noted that the fossils in different geological strata differed, and that as geological time passed, 'less perfect' organisms gave way to higher creatures: there was 'a gradation in creation'. (Although he commented that the term 'less perfect' was not to be interpreted too literally: all God's creatures were perfect in their own way.) Evolution, he thought, provided a beautiful illustration of nature's plan. He might be referred to as a theistic evolutionist. Perhaps it was as well for him that he worked in the mission field in remote parts of Australia. Had he been closer to the heart of Catholic orthodoxy in Europe he might have been exposed to theological pressures that were less severe in the Australian Catholic Dioceses, although there certainly were times when he had his difficulties.

Perhaps part of his success was that despite his work amongst the Catholic poor of the outback, he had important links with 'society', partly the legacy maybe, of his youthful days in London, and indeed his Anglican heritage. He knew Governor Frederick Weld of Tasmania, and it was through his offices, when Weld was later a colonial governor in Asia, that he received some of his scientific assignments in other parts of the Empire. He corresponded with the leading British scientists, including Sir Charles Lyell. He seems to have had the knack of getting along with people of all kinds.[12]

Charles Grenfell Nicolay: geographer, geologist, museum curator

C. G. Nicolay (1815–1897) provides another example of a nineteenth-century polymath, whose activities and interests were not confined to what would now be thought appropriate for a clergyman. He dabbled as farmer, land developer, engineer and newspaper editor. In a colonial environment a man had to be able to turn one's hand to more than one occupation.

Charles Nicolay had a well-connected, almost aristocratic background. He was born at Cadogan Place, Chelsea, and his father held a position in His Majesty's Treasury. An ancestor, Caspar Nicolay, had come to England in 1736 as part of the entourage of Augusta of Saxe-Gotha, who married Frederick Louis, Prince of Wales. A grandfather had been page to Queen Charlotte and confidante of George III. Alas, when Charles Nicolay was only two years old, his father died. His mother, with eight children, the youngest only a month old, was left destitute, and petitioned the Earl of Liverpool for financial help. It is not clear what education the young Charles Nicolay had, but it is certain that he did not go to university, to his lasting regret, presumably for financial reasons. Nevertheless, early in 1841 he was ordained deacon in the Church of England by the Bishop of Exeter: on 28 March of that year he was licensed to a curacy at Tresco in the Isles of Scilly. On 7 June he married Mary Ann Raven, by whom he eventually had eight children.

From 1843 to 1858 he held the position of librarian at King's College, London, and embarked on a period of self-education in geology, geography and history. He took an important part in the establishment of Queen's College in 1848. This was the first institution for the higher education of women in England. He held the positions of Dean, Deputy Chairman, and surprisingly in view of his lack of formal qualifications, Professor of Physical Geography. Regrettably, despite his apparent administrative abilities, disagreements with some of the female staff developed. He was asked to resign the position of Dean, and eventually relinquished all his posts at both colleges. It was alleged that Nicolay had shown 'defects of temper'. During this brief academic career, however, he wrote a number of papers and books, particularly on physical geography.

In 1858 Nicolay was appointed chaplain to Bahia (now Salvador) in Brazil, an important seaport, which in the nineteenth century had an appreciable British presence. Nicolay remained in Brazil for nearly ten years, retuning to England in 1867 on furlough. However, as in his academic position in London, he seems to have had the knack of annoying people, and some of the British community in Bahia requested Nicolay to resign, and for a year or so he was without a clerical position.

The church of St George, Bahia, had been consecrated by Bishop Matthew Hale, while *en route* to Australia to take up his position as Bishop of Perth, and part of Nicolay's stipend while he was in Brazil was paid by Bishop Hale. It may be, therefore, partly through this link that he obtained the position of chaplain at Geraldton, Western Australia in 1870. He arrived in Fremantle in April 1870, and seems to have impressed some of the leaders of the colony including Governor Frederick Weld, and the Colonial Secretary Frederick Barlee. Almost as soon as he arrived in Geraldton, with Weld's approval, Nicolay, possessed of the notion that the climate and environment were similar to those of Brazil, attempted to establish a coffee plantation. The venture was a pathetic failure and was abandoned within a couple of years.

A period as editor of a Perth newspaper followed, Nicolay for a while attempting to run his paper while retaining his clerical position. Bishop Hale resisted this strongly. At the same time he acted as scientific adviser to the colonial government on 'such diverse fields as engineering, geology, botany, astronomy and conchology' and was ridiculed. When in 1875 he was appointed to look into the reports of coal deposits in the Fitzgerald River area (a task which he completed competently – there was no coal), a rival local newspaper scathingly criticised the appointment on the grounds that he had no qualifications or experience in coal prospecting. He was described as 'whilom chaplain, whilom coffee-planter, whilom editor, whilom engineer, and the Fates alone know whilom what else'. Once again Nicolay's propensity to annoy appeared.

1877 saw Nicolay back in clerical employment, at least on a part-time basis. He was a curate in the parish of Perth, and from 1878 onwards chaplain to the Fremantle convict establishment. In the 1880s he assisted Bishop Parry with the training of theological students. For much of this time he advised the government on geological matters, reporting on minerals sent for examination, and on the geology of proposed railway routes. Very much in the spirit of the age he was responsible for the founding of Western Australia's first museum in 1881: he mounted an extensive display of rock and mineral specimens in what became the original display of the Western Australian Museum. He was also concerned, in the paternalistic way of the times, for the welfare of Aborigines, campaigning for the setting aside of a large reserve in the Murchison area, and serving as a member of the Aborigines Protection Board from 1892 until his death.

He died at Fremantle on 9 May 1897, his wife, who had converted to Catholicism some years previously, having predeceased him by ten years.

Like so many missionary clergy of his generation, Nicolay was an oddball. His heart never seems to have been fully in his priestly duties, and yet despite his activity in the fields of journalism, geology, education, plantation agriculture, government administration and so on, he never seems to have been able entirely to abandon the clerical life. His character seems to have been flawed, and yet he must have been a man of considerable ability. Perhaps the colonial environment, with its 'make do and mend' approach, and need to use talent wherever it lay was the right setting for such an individualist. It is hard to see him fitting into a rural parish in Victorian England.[13]

A missionary miscellany

Some missionary or overseas clergy spent their entire ministry in one part of the world. Cruttwell worked in Papua New Guinea, Clarke in New South Wales. Tenison Woods moved around a good deal more, but mainly within eastern Australia (he never touched Western Australia). There were others who moved from arena to arena, sometimes interspersing their years overseas with periods in an English parish. Nicolay conformed to some extent to this model, so too did the Reverend Thomas Basil Kitchen (1905–1987). Yorkshire born and bred, Thomas Kitchen was sometime President of the Yorkshire Naturalists' Union. He was a lifelong student and collector of Coleoptera (beetles): at the time of his death, his collection contained 13,497 specimens belonging to 2,782 species. After training at St

Augustine's College, Canterbury and a curacy in Bethnal Green, he spent five years in what was then Southern Rhodesia. Six years as Vicar of Brayton, Selby, followed, and then he served for two years as Railway Chaplain in Bengal. Later in life he undertook a series of chaplaincies in the extensive Diocese of Gibraltar, churches in Madrid, Oporto, Tangier, Tenerife and Malta among them.[14]

With some, the commitment to the missionary life, if such it can be called, was even more brief, the clergyman-naturalist being recruited for a single task or as a member of a particular expedition, the period overseas being limited to a few months, or a year or so at the most. Such seems to have been the case with the Reverend H. H. Slater, in his day President of the Vertebrate Section of the Yorkshire Naturalists' Union, who served as naturalist on HM Transit of Venus Expedition, to Rodriguez, a small island dependency of Mauritius in the Indian Ocean, in 1874. He wrote several articles on the geology, plants, animals, anthropology and human activities on the island.[15]

The occasional example has been quoted of a person who was a naturalist before he was a clergyman – usually the opposite is the case, a man being ordained before making a name for himself as a naturalist. William Woolls (1814–1893) was born in Winchester. He did not come from a clerical family, his father being a wholesaler. However, a family link was important, for he was profoundly influenced as a young lad by his godfather, Canon Westcombe of Winchester College. He emigrated to Australia at the age of sixteen, arriving in Sydney on 16 April 1832. Despite his young age, he was employed as a schoolmaster, and it was during this phase of his life that he became interested in botany. He was always a keen Anglican, and twice refused ordination, but was eventually ordained deacon on 8 June 1872, and priest some six months later. He was incumbent of Richmond, later becoming rural dean. His particular enthusiasm was the 'vegetable resources of Australia', and he wrote extensively on the subject, e.g. *The Plants of New South Wales*, 1885. Like many of his ilk, he had an extensive network of correspondents.[16]

It has been emphasized that the phenomenon of the parson-naturalist is distinctively English, many 'colonial' clergy who were naturalists, being English by birth, training or temporary residence. Nevertheless, important exceptions exist. Herbert Montague Rucher Rupp (1872–1956) was born at Port Fairy, Victoria on 27 December 1872. He was of Prussian ancestry, and received his entire education in Australia. He was another distinguished clergyman-botanist, specializing in orchids. He wrote the *Guide to Orchids of New South Wales*, published in 1939 and *The Orchids of New South Wales*, in 1943, revised with a supplement in 1969. He distinguished new species of plants in the genera *Acacia, Boronia* and *Prasophyllum*. Perhaps part of the explanation is to be seen in the fact that, despite his German-Australian background, he won scholarships to two of the most English of institutions in Australia – Geelong Grammar School, and Trinity College, at the University of Melbourne.[17]

More typical in many respects was the Reverend Richard Taylor (1805–1873). Another Yorkshireman, he took his Cambridge MA before becoming a vicar of a parish in the Isle of Ely, not far distant from his university. Orthodox in much of his theology, and an evangelical, he sailed with the Church Missionary Society in 1836. He was detained *en route*, being obliged to take up church duties in Sydney for a while, and did not arrive at the Bay of Islands in New Zealand – something of a centre of a missionary activity – until 1839. There followed what has been described as 'a life of extraordinary activity, both in his missionary duties and in his recording of New Zealand's natural history'. After working at Waimate, he moved to Wanganui, the suburb of Taylorville being named after him. In his orthodox, evangelical way, he saw everywhere around him the hand of the Creator. He was an all round naturalist, being elected a Fellow of the Geological Society of London, and being associated with the finding of the first bones of the extinct flightless bird, the moa. He collected plants, and like many missionary botanists, sent specimens to Kew. He discovered a new species of underground parasitic plant, *Dactylanthus taylori*. Although somewhat conservative in his theology, he was a great believer in the education and advancement of the Maories. He supported the Maories in disputes over land, understanding their customs, and made pleas for the dignity of the chiefs to be recognized. He often preached in Maori pas (fortified settlements). Such views and activities did not endear him to the white settlers, or to the CMS (Church Missionary Society) authorities. Like many missionary naturalists of his day, Richard Taylor attempted to harness scientific knowledge for the good of humanity. Thus he combined his close association with the Maoris, and knowledge of their lore, with his knowledge of plants in his preparation of the *Maori Pharmacopoeia*, attempting to preserve the native New Zealanders' knowledge of the healing properties of local plants.[18]

Another New Zealand clergyman-botanist, of a rather later vintage, was the Reverend Dr J. E. Holloway (1881–1945). Although New Zealand born and educated (Auckland University and St John's Theological College), and having an interest in natural history from his boyhood years, his interest in primitive plants was certainly encouraged during his time in English parishes (1909–1911). One of these parishes was in the midst of the Yorkshire coalfields, and in his spare time, Holloway used to collect Carboniferous fossil plants from the mine tipheaps. Ferns and the other primitive fern-like plants (the Pteridophyta) remained his lasting interest. His MSc was on *Lycopodium*, the club-moss. When he was vicar of a parish in Westland, on South Island, New Zealand (1916–1921), he had ample opportunity to study modern ferns, which abounded in the temperate rain forests of the district. *Timesipteris*, *Psilotum* and *Phylloglossum* are other primitive plants of which he made special studies – studies that earned him a DSc in 1919, the Hutton Memorial Medal in 1920 and a Fellowship of the Royal Society in 1921. He carried out his researches with 'notoriously minimal equipment'. In 1924 Holloway became lecturer in botany at Otago University, although he continued to work in parishes.[19]

Most of the examples of overseas parson-naturalists considered above have come from Australia and the Pacific. However examples illustrating similar themes could be found amongst those who served in Asia, Africa or the Americas. To some extent, in their background, education and family connections they shared characteristics of parson-naturalists at home. They varied as much in their theology – high, low, or broad – as did their brothers in England. Yet maybe differences can be discerned. They were independent-minded, sometimes almost eccentric individuals. They not infrequently combined secular employment with their clerical appointment. They tended to have extremely wide interests, to emphasize 'applied' or 'useful' aspects of science, and they tended to be called upon to advise governments: colonial administrators had few experts to call upon, and had to make the best use of the talent available. The Commonwealth, the world, owes them a special debt, not least through their English contacts, and continuing membership of the English clergy network, they provided a flow of specimens, ideas and information from the distant portions of the earth to the British scientific establishment.

The role of some of these clerical naturalists within the general pattern of colonial science, is perhaps worth a brief comment. One view of science in the nineteenth century in the British Colonies is that is was peripheral, and of lower standard, in, for example the colonies of Australia and New Zealand, than in the home country. Scientists in England, it is argued, saw colonial workers as useful fact-gatherers, while the real intellectual work, the forging of new theories was done in London, Oxford or Cambridge. To some extent, naturalists in the colonies acknowledged the position. The opposite view is that some, at least, of the scientists and naturalists in the Empire regarded themselves as colleagues of those in the home country, rather than their servants, and were original thinkers in their own right, striving to establish vigorous local scientific communities.[20]

The lives and activities of the parson-naturalists discussed in this chapter provide evidence to support both views. John White did see his role to provide materials for his brother Gilbert; Norman Cruttwell did send specimens to Kew. So did Richard Taylor the previous century. William Clarke, early in his time in New South Wales did feel that he was working in an intellectual wilderness and said so; H. H. Slater served as naturalist on the Transit of Venus expedition for a few months, and then hastened back to an English parish, showing no great affection for Rodriguez and its people. Julian Tenison Woods published his important book on South Australian Geology in London. All these represent the process of information passing from the periphery towards the centre. In this the model of the structure of scientific activity coincided closely with the ecclesiastical one. The Anglican Church is strongly hierarchical and centralized. A priest is always responsible to his bishop. Missionary priests might be employed by, or at least partly funded by, a missionary society in faraway London, that was ultimately responsible for their welfare. (A Catholic colonial priest like Tenison Woods, of course, worked in an even more centralized and hierarchical system.)

And yet Norman Cruttwell was also at pains to send specimens to the local herbarium at Lae. When he retired from his church appointment he stayed on in New Guinea to train local people in botanical conservation. Clarke was one of the founders of the Royal Society of New South Wales, and throughout his life attempted to build up the role of science in the life of the people. Nicolay established a Museum. All were attempting to build up local scientific resources (and succeeding). Woolls, Tenison Woods and Holloway had all been born in, worked in or visited England, and had a network of correspondents there, but were very much part of their local scientific communities. To some extent there was an evolutionary change here. In Australia (and elsewhere in the Empire) in the 1830s (and before), virtually all the small number of naturalists were European trained (usually English), and local institutions were absent: any contribution one was going to make had to be made through home country institutions. By the late 1870s and 1880s the situation was very different: local societies, libraries, museums and herbaria had been established and populations had grown markedly. Nevertheless the legacy remained: for many Australian and New Zealand scientists the ultimate accolades was (and indeed still is) an FRS. An accolade that Clarke and Holloway, for example, achieved.

Notes

1 Mabey, R., *Gilbert White: a Biography of the Author of The Natural History of Selborne* (London, Century, 1986); Foster, P. G. M., *Gilbert White and his Records: a Scientific Biography* (London, Christopher Helm, 1988).

2 Different Missionary Societies had their own churchmanship; for example, the

CMS (Church Missionary Society), founded in 1799, always had an evangelical theology. The SPG (Society for the Prorogation of the Gospel in foreign parts), founded in 1701 to minister to British people overseas and to evangelize non-Christian races subject to the Crown, tended to be 'higher church' in outlook. The latter merged with the UMCA (Universities Mission to Central Africa), which had been formed in response to an appeal by David Livingstone in 1857, in 1965.

3 Thomas, W. C., 'Notice of ferns from Old Calobar', *Edinburgh Botanical Society Transactions* 6, 1860, pp. 357–358. Dallman, A. A. and Wood, M. H., 'A biographical list of deceased Lancashire botanists', *Transactions of the Liverpool Botanical Society* 1909, pp. 4–59.

4 1996 issue of *The Family Magazine* and personal information from the Reverend Colin Holden, of Melbourne.

5 Clarke, W. B., 'On certain recent meteoric phenomenon . . . contemporaneous and in supposed connection, with emanations', *Magazine of Natural History*, 1833–1835, 6, pp. 289–308; 7, pp. 193–202, 289–309, 385–390, 609–630. Clarke W. B., 'Illustrations of the geology of south-east Dorsetshire', *Magazine of Natural History*, 1837–1839, New Series, 1, pp. 414–421, 461–469, 2, pp. 79–88, 128–136, 3, pp. 390–401, 432–428, 483–489.

6 Armstrong, P. H., *Charles Darwin in Western Australia: a Young Scientist's Perception of an Environment* (Nedlands, University of Western Australia Press, 1985); Nicholas, F. W. and J. M., *Charles Darwin in Australia* (Melbourne, Cambridge University Press, 1989).

7 Mozley, A., 'James Dwight Dana in New South Wales, 1839–1840', *Journal and Proceedings, Royal Society of New South Wales,* 97, 1964, pp. 185–191.

8 Letter, J. D. Dana to E. C. Herrick, Maitland, New South Wales, 28 January 1840, quoted in Gilman, D. C., *The Life of James Dwight Dana: Scientific Explorer . . .* (New York, 1899), p. 115.

9 Clarke, W. B., 'Effects of forest vegetation on climate', *Journal and Proceedings, Royal Society of New South Wales*, 10, 1876, pp. 179–235.

10 Organ, M. M., 'W. B. Clarke as scientific journalist', *Historical Records of Australia Science*, 9(1), 1992, pp. 1–16.

11 Fuller details of Clarke's life and work are given in Organ, M. (*ibid.*) and Grainger, E., *The Remarkable Reverend Clarke: the Life and Times of the Father of Australian Geology* (Melbourne, Cambridge University Press, 1982).

12 Press, M., *Julian Tenison Woods* (Sydney, Catholic Theological Faculty, 1979); ABC Radio broadcast, 2 December 1990; personal information from Mrs J. A. Day, Royal Society of New South Wales, and other sources. (He adopted the style Julian Tenison Woods in the 1850s in order to distinguish himself from several other clergyman-geologists who were publishing at the same time.)

13 Playford, P. E. and Pridmore, I., 'The Reverend C. G. Nicolay: a pioneer geographer, geologist and museum curator in Western Australia', *Royal Western Australian Historical Society, Journal and Proceedings*, 7(1) 1969, pp. 29–33.

14 Flint, J. H., 'Reverend Thomas Basil Kitchen (1905–1987)', *Naturalist,* 114, 1989, pp. 71–72.

15 Slater, H. H., 'The island of Rodriguez, and its fauna, and they were and as they are', *Naturalist*, [6–7], 1881–1882, pp. 177–181; 25–30.

16 *Australian Dictionary of Biography*, vol. 6 (Melbourne University Press, 1976).

17 *Australian Dictionary of Biography*, vol. 11 (Melbourne University Press, 1988).

18 'P.S.', 'Reverend Richard Taylor (1805–1873)', *New Zealand's Nature Heritage* (Wellington, Paul Hamlyn, 1974).

19 'P.S.', 'J. E. Holloway (1881–1945)', *New Zealand's Nature Heritage* (Wellington, Paul Hamlyn, 1975).

20 Butcher, B. W., 'Darwin's Australian correspondents – deference and collaboration in colonial science', in: MacLeod, R. and Roebock, P. F., eds., *Nature in its Greatest Extent* (Honolulu, University of Hawaii Press, 1988), pp. 139–157.

Chapter 10

Retrospect and prospect

The link between theology and science

All of Creation was an appropriate subject for admiration. The Reverend John Keble (1792–1866) put it thus:

> [W]e are taught to make every part of life, every scene in nature, an occasion – in other words a topic – of devotion.[1]

Many of the naturalists of the late eighteenth, nineteenth and early twentieth centuries would have been in full sympathy with this view. Those who peered through hand-lenses, or looked down microscopes to see the detailed form of plants and animals, or who spent a life-time collecting, studying and classifying a particular group of organisms – whether ferns, fungi, lichens, beetles, sponges, spiders, mites or tropical orchids – often rejoiced in the world's profusion of life, its complexity and the pattern of order to be discerned within in it. Whether or not they espoused all of William Paley's *Natural Theology* they would have seen themselves as researching the beauty and intricacy of God's world:

> The earth is the Lord's and the fullness thereof
> (Psalm 24. 1)

was their watchword. John Ray's heart leapt at the beauty of a flower or the colours on the wings of a butterfly. Nature represented God's work and so contributing to the understanding of nature was an entirely appropriate activity for a clergyman.

Amongst John Henslow's papers were the following notes by John Glyde:

> There is no species of study so refreshing and invigorating as

> Botany and none other that seems so well adapted to a clerical life. In this occupation the thoughts are not dissipated, they are merely set free for wholesome meditation. They are not tempted to wander from God, on the contrary they are naturally led to walk in closer communion with him and are drawn by everything around to admire and adore him not only in the wonders of his works, but in his abundant and gracious provision for the happiness of his creatures.[2]

There was much more to it: the fading flower declares eloquently the ephemeral nature of earthly things, and thus could move thoughts towards the temporary nature of life.

There were others, particularly in the middle years of the nineteenth century, who sought to bring together the Book of Nature and the Bible in a more direct way. The book of Genesis provided one account (or perhaps more than one account) of the Creation, or origin of the world and all that is therein. Some geologists and other naturalists sought to show how it could be married in every detail with the stratigraphical record (the evidence of the sequence of rocks). Buckland was the leader of the diluvialists who sought to explain many of the features of the geology of the British Isles by reference to the Flood. With the publication of Charles Lyell's *Principles of Geology* (1830–1833), with its emphasis on uniformitarianism or gradualism, the immensely long time-scale of the earth's history began to be understood, and attempts at this reconciliation or harmonisation of stratigraphy with the Genesis accounts became more difficult. Some clerical geologists adopted a slightly less literalist interpretation, espousing the 'day-age theory' maintaining that a day in the Genesis account represented a long geological period. The Reverend Samuel Kinns' *Moses and Geology*,[3] for example, found an exact correlation in the order of the fifteen 'creative events' described in Genesis with the order taught be science.

The publication of Charles Darwin's *Origin of Species* in 1859 posed real difficulties for some clerics, some of whom continued to maintain the literal truth of every word of Genesis (difficult in view of the fact that there are at least two distinct versions of the Creation story). Such persons were the antecedents of the creationists of the modern day. Such was the Yorkshire parson Francis Orpen Morris, who attempted to exterminate Darwinism from the intellectual scene with sermon and speech, pamphlet and poster. So too Galloway, whose mission was above all else 'the defence of scripture' and used geology (as he understood it) along with mathematics, in an attempt to demonstrate its absolute inerrancy. These were the type of persons who later became known as the fundamentalists – adhering to the 'fundamentals' of orthodox Christianity, including an inerrant Biblical text, to be interpreted literally.

Those affected by the biblical criticism of the day, seeing that even within the single book of Genesis there were a multiplicity of texts, with different sources, written over a long period, to serve different purposes, sought to reinterpret biblical sources in the light of modern knowledge, reflecting the current world. Some of these 'liberal' or 'modernist' theologians were quite welcoming of Darwin's views, and were pleased to find that scientific thinking was, like the critical study of the biblical texts, moving them away from a literalist approach. Some parson-naturalists, such as Canon Henry Baker Tristram, with his larks from north Africa, and Octavius Pickard-Cambridge with his spiders, enthusiastically utilized Darwin's ideas in their scientific work.

Henry Hugh Higgins, originally on the evangelical wing of the church, later became something of a 'broad' churchman. Faced with the difficult idea of the apparent cruelty of the notion of the 'struggle for existence' of and 'the survival of the fittest' in Darwin's thinking, he was not in the least put out. He saw a severity which he compared to that of a parent, surgeon or judge, rather than needless cruelty. Others saw the role of animals of prey as a means of shortening the distress of other creatures: carnivorous creatures, such as pike, stoats and weasels, hawks, cats – all, according to one clerical naturalist, tend to consume creatures already injured or diseased:

> . . . among the wise decrees of providence, the animal of prey is sent for the special purpose of terminating the suffering of accident or disease among animals.[4]

Charles Kingsley was an enthusiastic Darwinian, but as a popularizer of science rather than an original researcher, he had less call to relate the ideas to real-world examples, although he saw Darwin's work on the *Fertilisation of Orchids* (1877) as 'a most valuable addition to natural theology', a doctrine to which he was particularly devoted. He gave an address on 'The natural theology of the future' at Sion College in January 1871. Here is part:

> I sometimes dream of a day when it will be considered necessary that every candidate for ordination should be required to have passed creditably in at least one branch of physical science, if it be only to teach him the method of sound scientific thought. And if it be said that the doctrine of evolution, by doing away with the theory of creation, does away with that of final causes – let us answer boldly, Not in the least. We might accept what Mr. Darwin and Professor Huxley have written on physical science, and yet preserve our natural theology on exactly the same basis as that on

> which Butler and Paley left it. That we should have to develop it, I do not deny. That we should relinquish it, I do.[5]

This summary is of course a simplification: there were subtle shades within this spectrum. Even Tristram felt that there might be some scope for independent creation. The younger Henslow, George, enthusiastically campaigned for evolutionary ideas, but had reservations on details, for example, on the natural selection mechanism. William Purchas, when he got from his clerical colleague Symonds, a Lyellian description of his beloved Herefordshire for his *Flora* instead of a Mosaic reconciliation, wrote that as geology was such a young science, he expected closer harmonization to be possible in the future, as fresh scientific facts emerged.

Thus there were a variety of theological and scientific viewpoints, and others existed besides the above, from which a parson-naturalist might approach his work. Many therefore saw their studies of natural history as a logical extension of the work of a priest.

Space, time, technology and society

The geographical nature of the Church of England contributed to the success of the parson-naturalist phenomenon. The parish system that placed a parson in every village; the system of patronage, the parson's freehold, together with the nature of the *advowson*, whatever their failings, meant that some of the links between parish and parson became very strong indeed. Sometimes the link lasted for generations, and enabled an individual, or a father-and-son pair, or even a grandfather, father and son trio to gain a unique knowledge of a rural landscape, its human occupance and its natural history. (The full title of Gilbert White's book is *The Natural History and Antiquities of Selborne*.) The grouping of parishes into rural deaneries and archdeaconries,[6] and the existence of dioceses maintained a system of social links between clergy. We know, for example, from his diary that in the 1780s, every six months or so, usually in late April or May and in October, the Reverend James Woodforde (Parson Woodforde of Norfolk) used to receive a summons from his archdeacon to attend 'clergy generals' or 'archdeacon's generals' (general visitations) at a nearby centre. There would be a church service, then sometimes the archdeacon, or occasionally the Bishop of Norwich, or some other notable would address them or 'give them a charge'. This would be followed by a convivial meal in some local inn. Clergy were evidently expected to attend these, for on one occasion Parson Woodforde had to pay a 'forfeit' of one shilling (1s 0d, the equivalent of 5 pence, but much more in terms of purchasing power) for missing the previous 'general' through illness. Here is his account of the meeting held on 8 May 1789:

> After breakfast about half past 8 o'clock I mounted my old Mare and went to Foulsham, about 9 Miles from my House, to the Sign of the Ship, kept by one Blanchflower, very civil People, and there I dined with our Arch-Deacon Mr. Younge and other Brethren. At 11 o'clock we walked to Church where we heard Prayers read by Mr Wilson for the Revd Mr Harding of Ling. The Company at Dinner were the following Clergy. The Arch-Deacon Mr. Younge, Mr. Astley, Mr. Athill, Mr. Wilson, Mr. Jeans, Mr Priest, Mr. Whitmell, Mr. Carr, Mr. Addison, Mr. Taswell, Mr. Ivory, Mr. Norris, Mr. Brown, Mr. Churchill, Mr. Bulwer, Mr. Bryant Junr and myself. . . . and a very excellent dinner we had a whole Cod-fish and Cockle Sauce, boiled breast of Veal and Oyster Sauce, hashed calfs head, ham, boiled and rost beef, a leg of mutton boiled. Pies and Puddings &c. Quarter of Lamb rosted. We dined about 2 o'clock and broke up before 5. We each paid . . . 3. 0. . . . I got to my own House by 8 o'clock this Even' and I thank God safe and well after spending an agreeable Day . . . There were a great many dressy Ladies at Church to day at Foulsham, and some very handsome.
> (Capitalization, spelling and punctuation as given.)

The account is quite typical, although sometimes Mr Woodforde was less impressed with the food (or the feminine talent) and said so, and sometimes he comments on 'a very good port-wine' or something similar. We have no means of knowing how many of the seventeen clergy were interested in natural history (Woodforde wasn't), but in rural Norfolk there would have probably been some that were. Specimens and notes, as well as family and clerical gossip, might be exchanged at such clergy gatherings. Let us not forget the 'handsome, dressy ladies'. We have already noted that clergy frequently married clergy daughters, maintaining the social network, and perpetuating it. These meetings no doubt served a marriage-mart purpose as well as performing other functions.

The tightly knit nature of clergy families, including clergy-naturalist families, has been stressed. Through intermarriage and the existence of a family tradition of service to the Church of England, there existed a densely woven network of interconnections, a network that was strengthened by associations made at university. We have seen that some links forged at, for example, Christ's, Trinity and St John's

Colleges, Cambridge; Oriel College, Oxford; University College, Durham and King's College, London, remained important throughout a naturalist's career. Of course there were also particular teachers: the direct and indirect influence of Henslow, Sedgwick and Bonney, persisted for a century – indeed it still exists. Bonds established at reading parties in Wales with undergraduate contemporaries, or in discussions of field trips with university teachers remained lifelong.

Moreover, the nineteenth century saw the development of technology and of institutions so that *these networks could be maintained*. The appearance of the penny postage (1840), and the railways and the steam locomotive (1820s onwards), and towards the end of the century the telegraph enabled contact to be maintained with scientific and clerical colleagues quickly, efficiently and cheaply. Less important, but significant, was the development of the steamship, which allowed contact to be maintained with colleagues overseas. By the end of the century it was possible to send a letter query to someone in the 'mission field' or in the colonies of Australia or New Zealand, and receive a reply within a reasonable time. Space was effectively contracted. The development of institutions for the exchange of scientific news and views served to consolidate social links, as well as for the presentation of scientific papers. Local museums came into existence in their dozens in the middle years of the nineteenth century, along with local natural history societies and field clubs, often with the strong involvement of the clergy. National bodies were even more important. The Royal Society was founded in 1660: it was an efficient, prestigious if somewhat exclusive forum. The Geological Society of London came into existence in 1807, the Zoological Society of London in 1826, the Royal Geographical Society in 1830. Perhaps most important of all, was the British Association for the Advancement of Science, founded in 1831, which acted as an extremely important focus because of its annual meetings in regional centres, which many parson-naturalists attended, and at which they often presented papers. Their wives went along too, to renew family acquaintances – women valuing the maintenance of social links as much as, or more than men. Rectory daughters were no doubt occasionally included in such parties, perhaps with an eye to the possibility that they might meet a suitable young curate or don. The network not only expanded spatially, it became denser. The following quotation from Leonard Blomefield's (Jenyns') autobiography provides a good indication of the importance of the Association in the maintenance of social networks:

> I joined the Association very shortly after . . . [the first meeting of 1831 in York], and made my first appearance at the second meeting

> held the following year at Oxford. I remember well being one of four, who joined in hiring a carriage to post from Cambridge to Oxford on the occasion, the other three being Henslow, Clark, Professor of Anatomy, and Bowstead of Corpus College, afterward Bishop of Lichfield.[8]

Thus three of the four men sharing that coach from Cambridge to Oxford, for the second British Association meeting were Anglican clergy. The fact speaks volumes.

An Anglican tradition?

The tradition of the parson-naturalist is a distinctively English one, and, to some extent, a distinctively Anglican one. There are certainly notable exceptions. There have been Presbyterian ministers in Scotland (e.g. the Reverend Dr John Walker, 1731–1803, Church of Scotland minister, and Professor of Natural History at Edinburgh),[9] and Catholic priests in many parts of the world who have made important contributions to the life sciences and geology. One the most notable of the latter was the French priest, Father Pierre Teilhard de Chardin (1881–1955), a distinguished palaeontologist.

Perhaps the story of Teilhard provides part of the clue. His ideas were expressed in *La Phénomène Humain* (1955), translated as *The Phenomenon of Man* (1959) and *Le Milieu divin* (1957). He attempted to combine evolutionary and Christian thought in a unique way. His views were too advanced for the hierarchy of the Catholic Church at the time, and he came under severe pressure, and was not permitted to publish in his lifetime. The Church of England has, at least in recent centuries, been more tolerant of a modest degree of unorthodoxy. Extremism has not been the way of Anglicanism, but toleration has. The breadth of the Church of England has allowed High and Low, anglo-catholic and evangelical, liberal and traditional, to flourish under the same roof. Although certain dioceses have, from time to time displayed a distinctive 'temper' or emphasis, in the nineteenth century a scriptural geologist might be in the next parish from a liberal acceptor of Darwinian ideas. It is difficult to envisage this sort of 'broadness' and toleration existing in the Roman Catholic tradition. In any case, until quite recently the challenges of evolution have caused real difficulty in that church: in Ireland, for example, natural history has sometimes been seen as a 'Protestant' activity; an Irish Catholic priest of a scholarly turn of mind would be more likely to make a special study of his locality's local history. Tradition and historical continuity were ideas that were valued in Catholicism.

There is also the regretable fact that until well on in the nineteenth century it was difficult for free churchmen and Catholics to obtain a university education in England. Part of the rationale of the civic universities was to allow people of a wide variety of backgrounds to aspire to a university degree. It was only in 1871 that the University Tests Act was passed, laying it down that no person taking a degree at Oxford, Cambridge or Durham could be required to subscribe to any article or formulary of faith. Even then the difficulty of the cost of university education preserved distinction, free churchmen and Catholics being, in the nineteenth century, for example, less well off on average than the Anglican squirarchy. Although it has to be remembered for centuries scholarships have been available for the very able: several of the naturalists mentioned in these pages benefited from such schemes.

The Church of England has, since the Reformation, been rooted in the soil of the English countryside. The importance of the evangelical waves of Methodism should not be neglected, and many villages for one and a half centuries or so, have been divided between 'church' and 'chapel'. Although, however, many of the people would forbear rather than hear, the parson has always been in his pulpit, and willing (and indeed required) to baptize, marry or bury those from within his parish who came or were brought to him. The notion of an established Church (a church linked to the structures of the State) has often been criticized, but it made for continuity. The combined effects of patronage, parson's freehold and the network of family connections, together with the fact that many church of England clergy were long-lived, meant that there was possible the development of an association between parson, people and countryside. Possibly it was not always beneficial, and certainly the links are not as strong as they were. Yet the association existed, and enabled the parson-naturalist plant to grow and to blossom.

Catholicism has, since the Reformation, been a minority religion in England, and Catholic priests have tended to be located in the larger centres, where they can serve a greater number of their faithful. Large towns and cities are less suitable locales for natural history. Such a man although of course having a set of colleagues and associates (and parents and siblings), being celibate, cannot, by definition, be connected to the same type of family network that has penetrated the Church of England for centuries, and which provides such advantages to the naturalist. The role of clergy wives in helping and supporting their husbands in some of their natural history work has only occasionally been mentioned here: they must have assisted in a host of ways, and have certainly been undervalued. An unmarried amateur naturalist of any persuasion (and either gender) does not have this built-in support system. Celibacy enjoins a man to devote himself to his work; for a Catholic priest, whether in the countryside where his people were thinly spread, and he needed to travel, or in the cities where numbers were large, there was much work to be done. Some rural Anglican clergy may in former generations have suffered from a want of work, and they had the time to devote to natural history. Be these things as they may they perhaps go some way to explaining the distinctly Anglican flavour of English natural history. The association was not to the exclusion of others, and not necessarily always to the church's benefit, but the link exists.

Where exceptions occur, it is sometimes possible to identify certain special circumstances. Tenison Woods, the Australian Roman Catholic priest geologist, might be cited as an aberration. Yet part of his formation was Anglican. He was born in England and (not terribly enthusiastically) attended the services of the Church of England, and becoming a Catholic in the wake of Newman in 1848.

It is not altogether surprising that the centres of Catholic education should have produced a small number of notable Catholic priests who were naturalists. Such was the Reverend Sylvester Joseph Hunter, MA, SJ (1829–1896), who was associated with Stonyhurst College, near Blackburn, Lancashire, and who wrote on botany, including a paper on conjugation in *Spirogyra*.[10] Across the Pennines in North Yorkshire, at Ampleforth College, and in the twentieth century, two priests who showed an interest in natural history included Father Damian Webb, a botanist, and who experimented with time-lapse photography in producing natural history educational films, and Father Julian Rochford, who was interested in marine and freshwater biology, and in the biology of that important organism of the school science laboratory, the cockroach.[11]

Non-conformist ministers who made a contribution to natural history are perhaps rather more common. Again there is sometimes an educational link. The Reverend James Molineau (1791–1873), born in Leigh, Lancashire, was a warehouseman, and then for a while a schoolmaster at Wilmslow, and from 1837 minister of Baillie Street United Methodist Free Church in Rochdale. He lectured in botany to the local working people, and published *Botany Made Easy* in 1867.[12]

Much more distinguished was the Reverend James Yates (1789–1871), born at Toxteth Park Liverpool, educated at Glasgow University (MA, 1812), before he became a Unitarian minister in London. Political liberalism, or in the eighteenth and early nineteenth century, a 'whig' outlook on politics, an appreciation of scientific progress and Unitarianism have sometimes run together in English families, and it should be little surprise to find this denomination represented amongst those who made something of a name in science. James Yates was a botanist, studying both fossil plants and the modern forms. A particular enthusiasm was the cycad group, on the taxonomy of which he became a leading authority. He was elected to the Linnean Society in 1822, and achieved the honour of an FRS in 1839. He was a founder member, and secretary, of the British Association for the Advancement of Science (27 September 1831), the meetings of which were such a particularly important clearing house for ideas (see above). Yates was a metropolitan person, living close to the centre of ideas in Highgate, London: he is in fact buried in Highgate Cemetery.[13]

Charles Darwin is one person who has a number of characteristics of the parson-naturalist. He came from a well-to-do, upper middle class family, he studied some theology at Cambridge, had read Paley, enjoyed Church of England services (although some of his family were Unitarians, or were not very religious), had a Greek testament with him aboard the *Beagle*, and when he stepped aboard, expected to return to the life of a country parson, similar that of his close Cambridge friend and cousin, William Darwin Fox. The learned divines John Henslow and Adam Sedgwick were his teachers, and Leonard Jenyns was another collaborator. His wife Emma was a religious woman, and although Darwin himself abandoned much of Christian dogma, he was, in his own words, 'never an atheist' nor was his free-thinking, evolutionist grandfather Erasmus Darwin (1731–1802). In his researches Charles Darwin utilized the network for all it could provide: he corresponded freely with parson-naturalists, exchanging information with them. It was indeed through the network that his position aboard HMS *Beagle* was obtained The naturalists' network of the Victorian period, although strongly Anglican in temper, was not so rigid that those of other denominations, or of none, were unable to penetrate it, provided they understood its rules. It was thus used by those who were honorary rather than full members.

Towards the future: ecotheology

English clergy have thus played a role in the development of the science of ecology in Britain, the example of the Reverend E. A. Woodruffe-Peacock in emphasising the relationships between soils and plant communities, and in completing early studies in local ecology was discussed in chapter 3, and the extension of the ecological approach, linking animal committees with those of plants by the Reverend C. E. V. Kendall mentioned in chapter 6. We have noted that they played a significant role in the development of conservation, both in the early species-centred approach – the protection of individual species of seabirds for example, or in the more recent habitat or ecosystem approach.

In Britain, as throughout the world, concern for the environment, manifest in the problems of air and water pollution, the destruction of the habitats of many organisms, the extinction of rare species, has become a clamour. This concern is manifest in coverage of environmental problems in the press and the electronic media, the increase in the amount of environmental legislation and the development of environmental law. Another manifestation of this concern is the rapid increase in the membership of organizations with a concern for the environment, such as the National Trust and the Royal Society for the Protection of Birds. The clergy, of all denominations, as with lay members of churches, are represented in their membership, and in the active participation in these, bodies, but their voices are not loud. Where Canon Kingsley, or Orpen Morris campaigned for the protection of 'God's creatures', preached about the 'moral value of pure water', formed societies and organised meetings, their modern equivalents have other concerns. Maybe there is a feeling that many of the battles have been won. Perhaps issues of social justice are more to the fore; maybe, with more parishes to attend upon, and with an increasing 'admin' load they no longer have the inclination for this sort of activity.

Possibly there is a feeling that it is now more difficult for the amateur to make an impact on serious research in the scientific subjects, and such work, in the environmental or biological sciences and in practical conservation, is better left to the professionals of the universities and government and non-government conservation bodies.

New notes are now, however, being heard: some of them quite strident. Over the last two decades, just as the science of ecology has expanded enormously, academic theologians and philosophers have been wrestling with the philosophical basis of the root causes of the environmental crisis, and offering a spiritual dimension to the consideration of solutions. The challenge was laid down in an article by Lynn White in the American journal *Science* in 1967 that argued that it was the Judeo-Christian tradition, exemplified in the text:

> Be fruitful and multiply, and replenish the earth and subdue it: and have dominion over the fish of the sea, and over the fowl of the air and every living thing that moveth upon the earth.
>
> Genesis 1.28

that was the root-cause of the modern environmental crisis. This criticism has of course been fully answered, it being pointed out that there has, from Old Testament times onwards, been a spirituality that rejoiced in the glory of Creation, a spirituality that sees the whole created universe as a basis for devotion. There has been the developed a *creation theology*, a branch of theology that seeks to understand the philosophical basis of the created universe, and all that there is within it, and to analyse the moral dilemmas faced by humanity in utilizing it.

Ecotheology, related to, but distinct from creation theology, acknowledges the interconnectedness of the living world, and seeks to provide a philosophical understanding of it. At one level it could be seen as an extension of the natural theology of the nineteenth century, seeing for example, the complexity of ecosystems as evidence for the existence of a Creator. Yet ecotheology also seeks to adduce from the exegesis of biblical (and other sources), a moral, ethical dimension in the discussion of the earth's resources, especially living resources. Anglican clergy have certainly been involved in these debates of the 1970s, 1980s and 1990s, but it is interesting to see the extent to which the 'Celtic fringe' of the British Isles, the source of some of the nature stories mentioned in chapter 2 has assumed a dominant position in the discussions. This approach has also seen elements from the Roman Catholic and Free Churches enter strongly into the debate. For example the Reverend Ian Bradley, at one time Church of Scotland minister at St Leonard's, now a lecturer in theology at the University of Aberdeen, has been a leader in this line of thinking north of the border. In *God is Green* (1990), he traced ideas from the Early Fathers, and eastern Orthodox, into mediaeval thought (or some bits of it) to show that Christianity is in fact a 'green' faith. Utilizing the insights provided by contemporary science, including quantum physics and the new biology he develops this message that God is a Creator that cares about and sustains all of Creation, and Jesus is a Cosmic Christ.

Father Sean McDonagh is an Irish Columban missionary who has worked for many years in the Philippines. In *To Care for the Earth* (1986) and *The Greening of the Church* (1990) he makes a plea for the church to respond to the environmental crisis facing the earth.[14] He identifies much concern for the living environment in the Benedictine and Franciscan traditions of the church, but a particular concern is that in the Third World: the church in its liturgies and teaching should not be seen to be alien but should identify closely with indigenous peoples in their responses to the environmental challenges they face.

Perhaps these and similar individuals are indicative of the manner in which the churches will respond to Creation in the new millennium. Taxonomy, the cataloguing, identification, naming and classification of 'nature's plenty', the biodiversity of the planet, with its use of powerful computers, DNA-testing, and requiring access to vast museum and herbarium collections is indeed a field that is largely beyond the resources and expertise of a single individual, working as an amateur. The institutions for the popularization of science exist: it is not necessary to reinvent them. Could it be that in the development of a creation spirituality, a theology that both acknowledges the power of modern ecology, and also the more basic appreciation of 'God's World', in the manner of the Celtic saints and scholars, we have a new direction for the parson-naturalist beyond 2000?

Dull atheist, could a giddy dance
  Of atoms lawlessly hurl'd
Construct as wonderful, so wise,
  So harmonised a world?
Erasmus Darwin (1731–1802)[15]

Notes

1 Quoted in Foulkes, R., *Church and Stage in Victorian England* (Cambridge University Press, 1997), p. 51
2 Ipswich and East Suffolk Record Office. Henslow papers AD654/5.
3 Kinns, S., *Moses and Geology or the Harmony of the Bible with Science* (London, Cassell, 1892), pp. 13–16.
4 Letter, the Reverend R. H. Davies to the Reverend L. Jenyns, 12 September 1846, West Lexham, Norfolk. File of Naturalists' Letters, Bath Reference Library.
5 Kingsley, F., *Charles Kingsley: his Letter and Memories of his Life, edited by his wife,* vol. 2 (London. Henry S. King, 1877), p. 347.
6 Each diocese traditionally had several rural deaneries and rural deans. The office of rural dean was important in the mediaeval period, but had fallen into disuse in many English dioceses by the eighteenth century, with many of the functions of 'visitation' (i.e. inspection) and reporting to the bishop, being subsumed by the archdeacon. Sometimes there were several archdeaconries in a diocese, and so the hierarchical, nested structure was maintained. The office of rural dean, and the importance of rural deaneries were revived in the nineteenth century, especially by the Ecclesiastical Commissioners Act, 1836, which stated that each parish was within a rural deanery, and each rural deanery in an archdeaconry. Despite assertions, e.g. Sir Robert Philimore's, *Ecclesiastical Law of the Church of England*, vol. 1 (London, Henry Sweet, 1873), p. 258, that there is no conflict between the duties of the archdeacon and rural dean, the precise duties of the two offices have overlapped, and have been decided on the basis of local custom and practice, varying from diocese to diocese. See also Ravenscroft, R., 'The role of the rural dean', *Journal of Ecclesiastical Law*, 5 (22) January 1998.
7 Bereford, J., ed., *The Diary of a Country Parson: The Reverend James Woodforde*, vol. 3, 1788–1792 (Oxford University Press, 1927).
8 Blomefield, L. (late Jenyns), *Chapters in my Life* (Bath, privately printed, 1880), p. 103.
9 Withers, C. W. J., 'The Reverend Dr John Walker and the practice of natural history in late eighteenth-century Scotland', *Archives of Natural History,* 1991 18(2), pp. 201–220.
10 Dallman, A. A. and Wood, M. H., 'A biographical list of deceased Lancashire botanists', *Transactions of the Liverpool Botanical Society*, 1, 1909, pp. 4–59.
11 Anselm Camer, OSB, Ampleforth Abbey, York, and Jill Rutherford, Whitby, personal communication.

12 Dallman, A. A. and Wood, M. H., 1909, op. cit., 1971–97.
13 *Ibid*.
14 McDonagh, S., *To Care for the Earth: a Call to a New Theology* (London, Geoffrey Chapman, 1986). McDonah, S., *The Greening of the Church* (London, Geoffrey Chapman, 1990).
15 Quoted in Gillispie, C. C., *Genesis and Geology* (Cambridge, Mass., Harvard University Press, 1951), 197, p. 33.

Glossary of theological, scientific, ecclesiastical and legal terms

Advowson: The legal right to appoint the incumbent (rector or vicar) of a parish. The right of patronage.

Anglican Church: The term used for the institution of the Church of England, and those churches historically linked to it, including, for example, the Church in Wales, the Church of Ireland and the Anglican Church in Australia.

Anglo-Catholicism: The wing of the Anglican church that emphasizes the sacraments and tradition. Often Anglo-Catholics emphasize elaborate ceremonial in the church's services, the wearing of vestments (elaborate priestly clothing) and the use of incense. Sometimes Anglo-Catholics are seen as being closer, in their observance and theology, to the Roman Catholic Church than other Anglicans and 'higher' than the 'Low Church' or evangelical wing.

Archdeacon: A senior member of the clergy who assists the bishop in the running of a diocese. An archdeacon will conduct visitations of parishes, to inspect the fabric of the church and the general running of the parish. Today, an archdeacon is a senior administrator. A diocese may be (but is not always) divided into several archdeaconries.

Benefice: Traditionally the right to receive the income from lands, and to live in the house associated with a particular living or parish, and to take the services and act as parish priest in the associated church.

Botany: The scientific study of plants.

Bestiary: A 'book of beasts'. A book, in many cases of mediaeval origin, giving details of animals, often including mythological creatures.

Canon: 1. A rule of ecclesiastical or church law: hence **canon law**.

2. A member of the clerical (ie ordained) staff of a cathedral. Traditionally, where the office was attached to a particular benefice or living, the term **prebend** or **prebendary** was used.

Catastrophism: The idea that the earth's history is to be understood in terms of a number of sudden dramatic events or changes – earthquakes, etc.

Coleoptera: The scientific name for the biological group consisting of the beetles.

Consecration: The separation of something, or someone, for Divine service. Thus: of bread and wine at the Eucharist; of bishops when they assume office; of land or a church.

Creation: 1. The act of creating, or bringing into existence, the Cosmos, and everything in it, including organisms and humanity. In Christian theology, it is usually assumed that God created the world and the universe, although not necessarily all at one time.
2. The whole created universe (including organisms) as an entity.

Creationism: The body of beliefs that maintains that the whole of Creation (in the second of the senses above) was brought into existence by divine power, or *fiat*, within a short time, and in approximately its present form, in accordance with the Creation (in the first sense) narratives of the Old Testament book of Genesis.

Creation theology: That part of theology that deals with Creation (in both senses). Thus it attempts to explain the possible reasons for the formation of the Cosmos, its significance, and the spirituality associated with the Cosmos, the earth and the living environment.

Creation science: The attempt, through *scientific* means to demonstrate the literal truth of the whole of Scripture, including the creation stories in Genesis.

Curate: A clergyman assistant to a parish priest (the vicar or rector of a parish); hence **curacy**, the position itself. A curate is usually a deacon or recently ordained priest in a subsidiary or trainee position.

Darwinism: The system of ideas associated with Charles Darwin's *Origin of Species*, published in 1859, including not only the idea of evolution, but the mechanism of natural selection and the idea of gradual change in the environment and its living inhabitants over long periods of geological time (uniformitarianism).

Deacon: A person in the rank below a priest in the Anglican ministry (and in that of certain other churches). A person is usually ordained deacon, holding that position for about a year before becoming a priest in the Anglican church. Such a person is able to perform some, but not all, of the duties of the ordained ministry.

Dean: The senior clergyman in charge of a cathedral, or sometimes a college of a university.

Denudation: The slow, gradual process of erosion or wearing away and removal of the landscape by rivers and streams, glaciers, wind and wave-action.

Diocese: The territorial unit of administration of the Church, governed by a bishop.

Diluvialism: The belief in the literal truth of the story of Noah's Flood (the Deluge), as set out in the book of Genesis, and by extension, the belief by certain geologists that geological evidence for this idea could be found. The diluvialist school maintained that many of the drift or superficial deposits in Britain were left by the Flood.

Dissenter: See Free Churches.

Ecology: The science that deals with the relationships amongst organisms, and between organisms and their inorganic environments: the science of ecosystems. Sometimes, less correctly, the conservation and management of the environment, broadly in accordance with ecological principles.

Ecosystem: A segment of nature of any magnitude, with all its included organisms in their environment. A ecosystem thus includes the plants and animals that make up a community (natural, semi-natural, or even largely created by humans) and the inorganic component–soil, water, air. Examples might include: an oakwood, a rock pool, a decaying log, a churchyard.

Ecotheology: The theological, or philosophical basis for the understanding and management of the environment, including ecosystems. Usually, but not always, from a Judaeo-Christian perspective.

Entomology: The scientific study of insects.

Ethology: The scientific study of animal behaviour.

Evangelicalism: In the Anglican Church, a conservative strand of theology that emphasises Bible-centred teaching and the importance of personal experience and commitment. In some cases such persons have an extreme reverence for Scripture (the Bible) that comes close to fundamentalism. The 'Low Church', opposite wing of the church to Anglo-Catholicism or the 'High Church' movement.

Evolution: The theory that organisms have changed throughout geological time; descent with modification. Although theories of evolution were put forward earlier, the theory is most often associated with Charles Robert Darwin (1809–1882), who advanced the notion of evolution by natural selection in *The Origin of Species* in 1859.

Excommunication: The act of censure excluding an individual from communion; now very rare in the Anglican church.

Exegesis: The art of interpreting or explaining a text, usually a sacred text (such as the Bible) or some other much venerated writing.

Extinction: The disappearance or 'dying out' of a particular species of organism or biological group of organisms (family, class).

Fellow: A senior, graduate member of an Oxford or Cambridge college. Such a person might play a role in the governance of the college, and undertake some teaching or other scholarly work. A **fellowship** of which a college holds a limited number, is the appointment or position to which such a person is elected.

Fossils: The remains or traces of past life, preserved in the rocks.

Free Churches: The Protestant (i.e. non-Roman Catholic) denominations other than the Church of England or Anglican Church, including for example, Methodism, and the Presbyterian and Baptist Churches. The term 'Dissenting Church' was sometimes used in the past. Such churches share part of the doctrine with the Church of England, but not, for example, that on the authority of bishops.

Geology: The science that deals with the earth – the rocks and minerals of the earth's crust, their nature and arrangement, and the use of this information for the reconstruction of the the history of the earth. In also sometimes includes palaeontology.

Glebe: Traditionally land attached to the parish, and used as a source of income for the vicar or rector. The parson could either cultivate it himself, or (more usually) rent it out, the rent constituting part of the income of the benefice. Since 1976, glebe land in England has been vested in the diocese.

Holy orders: The ordained ministry. A **clerk in holy orders** is a priest or deacon. Hence the adjective clerical.

Igneous rock: A rock formed by the crystallization of a liquid magma. Examples include lavas (which solidified at the surface), and rocks such as granite which crystallized deep in the earth.

Incumbent: A person holding the position of vicar or rector in charge of a parish in the Church of England.

Institution: The legal act of installing of an incumbent (vicar or rector) into his benefice by a bishop. The term used for the installing of a dean or canon or prebendary to his seat in a cathedral is **installation**.

Invertebrate: An animal without a vertebral column or backbone, for example insect, spider, crab, mollusc, sponge.

Lamarckism: The set of evolutionary ideas put forward by French naturalist Jean Baptiste Lamarck (1744-1829), who asserted that evolution might take place as the result of the inheritance of acquired characteristics (those developing in the lifetime of the organism) and an internally rather mysteriously driven *pouvoir de vie* (or 'wish-power'). Darwin became familiar with Lamarck's ideas while studying in Edinburgh in the 1820s.

Lepidoptera: The 'scale winged' insects, i.e. butterflies and moths.

Liberalism: In theology this originally meant freedom from bigotry and over-close adherence to traditional ideas, together with a willingness to accept progress and change. More specifically, it has more recently implied a theological approach that attempted to reconcile the

Christian outlook with modern philosophical and scientific ideas.

Living: A Church of England benefice or parish, with the rights, incomes and duties associated with it.

Mesozoic: The period of middle life, including the period of the rocks of the Triassic, Jurassic and Cretaceous systems, i.e. the rocks formed approximately 40 to 120 to million years ago.

Metamorphic rock: A rock formed by the action of heat, pressure or chemical fluids (or a combination of these) on other rocks. Examples include the slates of the English Lake District and Wales, which have been converted from shales and clays.

Meteorology: The scientific study of the weather and atmospheric phenomena.

Natural theology: The set of beliefs that maintains that the existence of the world, especially the living world, its beauty and complexity provides evidence for the existence of, and concerning the nature of, God. The notion was expounded particularly by William Paley (1743–1805), although many of the ideas can be traced to John Ray's *Wisdom of God*. It may include the search for laws, or patterns of order governing the universe.

Ordination: The ceremony whereby a person is made a priest or deacon. Certain vows have to be taken and assurances as to belief, learning and character given.

Organism: Living thing (animal, plant or microorganism).

Ornithology: The scientific study of birds.

Palaeontology: The scientific study of fossils, and the use of these to reconstruct the history of life on earth.

Palaeozoic: The period of ancient life; the period of the formation of the rocks of the Cambrian, Ordovician, Silurian, Devonian, Carboniferous and Permian systems, i.e. approximately 120 to 600 million years old.

Parson's freehold: The right of a clergyman to remain permanently in the office to which he is lawfully appointed.

Perpetual curate: A person who carried out the duties of a priest in a parish, but who was not a vicar or rector; the position was a permanent one (hence perpetual) but the person did not have to be formally instituted; there were other legal differences. Perpetual curacies were abolished in 1968.

Phytology: Old term for botany, the study of plants.

Polymath: A person learned in many different subjects of study.

Prebend, Prebendary: See canon.

Priest: A person in the ordained ministry of the Church or England or certain other churches, including the Roman Catholic Church. Until very recently only a male could be a priest in the Church of England.

Rector: Traditionally the person who was entitled received the tithes from a parish, usually the parish clergyman; the usual title of a clergyman in rural areas. Hence *rectory*: the house in which the rector and his family live.

Rural deanery: A subdivision of a diocese, in the charge of a rural dean.

Sacrament: 'A outward and visible sign of an inward and spiritual grace', such as Baptism, or the Mass, Holy Communion or the Eucharist.

Scriptural geology: The set of ideas suggesting that the geological record of the rocks could be found to correlate with the record of the earth's history set out in the Old Testament of the Bible: the reconciliation of the 'Book of God' with the 'Book of Nature'. The notion was largely discredited by about 1840, but had a few adherents until the end of the nineteenth century, and even beyond.

Sedimentary rock: A rock formed by the accumulation of sediments, or particles in the sea, a lake or estuary (e.g. shales, clays, sandstones, limestones) or on land as the result of wind (desert sandstones) or ice action (glacial till).

Stratigraphy: The branch of geology that deals with the manner in which sedimentary rocks **(strata)** are laid down and arranged. The interpretation of the evidence of stratigraphy is a valuable source of information on the earth's history.

Taxon: A biological group; a category distinguished in the classification of organisms, e.g. species, genus, family. Plural: **taxa**.

Taxonomy: That part of biological science that deals with the identification and classification of organisms.

Tertiary: The 'third' period (after the Palaeozoic and Mesozoic), sometimes known as the **Cainozoic** or **Cenozoic** (the period of recent life), including the rocks formed in the last 40 million years.

Thirty-nine articles of religion: The set of doctrinal formulae accepted as defining the Church of England's position in relation to dogmatic controversies of the sixteenth century. They thus represent traditional orthodoxy in the Church of England. They are, however much outdated, and clergy are now at ordination required only to give 'general assent' to them, rather than indicate acceptance of each and every one of them.

Tithes: The right of the holder of a benefice (or occasionally a lay or non-ordained person) to receive one tenth of the production of the land in a parish. Now obsolete.

Uniformitarianism: The notion that the history of the earth is to be understood in terms of the long-continued action of very gradual changes, changes of the sort that can still be observed. The idea was set out by John Hutton in *Theory of the Earth* in 1785, and was expounded in Charles Lyell's *Principles of Geology* (1830–1833).

Vasculum: An elongate collecting box, usually of thin metal and having a strap for easy carriage, used by botanists for plants. Now largely displaced by the ubiquitous polythene bag.

Vertebrate: Animal with a vertebral column of backbone; a fish, mammal, reptile, bird or amphibian.

Vicar: Traditionally a parish clergyman who represented the rector, ie one who attended to the spiritual welfare of a parish, but who did not receive the tithes. The legal distinction between a rector and vicar has now largely disappeared.

Wrangler: One who obtains first class honours in mathematics at Cambridge University,

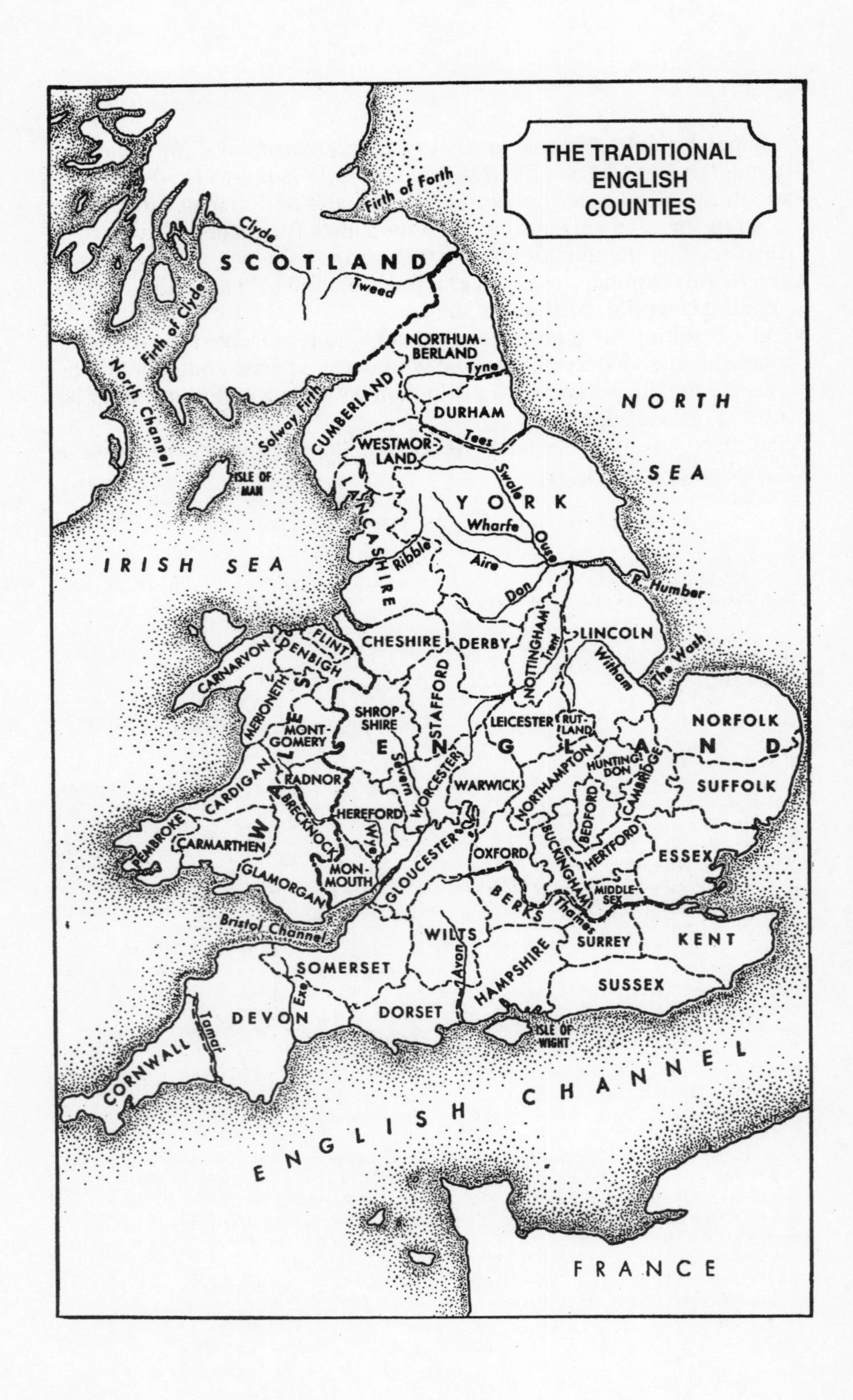
THE TRADITIONAL ENGLISH COUNTIES
SCOTLAND
Firth of Forth
Clyde
Firth of Clyde
Tweed
North Channel
Solway Firth
NORTHUM-BERLAND
Tyne
CUMBERLAND
DURHAM
Tees
WESTMOR LAND
NORTH SEA
ISLE OF MAN
LANCASHIRE
YORK
Swale
Wharfe
Ouse
Ribble
Aire
Don
R. Humber
IRISH SEA
FLINT
DENBIGH
CHESHIRE
DERBY
NOTTINGHAM
Trent
LINCOLN
Witham
The Wash
CARNARVON
MERIONETH
SHROP-SHIRE
STAFFORD
LEICESTER
RUT-LAND
NORFOLK
MONT-GOMERY
ENGLAND
WALES
CARDIGAN
RADNOR
Severn
WORCESTER
WARWICK
NORTHAMPTON
HUNTING-DON
CAMBRIDGE
SUFFOLK
PEMBROKE
CARMARTHEN
BRECKNOCK
HEREFORD
Wye
BEDFORD
HERTFORD
ESSEX
GLAMORGAN
MON-MOUTH
GLOUCESTER
OXFORD
BUCKINGHAM
MIDDLE-SEX
Bristol Channel
BERKS
Thames
WILTS
SURREY
KENT
SOMERSET
Avon
HAMPSHIRE
SUSSEX
Exe
DEVON
DORSET
Tamar
ISLE OF WIGHT
CORNWALL
ENGLISH CHANNEL
FRANCE

Index

Aborigines, Australian, 164
Adamnan, St (679–704), 38–40
Adder (*see* viper),
Addington, R., Suffolk, botanist, 66, 150
Advowson, 12, 174
Agriculture, 67
Algae, 52–53
Allen, David, historian of natural history, 54, 71, 77, 111, 144
Alps, 129, 132, 134
Alstonfield, Staffordshire, 19
Alton Locke, 6
Alnus glutinosa, 44
Amphibians, 84–86
Anglesey Abbey, 5
Animal Farm, 40
Anning, Mary (fossil hunter), 117, 118
Apethorpe, Northants, 52
Armstrong, Benjamin (1817–1890), Norfolk diarist, 10
Armstrong, Edward Allworthy (1900–1978) ornithologist, student of bird behaviour, 3–4, 80–81
Arnold, F.H., botanist, 55
Assisi, St Francis of (1182–1226), 10
Asplenium, 60
Aster tripolium, 57
Augustine, St (354–430), 27
Australia, 3, 121, 154–165, 176

Babington, Charles, Cardale, botanist, 55
Babington, Churchill (1821–1889), botanist, ornithologist, entomologist, 55, 76, 100, 117
Bacon, Roger (c. 1214–1292), author, 35–36
Bahia, South America, 163
Balliol College, Oxford, 149
Barrington, the Hon. Daines, correspondent of Gilbert White, 65, 83
Bartholomaeus Anglicus (Bartholomew the Englishman), thirteenth-century author, 36–37
Bath, Somerset, 5, 13, 19, 91, 112, 145
Beasts, fabulous, 29, 32, 33, 40
Bede (The Venerable) (c. 673–735), 36, 86, 105
Bedford, 12
Behaviour of birds, 4, 34, 36, 38, 80–81
Bees, 95–96, 97, 99
Beetles, 73, 100–102, 103, 164
Berkeley, Miles Joseph, FRS (1803–1889), mycologist, 5, 51–52, 67
Bestiary, 32
Betula, 24
Birds, 1, 3–4, 6, 14, 26, 31, 36, 70–81, 83, 173
Black Notley, Essex, 45
Blomefield, Leonard (*see* Jenyns, Leonard)
Boke of St Albans, 30
Bonney, Thomas, FRS (1833–1923), geologist, 2, 111, 121, 123, 132–135
Botany, study of, 2, 8–9, 12, 16–17, 43ff, 140–141, 156–157, 165–166, 179
British Association for the Advancement of Science, 7, 9, 79, 89, 90, 119, 120, 133, 134, 136, 176–177, 180
Buckland, William (1784–1856), geologist, 2, 8, 111, 118–120, 128–129, 132–133, 172
Burnet, Thomas (1635–1715), geologist, 125
Butler, Charles (c.1560–1647), bee-keeper, entomologist, 95–96
Butterflies and moths, 14, 37, 96–99, 171

Cambridge (*see also* names of colleges), 3, 4, 17, 24, 43, 45, 46, 58, 60, 61, 63, 79–81, 100, 111, 113, 120–123, 132–134, 140, 143, 146, 167, 177, 178, 180
Carex, 37
Catastrophism, 113ff, 122ff, 126, 127, 128, 135–136

Catalogus Plantarum Anglicae, 47–48
Catalogus Plantarum circa Cantabrigiam nascentium, 46–47, 54
Catherine's College, St, Cambridge, 45
Catholicism, 20, 140, 142–143, 160–162, 164, 168, 177–179, 182
Cephalaspis, 131
Chadwick, Owen, author of *The Victorian Church*, 13
Chaloner, John William (1811–1894), ornithologist, fisherman, 14, 73, 86
Chalk, 117, 124
Chamaenerion angustifolium, 57
Chester Cathedral, 26, 121, 139–143
Chester Society of Natural Science, 141–143
Chevalier, Temple (1793–1973), 102
Christ Church, Oxford, 119
Christ's College, Cambridge, 4, 19, 52, 125, 175
Churchyards, 150–152
Ciaran, St, 38
Clare College, Cambridge, 125
Clarke, William Bramwhite, FRS (1798–1878) geologist, 157–160, 161, 168
Classical authors, 32, 33, 36, 95, 126
Classification of animals, 89–90, 102–106
Classification of plants, 5, 48–50, 51–53, 65
Climate, 66, 91, 149
Coleoptera (*see* beetles)
Colonial science, 167–168
Colonsay, 39
Columba, St (521–597), 38–40
Columbanus, St (c. 543–615), 38
Common Objects of the Countryside, 76
Concise British Flora, 62
Coney, 35
Conservation, 10, 14, 24,77–79, 145, 147–152, 157, 181
Conybeare, John Josias (1779–1824), geologist, 110, 117, 132
Conybeare, William, Daniel, FRS (1787–1857), geologist, 117–118, 132
Cornewell, Revd Sir G. H., botanist, 55
Cornus suecica, 59
Cornwall, 11, 12, 13, 61, 141
Corpus Christi College, Cambridge, 50, 177
Corpus Christi College, Oxford, 154
County floras, 4, 18, 54–57, 62, 131
Countryside, Mediaeval, 23–25
Crabbe, George (1754–1832), Suffolk nature poet, 59
Crataegus, 24
Crosthwaite, near Keswick, 10
Cruciata, 44
Crusaders, 7
Cruttwell, Norman (1916–1995), botanist, 156–157, 168
Cumming, J. G., geologist, schoolmaster, 111–112
Cuscuta, 44
Cuthbert, St (c. 635–687), 37–38
Cuvier, Georges (1769–1832), French geologist, 127–128

Dana, James Dwight (1813–1895), American geologist, 158–159
Darwin, Charles (1809–1882), evolutionist, 3, 4, 6, 15, 31, 48, 52, 53, 54, 63–65, 88, 100–101, 102, 110, 120–121, 122, 131, 133, 135, 140, 147, 157, 161, 172–173, 180
Darwin, Erasmus (1731–1802), philosopher, poet, 180, 183
Davy, Sir Humphrey, Secretary of the Royal Society, 111
De Naturis Rerum, 34
Dereham, East, Norfolk, 10
Dew, Henry (1819–1901), Rector of Whitney-on-Wye, 11
Diluvial geology, 6, 9, 118ff, 123–132, 171
Dorset, 11, 102, 157
Drosersa, 5
Ducks, eider, 37
Dudley Caverns, 9, 19
Durham Cathedral, 6, 61, 72, 103
Durham, County, 4, 10, 55
Durham, monks of, 37
Durham, University of, 17, 57, 102, 103–104, 123, 176, 178

Eagle, 29, 34, 36, 75
East Anglian landscape, 23–25, 36
Ecology, 44, 57–61, 67, 81, 90–91, 105–107, 140, 181
Ecotheology, 182
Edwards, Bartholomew, Rector of Ashill, 11
Egg-collecting, 3, 12, 72–73, 77, 78–79
Ely, Bishops of, 23, 24, 30
Ely, Isle of, 26–27
Emblemes, 28
Emmanuel College, Cambridge, 79
Equisetum, 5
Evolutionary ideas, 6, 7, 54, 63–65, 102, 135–136, 161–162, 172–173, 174

Falconry, 29–31, 34, 41
Farringdon, Hampshire, 11
Feminine Monarchie, The, 95

Fenland, 26–27, 121, 132
Ferns, 5, 6, 59, 60, 61, 155, 166–167
Field clubs (*see* natural history societies)
Filipendula vulgaris, 60
Fisher, clerical family, 11
Fisher, Osmond, geologist, 122–123
Fishes, 14, 26, 31, 48, 83–88, 92, 148
Flint, 124
Flowers of the Field, 61, 141
Folkstone, Kent, 11
Forsyth, Alexander, Scots Presbyterian minister, wildfowler, 72
Fossils, 118–119, 122, 126–127, 128, 131, 159, 161, 166, 179
Fountains Abbey, Yorkshire, 60
Fowler, William (1835–1912), all-round naturalist, pioneer ecologist, 57, 101, 102
Fox, William Darwin (1805–1880), Charles Darwin's friend and cousin, entomologist,100–101, 180
Framlingham, Suffolk, 59
France, 30, 35, 48
Franciscan Order, 35, 36
Fremantle, Western Australia, 163–164
Frogs, 37, 84, 86
Fungi, 5, 52, 67

Galloway, William (1811–1903), scriptural geologist, 5–6, 123–125, 172
Gamekeepers, 77
Garnett, Philip Mauleverer (1906–1967), botanist, 59
Gatty, Mrs Margaret, authority on seaweeds, 53
Gawthorp, William, Yorkshire botanist, 60
Geese, barnacle, 31, 35
Geological Society of London, 110–112, 113, 117, 118–119, 123, 133, 136, 166, 176
Geology, study of, 3, 5, 110–136, 141–142, 157–162, 168, 172
Geraldton, Western Australia, 163
Geranium sanguineum, 47
Gibraltar, 18, 154–155, 165
Gilpin, Francis (1855–1945), Norfolk botanist, 59
Giraldus Cambrensis (Gerald de Barri) (c. 1146–1223), Welsh traveller and author, 30–32, 34, 43
Glaciation, 129, 134–135, 136, 161
Gleanings of British Algae, 52
Godric, St, of Finchale, 38
Gonville and Caius College, Cambridge, 24, 79
Goodenough, Samuel, FRS, Bishop of Carlisle, 111
Graham, Gordon, botanist, 4, 10, 55
Granite, 123
Grigson, Geoffrey (1905–1985), author, 13–14

Hadleigh, Suffolk, 67
Hale, Matthew, Colonial Bishop, 163
Hales, Steven (1677–1761), plant physiologist, 50–51
Handbook of British Birds, 77
Hartley, Peter Harold Trahair (1909–1985), ornithologist, 3, 10, 79, 147
Hayley Wood, Cambridgeshire, 24
Helleborus foetidus, 60, 67
Hempstead, East Anglian clerical family, 12, 56
Henslow, clerical family, 18–19, 63–65
Henslow, John Stevens (1796–1861), geologist and botanist, teacher of Charles Darwin, 3, 5, 8–9, 10, 15, 18, 19, 55, 63, 67, 146–147, 171, 180
Henslow, George (1835–1925), botanist, evolutionist, 19, 64–65, 174
Hereford, Bishop of, 30
Herefordshire, 19, 54, 55, 131, 174
Hey family, clergy and beetle-collectors, 100–101
Higgins, Henry Hugh (1814–1893), all-round naturalist, stalwart of Liverpool Field Club, 9, 144, 146, 173
Higham-on-the-Hill, Nuneaton, 11
Hild, St (Hilda) of Whitby, 38
Hildoceras, 38
Hind, William Marsden (1815–1894), Suffolk botanist, 55, 56
Hitcham, Suffolk, 3, 5, 8, 10, 67, 147
Holloway, J. E. (1881–1945), New Zealand botanist, 166–167, 168
Holy Land (*see* Palestine),
Hooker, family, botanists, 19, 52, 141, 147
Huitson, John, FRS, geologist, 110
Hull, John Edward (1863–1960), arachnologist, 103
Hutton, James (1726–1797), geologist, 113
Hyenas, 128

Ibis, 28
Incumbencies, lengthy, 10–15, 20
India, 66, 155, 165
Insects, 37, 95–103, 107–108
Iona, 38
Ireland, 3, 30, 31, 38, 40, 61, 66, 67, 160, 177, 182

Jameson, Robert, Scots geologist, 127

Jefferies, Richard (1848–1887), author, 1
Jenyns, Leonard (1800–1893), zoologist, 5, 14, 18, 64, 74, 76, 87–91, 98, 100, 105–106, 107–108, 145, 176, 180
Jesus College, Cambridge, 123, 157
Johnson, William (1844–1919), authority on lichens, 53
Johns, Charles Alexander (c.1818–1875), writer of popular natural history books, 61–62, 76, 141
John's, St, College, Cambridge, 57, 59, 63, 133, 175
Jourdain, Francis Charles Robert, ornithologist, 3, 10, 77, 148
Jurassic, 132

Keble, John (1792–1866), theologian, 171,
Kevin, St, 38
Kendall, C. E. V., zoologist, ecologist, 106–107, 180
Kew, near London, Herbarium and Botanic Gardens, 7, 15, 52, 146, 155, 168
Kilkhampton, Cornwall, 11, 12
Kilvert, Francis (1840–1879), diarist, 151–152
Kingsley, Charles (1818–1875), author, all-round naturalist, 6, 121, 139, 145, 147–148, 173, 181
Kinns, Samuel, scriptural geologist, 130–131,
Kirby, William, FRS (1759–1850), Suffolk botanist and entomologist, 56, 99–100, 147
Kirkdale Cavern, Yorkshire, 117, 128
Kitchen, Thomas Basil (1905–1987), 164–165
Knubley, E. Ponsonby (1850–1931), all-round naturalist, 12, 78–79

Lansborough, David, Scots authority on seaweeds, 52
Lamarck, Jean-Baptiste (1744–1829), evolutionist, 6, 64–65
Larks, 6
Lathbury, clerical family, 56
Leighton, W. A., friend of Charles Darwin, authority on lichens, 53, 54
Lewis, Thomas Taylor (1801–1858), geologist, 9
Ley, Augustus, botanist, 19, 54
Lichens, 53
Limonium vulgare, 57
Lincoln Cathedral, 99
Lindisfarne (Holy Island), Northumberland, 38, 43
Linnean Society of London, 56
Linnaeus, Carl (1707–1778), Swedish taxonomist, 47, 90
Lisbon earthquake (1755), 114–115
Liverpool, 9, 144–145, 146, 155
Lyell, Charles (1797–1875), geologist, friend of Charles Darwin, 54, 112, 118, 119, 129, 131, 133, 135, 141, 162, 171
Lycopodium, 5, 167

Macpherson, H. A., all-round Lakeland naturalist, 91
Magdalen College, Oxford, 95
Magdalene College, Cambridge, 12
Mammals, 83–93
Manchester Cathedral, 133
Maories, 166
Marcon, Canon, Rector of Edgefield (1875–1937), 11
Martin, William Keble, botanist, 62
Marx, Karl, political economist, 139
Mediaeval ideas, 25ff
Methodus Plantarum, 48–49
Misericords, 26, 29
Missionaries, 154–168, 176
Mitchell, John, FRS (1724?–1795), geologist, 3, 113–116
Mites, 103
Molluscs, 105–107
Morpeth, Northumberland, 2, 43, 45
Morris, Francis Orpen (1810–1891), ornithologist, anti-evolution writer, pioneer in conservation, 7, 14, 74–76, 77–78, 98, 148, 172, 180
Morris, Marmaduke Orpen, botanist, son of Francis, 15
Mulso, John (1720–1791), friend of Gilbert White, 18
Museums, 146–147, 164, 168

National Trust, 10, 149–150, 180
Natural History Museum, London, 7, 52, 99, 155
Natural History of British Birds, 75
Natural History of Selborne, The, 1, 10, 15, 83, 87, 96, 155, 174
Natural theology, 4–5, 17, 64–65, 75, 89, 107–108, 110, 135, 171, 173
Neckam, Alexander (1157–1217), author, 33–35
Newbould,W. W., botanist, 56
New Guinea, 156–157
New Herbal, 43
Newman, John Henry (1801–1890), theologian, 140, 160
Newton Kyme, Yorkshire, 14, 86
Newton, Sir Isaac (1642–1727), 51, 92

New Zealand, 3, 154, 161, 166–167, 176
Nicolay, Charles Grenfell (1815–1897), Australian museum curator, 162–164, 168
Norfolk, 10, 55, 56
Norman, Alfred, Merle, FRS (1831–1918) marine zoologist, 5, 103
Nightjar, 1
Nunburnholme, Yorkshire, 14–15, 74–75

Observations . . . made on a Journey, 48
Old Red Sandstone, 131
Orchids, 156–157, 165, 173
Orford, Suffolk, 56
Oriel College, Oxford, 2, 18, 91, 176
Origin of Species, On the, 6, 51, 63, 122, 172
Oriole, golden, 31
Orwell, George (1890–1950), author, 40
Otter, 26, 27, 29, 84
Owl, 28, 29
Oxford (*see also* names of colleges), 2, 15, 17, 31, 33, 35, 36, 60, 77, 110, 111, 118–120, 151, 156, 167, 176, 178

Palestine, 7–8, 64
Paley, William (1743–1805), author of *Natural Theology*, 4, 5, 135, 171, 180
Parasites, 90
Parson's freehold, doctrine of, 13, 20
Patrick, St, 38
Pelican, 28, 29
Pembroke College, Cambridge, 43, 45
Pennant, Thomas, correspondent of Gilbert White, 83–84, 89
Physiology, 50–51
Physiologus, 32
Phytophthora infestans, 67
Pickard-Cambridge, Octavius, FRS (1828–1917), 5, 6, 11, 102–103, 173
Pleisiosaurus, 117, 130
Potter, Beatrix (1866–1943) children's author, 10, 150
Pteraspis, 131
Purchas, William (1822–1903), botanist, 19–20, 54, 131, 174

Quarles, Francis, seventeenth-century author, 28
Queens' College, Cambridge, 113

Rawnsley, Robert Drummond Burrell (1851–1920), founder of the National Trust, 10, 149–150
Raven, Charles Earle (1885–1964), all-round naturalist, theologian and historian of science, 31, 32, 34, 36, 37, 47, 49, 79, 97
Ray, John (1627–1705), theologian and naturalist, 2, 4, 17, 45–50, 54, 60, 67, 80, 84, 85, 96–97, 110, 126–127, 171
Reliquiqae Diluvianae, 118, 129
Reptiles, 84, 118, 119
Richmond, Yorkshire, 26
Ripon Cathedral, 29
Roman Catholic church, *see* Catholicism
Romanticism, 113
Royal Society, 48, 50, 52, 72, 92, 111, 113, 115, 128, 133, 136, 168, 176, 180
Royal Society for the Protection of Birds, 77, 78, 79, 148, 181
Royal Society of New South Wales, 160
Rupp, Herbert Montague Rucher (1872–1956), Australian botanist, 165–166, 167
Rydal, 123

Savile, B. W., correspondent of Charles Darwin, 136
Scotland, 3, 47, 52, 53, 72, 91, 120, 148, 177, 182
Scriptural geology, 124–125, 129–132, 136, 174
Sea-Birds Preservation Act, 78
Sedgwick, Adam (1785–1873), geologist, 2, 19, 63, 111, 118, 120–123, 133, 146, 180
Selborne, Hampshire, 1, 2, 10, 18
Sherington, Richard, of Folkstone, Kent, 11
Shooting, 72–73, 74, 77–78, 148
Silurian, 130, 159
Skye, Isle of, 40
Slater, H. H., wildfowler, bird-collector, traveller, 165, 168
Sloth, giant, 6
Smith, Charles (1795–1862), lepidopterist, 99
Smith, Gerald (1804–1881), botanist, 15–17
Smith, William, 'Strata', (1769–1939), geologist, engineer, 112, 122
Snakes, 31, 38, 85, 92
Societies, natural history, and field clubs, 9, 19, 55, 141–146
Southcomb, clerical family, 11
Southwell Minster, 25–26
Sowerby, James (1757–1822), botanist, 12, 56
Spiders, 6, 102–103
Sponges, 5, 103
Stanley, Arthur Penryn (1815–1881), stalwart of Palestine Exploration Fund, 7

Steeple Ashton, Wiltshire, 12
Stonegate, Sussex, 71
Stonehenge, Wiltshire, 93
Stowell, Hugh (1829–1886), beetle collector, 101
Stukeley, William (1687–1765), topographer, medical doctor, eccentric, 92–93
Suffolk, 3, 9, 23, 36, 55, 56, 60, 98, 99, 157
Sutton, Charles, botanist, 56
Swift, Jonathan (1667–1745), 66
Symonds, W. E., geologist, 19–20, 54, 131, 174
Synopsis Britanicum, 50

Tansley, Sir Arthur G. (1871–1955), ecologist, 58, 106
Taylor, Richard (1805–1873), all-round naturalist, missionary in New Zealand, 166, 168
Teasel, 44
Teesdale, 5
Teilhard de Chardin (1881–1955), French Catholic priest, evolutionist, 177
Thomson, William Cooper, missionary doctor, priest and botanist, 155
Thornhill, Yorkshire, 3, 114
Thynne family, 12
Ticehurst, Norman, Suffolk ornithologist, 76
Tiree, 39
Toad, 84
Townsend, Joseph, geologist, 112
Trinity College, Cambridge, 26, 99, 121, 175
Tristram, Henry Baker, FRS (1822–1906), ornithologist, 6, 7–8, 72–73, 78, 148, 173
Tuck, Julian George, Suffolk ornithologist, 76
Turner, William (c. 1508–1568), 2, 43, 67, 81

Uniformitarianism, 113, 122, 135
Uniformity, Act of, 45
University Tests Act, 178

Vegetable Statics, 51
Viola, 16
Viper, 85
Vulcanicity, 114, 122, 123

Wadham College, Oxford, 131
Wales, 30–31, 34, 47, 48, 60–61, 120, 121, 122, 145, 148, 157
Walker, John (1731–1803), Church of Scotland minister, Edinburgh professor, all-round naturalist, 177
Walker, Richard (1791–1870), botanist, 54
Wallace, Alfred Russell (1823–1913), evolutionist, 6
Ward, J. Clifton (1843–1880), 123
Water Babies, The, 6
Weather, *see* climate
Wells, Somerset, 43, 45
Wescott, Brooke Foss (1825–1901), theologian and bishop, amateur botanist, 61
Whale, 36, 39, 92
Whewell, William, FRS (1794–1866), geologist, mathematician, 111
Whitby, Yorkshire, 38, 126
White, clerical family, 18, 154–155, 167–168
White, Gilbert (1720–1793), author of *The Natural History of Selborne*, 1–2, 3, 10, 11, 17, 65–66, 67, 80, 83–86, 87, 96, 166, 175
Whittlesey Mere, 5
Wickham, Archdale Palmer (1855–1935), lepidopterist, 99, 106
Wilkins, Bishop, seventeenth-century fellow of Royal Society, 48
Wisdom of God, The, 4, 46, 84
Woodforde, James (1740–1803), Norfolk diarist, 174–175
Wood, J. G., author of popular books on natural history, 76
Woodruffe-Peacock, Edward Adrian (1858–1922), botanist and ecologist, 57–59, 62–63, 180
Woodpecker, 31
Woods, Julian Tenison (1832–1889), Catholic priest, geologist, 160–162, 168
Woolls, William (1814–1893), Australian geologist, 165, 168
Wooton St Lawrence, Hampshire, 95
Worcester Cathedral, 33
Worcester College, Oxford, 74
Wren, 4, 34, 80–81

Yates, James, FRS (1789–1871), botanist, palaeontologist, 179–180
Young, Andrew John (1885–1971), poet, eccentric, naturalist, 71